Cultural Responses to the Volcanic Landscape: The Mediterranean and Beyond

Cultural Responses to the Volcanic Landscape: The Mediterranean and Beyond

Edited by

MIRIAM S. BALMUTH

DAVID K. CHESTER

PATRICIA A. JOHNSTON

ARCHAEOLOGICAL INSTITUTE OF AMERICA

BOSTON, MASSACHUSETTS

Colloquia and Conference Papers 8

Cover illustration: Base of the Üçhisar ignimbrite castle near Urgüp. (Photo by R. Mussoli-Novelli)

∞ The paper in this book meets the guidelines for permanence and durability of the Committee on Production Guidelines for Book Longevity of the Council on Library Resources.

Cover and text designed by Peter Holm, Sterling Hill Productions
Printed in the United States of America by Sheridan Books

06 05 04 03   5 4 3 2 1

Library of Congress Cataloging-in-Publication Data

Cultural responses to the volcanic landscape: the Mediterranean and beyond / edited by Miriam S. Balmuth, David K. Chester, Patricia A. Johnston
       p. cm. – (Colloquia and conference papers ; 8)
Includes bibliographical references
ISBN 1-931909-06-7 (alk. paper)
1. Volcanism—Social aspects—History—Congresses. 2. Volcanic eruptions—Social aspects—History—Congresses. 3. Natural disasters—Social aspects—History—Congresses.
I. Balmuth, Miriam S. II. Chester, David K. III. Johnston, Patricia A. IV. Colloquia and conference papers ; no. 8.

QE521.5.C85 2005
551.21—dc22
                                                                2005048297

CONTENTS

CONTRIBUTORS

MIRIAM S. BALMUTH
Department of Classics, Tufts University

EZIO BURRI
Dipartimento Scienze Ambientali, Università L'Aquila

DAVID K. CHESTER
Department of Geography, University of Liverpool

RAFFAELLO CIONI
Dipartimento di Scienze della Terra, Università di Pisa

BALDASSARE CONTICELLO
Former Director of Antiquities, Pompeii

DONATELLA DE RITA
Università degli Studi di Roma Tre

SANDRO DE VITA
Osservatorio Vesuviano, Ercolano (Napoli)

MAURIZIO DI ROSA

MAURO DI VITO
Osservatorio Vesuviano, Ercolano (Napoli)

ANGUS M. DUNCAN
Department of Geology, University of Luton

KAREN POLINGER FOSTER
Department of Near Eastern Languages and Civilizations, Yale University

FABIO FRATINI
Centro di Studio sulle Cause de Deperimento e sui
Metodi di Conservazione della opere d'Arte, C.N.R.

CIRIACO GIAMPAOLO
Università degli Studi di Roma Tre

CLAUDIO GIARDINO
Università degli Studi "Suor Orsola Benincasa"– Napoli

SERGIO GINESU
Istituto di Scienze Geologico Mineralogiche, Università di Sassari

JOHN E. GUEST
University of London Observatory

ROBERTO ISAIA
Osservatorio Vesuviana, Ercolano (Napoli)

PATRICIA A. JOHNSTON
Department of Classical Studies, Brandeis University

ANN OLGA KOLOSKI-OSTROW
Department of Classical Studies, Brandeis University

SARA LEVI
Dipartimento di Scienze Storiche Archeologiche ed
Antropologiche dell' Antichità dell'Università, La Sapienze, Roma

LAURA MANISCALCO
Office of Antiquities, Catania, Italy

PAOLA MARIANELLI
Dipartimento di Scienze della Terra, Università di Pisa

ALDO MARTURANO
Osservatorio Vesuviano

RANIERO MASSOLI-NOVELLI

FABRIZIO NICOLETTI
Istituto Universitario Suor Orsola Benincasa

GIOVANNI ORSI
Dipartimento di Geofisica e Vulcanologia, Università Federico II, Napoli, Italy

ELENA PECCHIONI
Dipartimento di Scienze della Terra dell' Università di Firenze

CARLA PEPE
Università degli Studi "Suor Orsola Benincasa" – Napoli

MARCO PETITTA
Dipartimento Scienze della Terra, Università La Sapienze di Roma

PATRICIA PLUNKET
Universidad de Americas-Puebla

ROBERTO SANTECROCE
Dipartimento di Scienze della Terra, Università di Pisa

ALESSANDRO SBRANA
Dipartimento di Scienze della Terra, Università di Pisa

STEFANIA SIAS
Istituto di Scienze Geologico Mineralogiche, Università di Sassari

JOHANNES JACOBIUS LUIS SMOLENAARS
Klassiek Seminarium, University of Amsterdam

GABRIELA URUÑUELA
Universidad de Americas-Puebla

ALESSANDRO VANZETTI
Dipartimento di Scienze Storiche Archeologiche ed
Antropologiche dell' Antichità dell'Università, La Sapienze, Roma

ANTONIO VARONE
Soprintendenza Archeologica di Pompei

— INTRODUCTION —

Volcanoes are a mixed blessing for human societies: while they pose a persistent threat, they also provide riches from the earth that, until recent centuries, would not ordinarily be accessible through technological or industrial means. Rich volcanic soils, building materials, and mineral wealth are only some of the blessings resulting from destructive eruptions. Archaeologists are much indebted to volcanoes for having preserved remnants of societies that would have disappeared long ago. The chapters in this volume are the result of two interdisciplinary symposia held by a group of volcanologists, engineers, Near Eastern and Classical philologists, and Old and New World archaeologists. The first symposium was held in October 1995, in Cumae (Naples), Italy, at the Villa Vergiliana, in the heart of the Italian volcanic region. The second was held in November 1996 in Medford, Massachusetts. The symposia were supported by the Vergilian Society, Brandeis University, Tufts University, and the Kress Foundation.

The participants contemplated the complex problems that arise in volcanic environments and the various ways in which societies respond. Many scholars have dealt, and continue to deal, with specific aspects of volcanism and its impact on local populations. If the scope and content of volcanology at the present time is compared with that of 30 years ago, the contrast could be not be more stark. Whereas in 1970 the subject was dominated by the study of volcanic processes, with scholars being largely drawn from the earth sciences in general and geology, igneous petrology, and geochemistry in particular, today volcanology has become truly multidisciplinary and addresses an increasingly wide variety of issues.

One reason for the changing emphasis has been the stimulus given to volcanic hazard studies through the designation by the United Nations of the 1990s as the International Decade for Natural Disaster Reduction (IDNDR).[1] Put into practice by scientific organizations, especially the International Association of Volcano and Chemistry of the Earth Interior (IAVCEI), the IDNDR has involved the designation of so-called Decade Volcanoes that represent differing styles of activity, are located in a variety of countries (some developed, others developing), and have become the focus for much integrated and multidisciplinary research (IAVCEI, IDNDR 1990; McGuire 1995). During the 1990s there was a perceived need for applied, problem-oriented research by international organizations and scientific policy makers, and this zeitgeist has rapidly diffused through volcanology as a whole, greatly assisted by funding opportunities from both national governments and supranational trading blocs. The European Union's Laboratory Volcanoes Initiative has, for instance, funded research on: Etna in Sicily; Santorini (i.e., Thera) in Greece; Teide in the Canaries; Furnas in the Azores; Krafla in Iceland; and Piton de la Fournaise, Réunion in the Indian Ocean. The Volcano Hazards Program in the U.S. has been a broadly similar policy (Wright and Pierson 1992), as have initiatives in countries as diverse as Italy, Argentina, Japan and Indonesia. Volcanology has clear interdisciplinary ties with medicine, the social sciences, planning and administrative studies. Fields such as evacuation planning, hazard mapping and civil defense have also formed strong but less obvious relationships with the humanities, since all volcanic hazard research requires an understanding of both the past behavior of volcanoes and their impact upon the people who live in the vicinity.

Today volcanologists often work with scholars drawn from archaeology, literary studies and history. One example of this new spirit of cooperation is the reconstruction of the character and impact of the eruptions of Mount Etna in Sicily during the Classical Period using data drawn from geology and ancient literature (Chester et al. 2000).[2] The research of Haraldur Sigurdsson and colleagues from archaeology and volcanology, who have successfully reconstructed events at Vesuvius during the eruption in A.D. 79 (Sigurdsson et al. 1985), is another example. Many of the chapters in the current volume continue and develop this now well-established tradition.

A second reason for the increasingly interdisciplinary character and widening scope of volcanology has been the realization that volcanoes have had major effects on human societies. Since the initial studies of the impact of volcanic eruptions on climate and society in the 1970s (e.g., Lamb 1970), the field has burgeoned and today there are many research teams examining the putative links among volcanoes, climate and weather, and a range of social, economic and political issues. The impact of eruptions on monsoon reliability and strength in India (Mukherjee et al. 1987), historic crop yields in the U.S. (Handler 1985), and European grape harvests (Stommel and Swallow 1983), are just a few examples of such studies. Neo-catastrophism is a frame of reference which acknowledges the significance of high magnitude and low frequency geological and meteorological events as major agents of environmental change and human impact (Gregory 2000; James et al. 2000). The rise and fall of ancient civilizations such as Thera (e.g., Baillie 1995; Polinger-Foster and Ritner 1996; Dalfes et al. 1996; McGuire 1999) is another subject of study. Although in our opinion some of the causal linkages may be over-deterministic and speculative (cf. Keys 1999), we are convinced that this is an exciting new field into which many of the contributions to this volume naturally fall.

Some idea of just how rapidly the field of volcanic impacts on historical societies is developing may be judged by the number of international multidisciplinary volcanological conferences that were held during the 1990s. The Cumae (Naples) and Tufts (Massachusetts) conferences in 1995 and 1996, where the chapters contained in this volume were first presented, and the congress convened by the Geological Society of London in 1997, were notable for the profitable interchange of ideas and the focus on research themes that have eluded single subject perspectives for many years (cf. McGuire et al. 2000). Rather than try to fit these chapters into a single pattern, we have arranged them under a series of topics. This is consistent with the very nature of the subject. Every eruption has its own signature, and thus can only be predicted to a limited degree; this variability is part of the fascination of this topic.

"*Ne plus haustae aut obrutes urbes*" ("no more shall the cities be burned and destroyed"), is the unofficial motto of the Hawaiian Volcano Observatory. This is an unachievable goal, but volcanology seeks to work within its spirit: to reduce the damages of eruptions; to understand why societies have been attracted to and lived in hazardous volcanic regions; and to learn to maximize the resource potential of volcanoes. We trust that this volume successfully captures the comprehensiveness and excitement of the new multidisciplinary research frontier.

The chapters in this volume attempt to cross the barriers between the volcanological, geological, and antiquarian perspectives. In this collection we examine the human response to the changing shape of the volcanic landscape, the assessment of risk, the use of volcanic materials for human habitation and artifacts, and new insights into discoveries at Pompeii after the Vesuvian eruption of A.D. 79. We conclude with the literary evidence of mythological, scientific, and poetic interpretations of volcanic activity in the ancient world.

In the first chapter, "Developments in Volcanology during the Past 30 Years," Chester and Duncan provide an overview of technical and sociological developments in volcanology. They show how the field of applied volcanology has progressed markedly, particularly in methods of volcano prediction and hazard reduction, since Gordon Macdonald's seminal textbook on volcanoes was published (1972). This chapter and others show the necessity of including cultural considerations in any program of hazard reduction for populations living near volcanoes.

"Understanding Vesuvius and Preparing for Its Next Eruption" (Santacroce, Cioni, Marianelli, and Sbrana) demonstrates how eruptions actually occur. The authors examine the history of eruptions of Mount Vesuvius, on the Bay of Naples, and propose some possible future scenarios. Duncan, Chester, and Guest then review the history of eruptions of Mount Etna, which has been continuously active during most of the past 400 years and was the most frequently recognized active volcano in the ancient world. "The Campi Flegrei Nested Caldera (Italy): A Restless, Resurgent Structure in a Densely Populated Area" (Orsi, de Vita, Di Vito, and Isaia) provides a detailed account of the volcanic history of the Campi Flegrei caldera on the Bay of Naples.

The chapters in the next section evaluate risks posed by volcanic eruptions in both the Old and New World and present examples of the manner in which various societies have attempted to adapt to them. "Responses to Eruptions of Etna from the Classical Period to 1900" (Chester, Duncan, and Guest) compares the response of the pre-industrial communities surrounding Mt. Etna to losses caused by eruptions and their methods of recovery. The authors argue that pre-industrial peoples often recovered by harmonizing with nature rather than by trying to manage and control it, as industrial and post-industrial populations have tended to do. They propose a new model of response incorporating the best of these two opposing models. A pre-Hispanic settlement on the slopes of the Popocateptl volcano in central Mexico, which was buried by a plinian eruption in the first century B.C., has been excavated by Plunket and Uruñuela. In "Cultural Responses to Risk and Disaster: An Example from the Slopes of Popocatéptl Volcano in Central Mexico," they reveal artifacts found there, including its altars and shrines, that shed light on this village and its culture and suggest their response to the volcanic environment.

Maniscalco discusses the settlements of the Copper and Early Bronze Ages located on the western slopes of Mount Etna in Sicily, near the salt-flats of San Marco Paternò. The unique springs of Paternò continue to provide much-valued mineral waters. Exploration of these settlements is yielding evidence of an interesting reaction to volcanic activity, including a large Neolithic wall built by the Castelluccian culture (1600–1400 B.C.) to channel the volcanic mudflow from Mt. Etna. From the same site, Nicoletti examines prehistoric chipped stone tools, and Di Rosa analyzes human skeletal remains.

The volcanic island of Vivara in the Bay of Naples provides evidence of the early Aegean-Mycenaean trade with western Mediterranean countries, as shown by Giardino and Pepe in "The Island of Vivara: An International Port of Trade of the Middle of the Second Millennium B.C. in a Volcanic Landscape."

The use of volcanic materials for human habitation in Rome, Sardinia, and Turkey is the focus of the next group of chapters. De Rita and Giampaolo ("Local Volcanic Building Stones Used in the Construction of Ancient Rome") closely analyze the volcanic materials used in the development of the city of Rome, providing a history of construction technology between the Archaic and Imperial Ages. Balmuth in "Pozzolana: The Contribution of the Volcanic Landscape to the Creation of a New Architectural Aesthetic," continues in this vein by demonstrating the impact of volcanic materials, specifically tuff and pozzolana, on the development of Roman construction technology. Ginesu and Sias, in "Landscape Evolution and the First Human Settlements in Sardinia," examine the development of monuments, tombs, and walls which reflect the peculiar Sardinian response to the volcanic landscape. In Turkey, the curious, "fairy chimneys" of Cappadocia now house a wide range of structures, from simple dwellings to apartment houses to great cathedrals. Burri, Massoli-Novelli, and Petitta examine the volcanic origins of these "fairy chimneys" in "Ignimbrites, Rock-Hewn Churches and Underground Settlements in Cappadocia (Turkey)."

In "Pyroclastic Temper in Apulian Bronze Age Pottery: The Far-reaching Impact of a Vesuvian Eruption," the authors (Levi, Vanzetti, Cioni, Fratini, and Pecchioni) identify traces of an early Vesuvian eruption. These traces indicate that an eruption of Vesuvius spread its materials much farther than previously realized, since Vesuvian pumice was used as temper in Apulian prehistoric pottery. Their results also remind us of the unique chemical signature of each volcanic eruption.

The evidence provided by Vesuvius and Pompeii during the first century A.D. is then examined in light of the human response to the volcanic threat. Varone and Marturano, in "The A.D. 79 Eruption: Seismic Activity and Effects of the Eruption on Pompeii," present new finds that show the effects of the eruption on the topography of the city. Conticello, former Director of

Pompeii, discusses his attempts to preserve the site while making it more accessible to the general population in "The Introduction of Applied Sciences in the Study of an Ancient Site: Pompeii." Koloski-Ostrow then reports on studies of "Water Use in Pompeii Between the Earthquake and the Eruption."

Finally, the literature of antiquity is considered as another important source of information concerning the human response to volcanic environments. In "Volcanic Echoes in Ancient Near Eastern Tests," Foster identifies ancient texts relating to the Bronze Age eruption of Thera and to volcanic activity in Mesopotamia from the third millennium on. In "Volcanoes in Classical Mythology," Johnston surveys mythological accounts of volcanic activity in Greek and Roman literature from the Classical period. The explanations she finds include the restless rage of a giant pinned there against his will, activity in the god Vulcan's smithy, and a passageway to the Underworld. In the final chapter, Smolenaars examines early "scientific" explanations of volcanism in Lucretius and later Roman literature in "Earthquakes and Eruptions in Latin Literature: Reflections and Emotional Responses."

It is hoped that this blend of articles will lead to increased appreciation across the disciplines for contributions that have previously been considered discrete modes of inquiry and that they will encourage future interactions between these and other fields of study. Because of the interdisciplinary character of this collection, a Glossary of Terms has been provided at the end of this volume.

REFERENCES

Baillie, M.G.L. 1995. *A Slice through Time*. London.

Chester, D.K., A.M. Duncan, J.E. Guest, P.A. Johnston, and J.J.L. Smolenaars. 2000. "Human Response to Etna Volcano during the Classical Period." In *The Archaeology of Geological Catastrophes*, edited W.J. McGuire, D.R. Griffiths, P.L Hancock, and I.S. Stewart, 179–188. Geological Society Special Publication 171. London.

Dalfes, H.M., G. Kukla, and H. Weis. 1996. *Third Millennium B.C. Climate Change and Old World Collapse*. Berlin and New York.

Gregory, K.J. 2000. *The Changing Nature of Physical Geography*. London.

Hamilton, R. 1999. "Natural Disaster Reduction in the 21st Century." In *Natural Disaster Management*, edited by J. Ingleton, 304–7. Leicester.

Handler, P. 1985. "Possible Association between the Climatic Effects of Stratospheric Aerosols and Corn Yields in the United States." *Agricultural Meteorology* 35:205–28.

Fisher, R.V., G. Heiken and J.B. Hulen. 1997. *Volcanoes: Crucibles of Change*. Princeton.

IAVCEI IDNDR Task Group. 1990. "Reducing Volcanic Disasters in the 1990s." *Bulletin of the Volcanological Society of Japan* 35:80–95.

James, P.A., D.K. Chester, and A.M. Duncan. 2000. "Soils of Quaternary Volcanic Lavas: Some Archaeological Considerations." In *The Archaeology of Geological Catastrophes*, edited by W.J. McGuire, D.R. Griffiths, P.L Hancock, and I.S. Stewart, 317–38. Geological Society Special Publication 171. London.

Keys, D. 1999. *Catastrophe: An Investigation into the Origins of the Modern World.* London.

Lamb, H.H. 1970. "Volcanic Dust in the Atmosphere; With a Chronology and Assessment of Its Meteorological Significance." *Philosophical Transactions of the Royal Society of London* A266: 425–533.

Macdonald, Gordon. 1972. *Volcanoes.* Englewood Cliffs.

McGuire, B. 1999. *Apocalypse: A Natural History of Global Disasters.* London.

McGuire, W.J. 1995. "Prospects for Volcano Surveillance." In *Monitoring Active Volcanoes*, edited by W.J. McGuire, C. Kilburn, and J. Murray, 403–10. London.

McGuire, W.J., D.R. Griffiths, P.L. Hancock, and I.S. Stewart, eds. 2000. *The Archaeology of Geological Catastrophes.* Geological Society Special Publication 171. London.

Mukherjee, B.K., K. Indira, and K.K. Dani. 1987. "Low Latitude Volcanic Eruptions and Their Effects on Sri Lankan Rainfall during the North East Monsoon." *Journal of Climatology* 7:145–55.

Polinger-Foster, K., and R.K. Ritner. 1996. "Texts, Storms and the Thera Eruption." *Journal of Near Eastern Studies* 55(1):1–14.

Sigurdsson, H., S. Carey, W. Cornell, and T. Pescatore. 1985: "The Eruption of Vesuvius in A.D. 79." *Natural Geographic Review* 1(3):332–87.

Stommel, H. and J.C. Swallow. 1983. "Do Late Grape Harvests Follow Large Volcanic Eruptions?" *Bulletin of the American Meteorological Society* 64:794–5.

United Nations. 1999. *International Decade for Natural Disaster Reduction: Successor Arrangement.* New York.

Wright, T.L., and T.C. Pierson. 1992. *Living with Volcanoes: The U.S. Geological Survey's Volcano Hazards Program.* United States Geological Survey Circular 1073. Washington, D.C.

NOTES

[1] IDNDR ended in 2000 and has been replaced by a new United Nations initiative, the International Strategy for Disaster Reduction (ISDR). Key words and phrases in this new strategy are: public awareness; moving from cultures of reaction to cultures of prevention; vulnerable groups, and maintaining the sustainability of hazard-prone areas. The interdisciplinary focus is likely to be further strengthened and historical perspectives are again going to be vital (cf. Hamilton 1999; United Nations 1999).

[2] Some idea of the interface between volcanology and archaeology may be gleaned from McGuire et al. 2000.

PART I

VOLCANOLOGY, RISK ASSESSMENT, AND EMERGENCY PLANNING

— I —

Developments in Volcanology
during the Past 30 Years

◈

David K. Chester and Angus M. Duncan

Thirty years ago, Gordon A. Macdonald's seminal textbook, *Volcanoes*, was published (1972). This fluently written and highly accessible work integrated several strands which were extant in volcanology at the time. As the papers in the present volume make clear, volcanoes have proved of great interest to humanity for thousands of years. Sometimes this fascination has proved fatal, but from the 18th century onward, descriptive volcanology has been placed on a more scientific basis, becoming part and parcel of the developing science of geology which emerged in the wake of the European Enlightenment (e.g., Hamilton 1772; Scrope 1825; Lyell 1830; Judd 1888; Dana 1890; Daly 1911; Rittmann 1936; Cotton 1944; Bullard 1962). From the early years of the present century, this essentially descriptive tradition has been strengthened by the integration of important insights which were emerging from the rapidly developing field of igneous petrology (e.g., Hatch, Wells, and Wells 1972; Bowen 1928; Daly 1933). As the century progressed, some preliminary attempts were made at volcano prediction and hazard reduction (Neumann van Padang 1934; Jaggar 1931, 1945; Macdonald 1958; Minakami 1960) and the possible impact of volcanoes on climate was considered, especially by Hubert Lamb (Lamb 1970; see also Symons 1888; Wexler 1952; Budyko 1968).

It became apparent that the most important variable controlling eruptive style, climatic impact, and degree of hazard was magma type (fig. 1.1 and

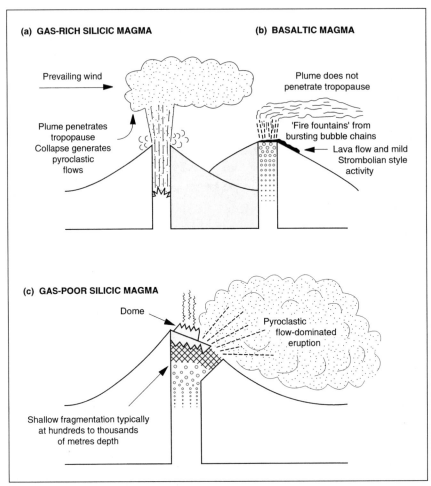

Fig. 1.1. Three distinctive types of eruption produced by basaltic and silicic magmas. Silicic magmas include andesitic, trachytic, dacitic, and rhyolitic. (Modified from Clapperton 1977, fig. 1.7)

table 1.1), specifically whether the melt was silicic (gas-rich or gas-poor) or basaltic. It was recognized that volcanoes could interact with the wider physical environment, but the areas of interaction were confined largely to climate and the generation of volcanic mud and debris flows, also known as lahars (Macdonald 1972, 170–82; see fig. 1.2 and table 1.2).

Macdonald's review was partial in one important respect; volcanism was only tentatively related to the model of plate tectonics, which by 1972 was rapidly becoming accepted as foundational to all understanding within the earth sciences. The 1960s saw significant attempts being made to link volcanic

Table 1.1. Summary of pure and applied volcanological knowledge in the early 1970s. Magma type was viewed as the major causal mechanism. The table should be read in conjunction with figure 1.1. (After Chester 1993)

	Magma Type		
	Basaltic	**Andesitic/Trachytic**	**Rhyolitic**
Morphology	Low angle lava *shields*. More silica-rich basalts produce higher angle *strato-shields*.	Interbedded lavas and pyroclastic materials produce *strato* cones. Angles of 30° are not uncommon.	Domes and calderas are dominant.
Eruptive Style	Hawaiian/Strombolian	Plinian	Peléan/Ignimbritic
Products	Mostly lava flows. Eruptive columns do not penetrate the tropopause. Dispersals of airfall material are localized.	Widespread dispersal of airfall ashes from eruptive columns reaching the stratosphere. Pyroclastic flows (i.e., glowing avalanches, nueé ardente) are produced. Ashfall and pyroclastic flows.	Large volume ignimbrites. Lavas of limited volume and length; domes are common.
Climatic Impacts	Local and regional.	May cause global climatic effects.	Airfall material may be injected into the stratosphere and cause climatic effects.
Hazard	Lava flows sterilize land. Limited risk of mortality.	Major cause of death in historic eruptions.	Ignimbritic eruptions are very infrequent. Peléan eruptions are similar to plinian, but the effects are more widespread.
Examples	Etna, volcanoes of Hawaii and Iceland.	Vesuvias, volcanoes of the Cascades and Andes.	Mont Pelée (Martinique), large ignimbritic and caldera forming eruptions of Campi Flegrei.

Table 1.2. The principal causes of volcanic debris flows (lahars) (After Macdonald 1972, 170–81) Each of the types involves water being mixed with loose rock fragments. Types 2, 3, 9, and 10 may occur independently of any eruption.

Types of Flow	Description
1	During an eruption water is ejected from a crater lake.
2	Release of water from a crater lake, caused by the breaking of its walls.
3	Rapid melting of snow and ice on the slopes of a volcano.
4	Avalanches of rock enter stream and river courses during an explosive eruption.
5	Descent of glowing avalanches (i.e., pyroclastic flows) into stream and river courses.
6	Entry of autobrecciated (i.e., self-broken) lava flows into stream and river courses.
7	Lava flows over snow, ice, or saturated ground on the slopes of a volcano, causing it to break into fragments, by processes of brecciation.
8	Extrusion of already brecciated lava from a volcano conduit before it reaches the ground surface.
9	Heavy rainfall on loose material on the slopes of a volcano.
10	The movement of water-saturated fragments down the slopes of a volcano caused by seismic activity.

activity to a global pattern of plate movements and boundaries (Hess 1962; Vine and Matthews 1963; Wilson 1965).

Macdonald's book was a masterly overview of the current thinking in volcanology and provided a firm foundation for the emerging studies of the physical mechanisms of volcanic processes, experimental and modeling studies, and the increasing awareness of the social implications of volcanology. It is the purpose of this chapter to indicate the flavor of developments in the broad field of volcanology over the succeeding 30 years. As such, the coverage is not intended to be comprehensive and not all significant achievements are mentioned. For more comprehensive reviews reference should be made to Sigurdsson (2000) and Schmincke (2004).

Progress in Research on Physical Processes

It is possible to review progress in the understanding of volcanic processes at two closely related scales: the global and planetary scale; and the scale of the individual volcano.

Planetary and Global Volcanism

According to Ron Greeley (1994:1), two scientific revolutions in the 1960s had profound effects on the earth sciences, which are still being felt today. One revolution was the insight into the long-term internal workings of the Earth provided by exploration of the inner, or terrestrial, planets of the solar system (i.e., the Earth, Mars, Mercury, and Venus) which established that volcanism was an important process on all the terrestrial planets (Guest et al. 1979; Murray et al. 1981; Condie 1982, 1989; Guest and Greeley 1985; Greeley 1994). Because volcanism was so critical to an understanding of the solar system, research into volcanoes on Earth was well funded and received in depth attention from physicists and mathematical modelers as well as from geologists and geochemists.

Greeley's second revolution involved the plate tectonics model, which by the middle of the 1970s had become the accepted paradigm for the whole of the earth sciences (see Ringwood 1975; Windley 1977; Brown and Mussett 1981). For the first time volcanism could be related to global tectonic movements in a convincing fashion (fig. 1.2 and table 1.3). Debate still surrounds some aspects of the model and in certain regions the detailed relationships of global tectonics and igneous processes remain controversial (Van Andel

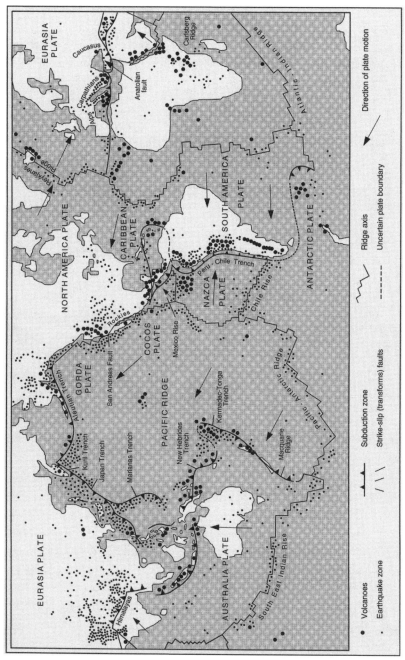

Fig. 1.2. The distribution of active volcanoes, major lithospheric plates, and divergent (ridge) and convergent (subduction) plate margins (Based on Chester 1993: 28, with additions and amendments)

Table 1.3. The workings of the plate tectonics model and its relationship to processes of magma generation and eruptive style. This table should be read in conjunction with figure 1.2. (Based on the sources cited in the body of the table and Condie 1989; Cox 1989)

Intra-Plate	Divergent	Convergent
Predominantly basaltic. Fed by partial melting in the Upper Mantle.	*Magma Type* Mid-Ocean ridges (MOR) are composed of MOR basalt (*tholeiite*), as are the ocean floors. Continental rifts show a more varied petrological assemblage, (i.e., basalt to more silica-rich trachyte/rhyolite). Magma originates in the upper mantle, but MOR and continental magmatism may represent different depths of petrogenesis. Crustal contamination may be significant in the case of continental rift magmas.	A wide range of magmas, but more silica rich (andesitic and rhyolitic/trachytic) melts predominate. Magmas are generated by subduction (slippage of one plate under another).
Oceanic Typified by Hawaii. Basaltic lava flows are dominant.	*Oceanic* MOR ~85% intruded to form ocean floors, the remainder erupted to form islands and seamounts.	*Continental Margin* Explosive volcanic activity, e.g., Andes and Cascade mountain ranges.
Continental Eruption of large areas of 'flood' basalt (e.g., Deccan Region, India)	*Continental* Typified by the East African Rift and the Basin and Range Province (U.S.). Basaltic eruptions produce mostly lava. More silica-rich melts produce domes, pyroclastic flows (including ignimbrite), air-falls, and surges.	*Island Arc* Varied suite of magmas depending on detailed morphology and geometry of the arc. Typified by the volcanoes of the East Indies.

1984; Cox and Hart 1986; Hamilton 1988; Nance et al. 1988; J.T. Wilson 1988; Cox 1989).

The effects of volcanism on climate at the global scale are also much better understood today than they were in the early 1970s. Hubert Lamb's (1970) thesis stated that dust injections into the stratosphere had worldwide climatic effects if eruptions were close to the equator, but that those at higher latitudes affected only the hemisphere in question. The effects, including a lowering of temperature by 1–3°C, lasted 1–3 years and dust injections could be measured by the dust veil index (DVI), which was scaled to produce a notional value of 1000 for the Krakatau, Indonesia, eruption of 1883.

Over the past quarter century, close study of contemporary and historic eruptions and the tracing of the sedimentological signatures of eruptions, particularly in ice (Hammer 1977; Hammer et al. 1981; Stothers and Rampino 1983a) and deep sea cores (Self and Sparks 1981), has greatly improved knowl-

Criteria	VEI	0	1	2	3	4	5	6	7	8
Description		Non-explosive	Small	Moderate	Mod-large	Large	Very large ---------			
Volume of ejecta (m^3)		<10^4	10^4-10^6	10^6-10^7	10^7-10^8	10^8-10^9	10^8-10^9	10^{10}-10^{11}	10^{11}-10^{12}	10^{12}
(Tsuya classification) *		(I)	(II-III)	(IV)	(V)	(VI)	(VII)	(VIII)	(IX) --------	
Column height (km)		<0.1	0.1-1	1-5	3-15	10-25	>25			
Qualitative description		-------- 'gentle, effusive' ------- -------- 'explosive' -------- 'cataclysmic, paroxysmal, colossal' --------								
						'severe, violent, terrific' ----------------------------				
Classification		---------------------- 'Strombolian' ----- --------- 'Plinian'								
		----------- 'Hawaiian' ------ --------------------- 'Vulcanian' ----------- 'Ultra-Plinian' --------								
Duration (hours)		--------------- <1 ---------------------				---------------- >12 --------------			
of continuous blast				-------------- 1-6 -------------						
					-------------------------------- 6-12 -----------------					
CAVW max explosivity ●		Lava flows ----------------------- Explosion or nuée ardente ------------								
		----------- Phreatic --------- -----------------------------------								
		Dome or mudflow								
Tropospheric injection		Negligible	Minor	Moderate	Substantial ------------------					
Stratospheric injection		None	None	None	Possible	Definite	Significant -------			

* If all eruptive products were pyroclastic ejecta
● The most explosive activity indicated for the eruption in the Catalogue of Active Volcanoes
Criteria are listed in decreasing order of reliability

Fig. 1.3. Criteria used in the estimation of the volcanic explosivity index (VEI) (From Newhall and Self 1982, table 1.1) As the table shows, the index is based solely on volcanological criteria to avoid the circular reasoning inherent in the DVI. The size of an eruption may be calculated using any one or more of five parameters to allow both historical and present day eruptions to be scaled: magnitude (volume of *ejecta*), intensity (volume of *ejecta* per unit time, calculated from column height and exit velocities), dispersive power (measured by column height), violence of release of kinetic energy (similar to intensity, but relevant to instantaneous rather than sustained eruptions), and destructive potential. Further details about the conventions used in calculating the VEI are given in Newhall and Self (1982). It should be noted that current nomenclature favors pyroclastic flow over nuée ardente and hydrovolcanic in place of Vulcanian.

edge of the links between volcanoes and climate. This has lead to modification of many of Lamb's conclusions. First, it is clear that the DVI involves circular reasoning in the calculation of some of its formulae. The volcanic explosivity index (VEI), developed by the Smithsonian Institution (Newhall and Self 1982), is now generally accepted as a better measure of eruption magnitude (fig. 1.3). Secondly, studies of eruptive columns, especially those produced in 1981 by Mt. St. Helens, United States, in 1982 by El Chichón, Mexico, and in 1991 by Mt. Pinatubo, Philippines, using satellite and aircraft-based remote sensing techniques, particularly correlation spectrometry (COSPEC), have demonstrated that sulphate aerosols, rather than silicate particles, are the main agents producing temperature depression (Newell 1981), since the former have a much longer residence time in the atmosphere than the latter. Thirdly, investigation into the effects of volcanoes on climate has been extended to many scales of study, both temporal and spatial. At the largest scale and over the longest

time period, the relationships between volcanic degassing and atmospheric evolution of the earth and other terrestrial planets, (Cogley and Henderson-Sellers
1984; Kasting et al.) and the complex questions of causality between volcanic
injections to the atmosphere and Pleistocene Ice Ages have been investigated
(Rampino et al. 1979; Rampino and Stothers 1985). Volcano-induced climatic
change has also been invoked to explain the nature and reliability of Pacific
Ocean El Niño events (Handler 1986a, 1989), Indian monsoons (Handler
1986b; Mukherjee et al. 1987), varying crop yields in the United States
(Handler 1985), and European grape harvests (Stommel and Swallow 1983).
The possible links between volcanoes and climate have also been explored at
more local scales of analysis (see Chester 1993, 178–80).

The study of gases has yielded valuable information about magmatic
processes, and is also being used as an aid to predicting eruptions (Tedesco
1995; also, see below). While a high loss of life was caused in 1986 when volcanic gas was discharged from Lake Nyos in the Cameroons (Sigvaldason
1989), it is now widely recognized that gases may present a potential threat to
long-term health on active volcanoes as well (Baxter 1990). The field of volcanism, gas emission, and climatic change is one in which extremely rapid
progress has been made in little over a quarter of a century and general reviews
are found in Chester (1988, 1993) and Francis (1993). Of particular interest to
the archaeologist and historian is Michael Baillie's book, *A Slice Through Time*
(1995), and recent papers by Stothers and Rampino (1983b), Lough and Fritts
(1987), Forsyth (1988), Burgess (1989), Blackford et al. (1992), Stothers
(1996), and the chapters by Karen Polinger-Foster and Patricia Plunket and
Gabriela Uruñuela in this volume.

The Scale of the Individual Volcano
Processes of global tectonism and magma generation explain in a general
sense why magma type varies between different volcanic provinces (table
1.3). To understand mechanisms of magma delivery and eruption more
specifically necessitates the detailed study of individual volcanoes and eruption sites. As was noted earlier, progress has been rapid since the early 1970s
and has occurred in several research fields.

Internal Plumbing
Once a batch of magma approaches the surface of the earth, it may become
ponded in a magma chamber. Magma reservoirs are typically located at depths

of between approximately 1 and 15 km and may comprise a plexus of sills and dykes. The internal structure of volcanoes and the nature of magma reservoirs have been explored by a number of geophysical techniques including seismology and more recently seismic tomography (Sharp et al. 1980; Cardaci et al. 1993), geomagnetism (Stuart and Johnston 1975), gravity anomalies and changes in microgravity prior to and during eruptions (Eggers et al. 1976; Brown et al. 1991; Rymer 1995), and precise leveling of the ground surface (Fiske and Kinoshita 1969). It has been known since the 1920s that the residence of magma within a chamber allows geochemical changes to take place during cooling, through processes such as fractional crystallization, which will result in more silicic derived magmas being generated (Bowen 1928; Eaton and Murata 1960). Over the last 30 years, however, many additional geochemical processes have been inferred both from field data and from experimental testing in the laboratory. A detailed review of this complex and fascinating field is beyond the scope of the present introductory summary; for detailed discussion, see O'Hara and Matthews (1981); Marsh (1984), and Ryan (1990).

A simpler summary is to be found in Chester (1993, 61–5), while Guest and Duncan (1981) and Santacroce et al. (this volume) provide interesting case studies for Etna and Vesuvius respectively; which demonstrate how changes in magma chamber dynamics and volcano internal plumbing can lead to differing eruptive styles, posing a range of threats to people and their activities.

Lava Flows and Domes

Major advances in understanding lava landforms have come about through the stimulus and funds provided as a spin-off from space programs, since terrestrial lavas provide easily studied analogues of processes which may have operated on other terrestrial planets, and through the investigation of the physical properties of lava, particularly their rheology (Hulme 1974; Pinkerton and Sparks 1978; McBirney and Murase 1984; Chester et al. 1995, 188–228; Wilson et al. 1987). For detailed discussion of lava flows and domes, reference should be made to books by Fink (1990) and by Kilburn and Luongo (1993). Significant advances have been made in the following areas:

1. For basaltic volcanoes on land, it is now firmly established that lava flow length and plan area are related to effusion rate, that is, volume erupted per unit time and duration (Walker 1973; Lopes and Guest 1982; Pieri and Baloga 1986). Differences in

morphology (i.e., between *aa*, *pahoehoe*, and *toothpaste* flows), may be explained by the relationship between viscosity and rate of shear (Peterson and Tilling 1980; Kilburn 1981; Rowland and Walker 1987; Pinkerton 1989).

2. Flood basalt terrains, such as the large volume basaltic provinces of the Deccan of India and the Karoo of South Africa, are related to large mantle plumes, but the vast amounts of lava involved require that processes of melting are supplemented by the decompression forces produced by large-scale uplift of near-surface layers of the Earth by rising plume heads (Cox 1989; White and McKenzie 1995).

3. On volcanoes fed by more silica-rich magmas, lavas are generally too viscous to flow far from their source vents. On andesitic volcanoes, short blocky lavas are typically produced, but for rhyolitic melts, the most characteristic landform is the volcanic dome. Understanding the physical processes responsible for producing differing dome morphologies has shown significant advance over the past quarter century (Fink 1990).

4. Progress has also been made—albeit more modest because of difficulties of accessibility—in understanding processes of subaqueous lava emplacement (see Chester 1993, 96–101 for a review).

The Pyroclastic Suite

Perhaps the greatest change to have occurred in volcanology over the past 30 years is that knowledge of the pyroclastic suite (i.e., fragmental materials produced by eruptions) has burgeoned, so that today the field would be unrecognizable to a scholar active in the early 1970s. Comprehensive accounts are to be found in Fisher and Schmincke (1984), Wilson (1986), Cas and Wright (1987), and Francis (1993).

Of primary importance is that a completely new set of processes and deposits are now recognized. Known as cold, wet, or base surges, they result from explosive activity produced by so-called fluid/coolant reactions, in which water interacts with magma (at ideal ratios of 0.3 to unity) to produce highly mobile, highly dangerous mixtures of steam, water, and fragments. Although some early papers pointed to the importance of water/magma interaction (Jaggar 1949; Moore et al. 1966), it was a combination of careful observation of eruptions, theoretical modeling, and laboratory simulations which allowed a series of seminal papers to be published that explicitly addressed the importance of what is now called hydrovolcanism (Self and Sparks 1978; Wilson et al. 1978; Kokelaar 1983, 1986; Sheridan and Wohletz 1981, 1983; Wohletz 1983, 1986; Heiken and Wohletz 1985; Wohletz and McQueen 1984; Carey et al. 1996).

Second in importance only to the hydrovolcanism have been improvements in the scientific understanding of hot fragmental flows—perhaps the most dangerous manifestation of volcanic activity. Until recently these highly mobile hot fragmental flows were known by a variety of names, including glowing avalanche deposits, ignimbrites, and nuée ardente—but a two-fold classification, pyroclastic flows and surges (see Chester 1993, 102–57, for a discussion), is generally adopted today. Pyroclastic flows have been exhibited in many historic eruptions, including: Vesuvius, Italy, in A.D. 79; Mt. Lamington, Papua, in 1951; Mt. St. Helens, United States, in 1980, and Mount Pinatubo, Philippines, in 1991, and may be produced by a variety of mechanisms which include collapse of the erupting column (at Vesuvius); boiling over of a mass of material too dense to form a eruptive column (at Mt. Lamington) or a directed blast (at Mt. St. Helens). Important papers include Wilson (1976, 1980), Sparks and Wilson (1976), Wilson et al. (1978), Carey and Sparks (1986), Branney and Kokelaar (1992), and Santacroce et al. (this volume).

Ignimbrite is a term that is generally reserved for the deposits of pumiceous pyroclastic flows (Sparks et al. 1973; Walker 1981, 1982). For many pyroclastic flows, like those of Thera (Santorini) and Vesuvius in A.D. 79, models of column collapse have been invoked (Sparks and Wilson 1976), but for the largest examples there remains a conspicuous lack of consensus. Many large ignimbrites (e.g., Crater Lake, Mount Mazama, United States), however, are related to calderas and in many cases may have been formed by high magnitude caldera forming eruptions (Francis 1983; Self and Wright 1983; Cas and Wright 1987; Scandone 1990; see also Orsi et al., this volume).

Pyroclastic surges are often associated with pyroclastic flows. Although of low particle concentration, they are highly dangerous, move at great speed, and, like flows, kill by heat and asphyxiation (Baxter 1990; Francis 1993, 208–65).

Table 1.4. Aspects of volcano instability. (Based on McGuire 1996, with additional information from Foxworthy and Hill 1982; Ui 1983; and Siebert 1984, 1992)

Type of Instability	Characteristics
Directed (or lateral) blast	Explosive blasts caused by the lateral failure of a volcano's wall rocks. Produced by either a sudden decompression of magmatic gases or the explosion of a high-pressure hydrovolcanic system, blasts may be triggered by the sudden removal of the confining rocks by some outside agency. In the case of Mt. St. Helens, a tectonic earthquake was responsible for slope failure around a large bulge on the north side of the volcano. This led to an unroofing of the magma chamber. Eruption products were blasted preferentially to the north.
Debris, avalanches/slope failures, and collapse events	Avalanche deposits may be generated not only as rockfall but also from collapse of whole sectors of a volcano. Instability and collapse are common on volcanoes and occur at different scales. Volcanological and external environmental factors may encourage the initiation of debris avalanches, collapses and slope instability. Volcanological factors include: 　i.　steep slope 　ii.　over-steepening caused by lava intrusion 　iii.　high surface loading by lava flows and pyroclastic deposits 　iv.　dyke emplacement 　v.　spreading of the edifice under its own weight 　vi.　seismic activity associated with magma movement. Environmental factors include: 　i.　meteorological events (e.g. high rainfall causing saturated ground) 　ii.　in the case of coastal volcanoes, sea level changes and coastal erosion 　iii.　long-term climatic changes 　iv.　processes of human-induced slope instability (e.g. induced erosion, changes to hydrological systems) 　v.　tectonic earthquakes and fault activity in adjacent non-volcanic terrains.

Volcano Instability

One of the major growth areas in research since 1980 has been stimulated by the realization that hazards are not simply a function of magma type (table 1.1 and fig. 1.1), but that volcanoes are often intrinsically unstable landforms that are capable of interacting with the environment in a number of ways. The generation of lahars and hydrovolcanism are discussed above, but, directed blasts, debris avalanches, edifice collapses and other forms of instability have also been given much prominence in the recent research literature (McGuire 1996; McGuire et al. 1996). A summary of these exciting and new research areas is given in table 1.4, which shows that volcanoes may present a significant hazard to people and their activities even when they are not in eruption.

Progress in Hazard and Risk Assessment

Applied volcanology has had a long history. During the 1669 eruption of Etna which threatened Catania, Diego Pappalardo and his colleagues attempted to divert a lava flow which was threatening their city (see papers by Chester et al. and Duncan et al. in this volume). In 1855 L. Palmieri, working on Vesuvius, recognized that seismic activity may precede eruptions (Hoernes 1893). Early in the last century there were early attempts at hazard mapping in Indonesia (Neumann van Padang 1960), while in the 1940s and 1950s attempts were being made to divert lava flows in Hawaii (Macdonald 1958). It is only since the early 1970s, however, that volcanic hazard and risk assessment have become important fields of applied research in their own right.

Procedures of hazard prediction belong to two families (Walker 1974). First, there is general prediction, also known as hazard mapping or assessment (Latter 1989a). This approach investigates "the past behavior record of a volcano to determine the frequency, magnitude and style of eruptions, and to delineate high-risk areas" (Walker 1974, 23). The result of this methodology has generally been a hazard map, which may be used as a basis for civil defense measures, evacuation planning, zoning for insurance purposes, and as a tool to guide new development. Figure 1.4 is an example of a conventional hazard map for the Etna volcano (Duncan et al. 1981). A major trend in recent years has been the development of computer-based mapping techniques (Wadge and Isaacs 1988; Wadge 1994). These techniques allow maps to be rapidly updated even during the course of an eruption and enable other relevant data on features such as population density, evacuation routes and emergency facilities to be stored on the same database. Over the past 30 years general prediction has been a—perhaps *the*—success story of applied volcanology and a significant factor in hazard reduction in many parts of the world (Crandell and Mullineaux 1978; Tazieff and Sabroux 1983; Chester 1993, 196–213; Wadge 1994).

Specific prediction, which involves surveillance and monitoring, has been developed to forecast the actual time, place, and magnitude of an eruption. This requires the recognition of the precursors of activity and calls for the long-term geophysical observation of a volcano. The major precursors that are used to predict volcanoes are seismicity, deformation of the ground surface, changes in gas volume and species, changes in heat flux, and a wide variety of other less common techniques including procedures based on gravity, geo-electrical, and geomagnetic measurements (Latter 1989b; McGuire et al. 1995). Techniques of specific prediction are costly and require long-term research programs, skilled personnel, and expensive equipment (Chester

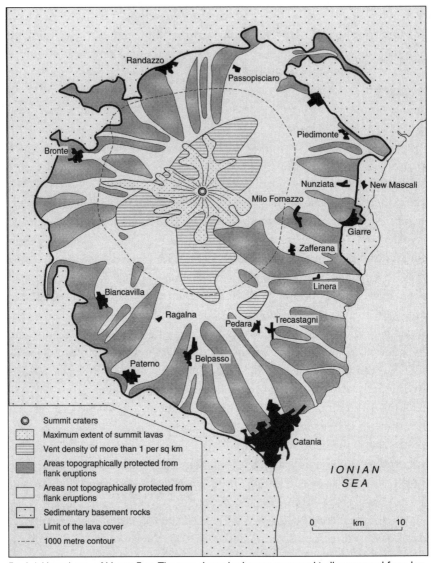

Fig. 1.4. Hazard map of Mount Etna. The map shows both areas topographically protected from lava flows and areas of high eruptive vent density where most future eruptions will be initiated and settlements will be at risk. (From Duncan et al. 1981, 176, with permission)

1993, 213–4). The most extensive applications of specific prediction, therefore, tend to occur in economically developed countries, with the United States, Japan, Italy, Iceland, and New Zealand leading the way. Many dangerous volcanoes in poor countries remain unmonitored (see below).

The detailed behavior of each individual volcano is unique. Many volcanoes erupt infrequently, providing little opportunity to establish the nature of their precursory phenomena. Identification and interpretation of precursors is a challenging task, and it is arguable that the success of specific prediction has not been so marked as that which has occurred for general prediction (McGuire et al. 1995). In 1987, the General Assembly of the United Nations designated the 1990s as the International Decade for Natural Disaster Reduction (IDNDR). This encouraged the applied volcanological community to widen its net, particularly in seeking to reduce hazard exposure in economically less developed countries. The impact of the social sciences has been considerable and has emphasized that to be effective, the technology and procedures of hazard reduction cannot simply be transferred from one volcanic area to another regardless of social context (see Hewitt 1983, 1997, for powerful critiques of traditional hazard reduction studies). It is now widely recognized that for maximum effectiveness planning policies developed from hazard reduction programs have to be tailored to the specific vulnerability of the population living on the volcano. Policies have to be strongly incultured within the unique social milieu of a volcanic region (Blaikie et al. 1994). An example of this new approach is research currently being undertaken by the authors and others on identifying issues pertinent to the evacuation of people living in the vicinity of Furnas Volcano, São Miguel, Azores (Guest et al. 1994; Chester et al. 1995). Here conventional hazard mapping has been combined with detailed cultural, social, and economic surveys, so that evacuation plans can be tailored specifically to the social and cultural characteristics of the people who will require evacuation in the event of a future eruption. Such an approach is also being developed for the areas around the volcanoes of Campi Flegrei and Vesuvius in Italy (Orsi et al. 1996 and Santacroce et al., this volume).

Conclusions

Both pure and applied volcanology has changed rapidly over the past 30 years and change is still occurring (See Sigurdsson 2000 and Schmincke 2004). One major area of development is the recognition that eruptions and the processes causing them are important in many academic disciplines and that joint research has the potential to be mutually enriching. Many such fields have been discussed in this short review, but there are two others that deserve mention. Volcanologists and historians study the effects of volcanic eruptions from differing perspectives. The present authors and others have, for example, used historical data sources and interviews with survivors to reconstruct the nature and effects of the very destructive 1928 eruption of Etna (Duncan et al. 1996). A similar approach has been used to investigate many aspects of the lengthy (1943–1952) eruption of Parícutin volcano in Mexico (Luhr and Simkin 1983). Over a wider canvas, a pioneer study by Stommel and Stommel (1983) has successfully unraveled the complexities of climate history, the eruption of Tambora, Indonesia, in 1815 and the political and social events that followed it. What is perhaps the most intriguing research also concerns Tambora; the global climatic effects of this eruption have been enlisted to account in part for the defeat of Napoleon's army at the Battle of Waterloo (McWilliam 1996).

In all such volcanological and historical studies, there is a danger of introducing unwarranted environmentally deterministic links between eruptions and human responses to them. Such pitfalls are carefully avoided by the authors quoted above but, as the history of geography in the early 20th century has shown, the danger of unfounded determinism is present in all research fields which lie at the interface between the earth sciences and the humanities (Johnston 1995, 40–1): great care is required.

In the field of volcanology and archaeology, a pioneer paper on the A.D. 79 eruption of Vesuvius (Sigurdsson et al. 1985) yielded important information of mutual benefit to both disciplines. Research involving archaeologists, classicists, volcanologists, paleoclimatologists, and linguists, has already helped to answer some—but by no means all—the questions raised by the high magnitude eruption of the Thera (Santorini) volcano in the Aegean Bronze Age (Hardy et al. 1990; Hardy and Renfrew 1990; see Polinger-Foster, this volume). The present volume builds on this fruitful interdisciplinary focus.

REFERENCES

Baillie, M.G.L. 1995. *A Slice through Time*. London.

Baxter, P.J. 1990. "Medical Aspects of Volcanic Eruptions. 1. Main Causes of Death and Injury." *Bulletin of Volcanology* 52:532–44.

Blackford, J.J., K.J. Edwards, A.J. Dugmore, G.T. Cook, and P.C. Buckland. 1992. "Icelandic Volcanic Ash and the Mid-Holocene Scots Pine (*Pinus Sylvestris*) Pollen Decline in Northern Scotland." *The Holocene* 2:260–5.

Blaikie, P., T. Cannon, I. Davis, and B. Wisner. 1994. *At Risk: Natural Hazards, People's Vulnerability, and Disasters.* London.

Bowen, N.L. 1928. *The Evolution of Igneous Rocks.* Princeton.

Branney, M.J., and P. Kokelaar. 1992. "A Reappraisal of Ignimbrite Emplacement. Progressive Aggradation and Changes from Particulate to Non-Particulate Flow During Emplacement of High-Grade Ignimbrite." *Bulletin of Volcanology* 54:504–20.

Brown, G.C., and A.E. Mussett. 1981. *The Inaccessible Earth.* London.

Brown, G.C., H. Rymer, and D. Stevenson. 1991. "Volcano Monitoring by Microgravity and Energy Budget Analysis." *Journal of the Geological Society* (London) 148(3):585–93.

Budyko, M.I. 1968. "On the Causes of Climatic Variations." *Sveriges Meteorologiska Och Hydrologiska Institut Medd.* Ser. B, 28:6–13.

Bullard, F.M. 1962. *Volcanoes: in History, in Theory, in Eruption.* Austin.

Burgess, C. 1989. "Volcanoes, Catastrophe and the Global Crisis of the Late Second Millennium B.C." *Current Archaeology* 117:325–9.

Cardaci, C., M. Coviello, G. Lombardo, G. Patane, and R. Scarpa. 1993. "Seismic Tomography of Etna Volcano." *Journal of Volcanology and Geothermal Research* 56:357–68.

Carey, S.N., and R.S.J. Sparks. 1986. "Quantitative Models of the Fallout and Dispersal of Tephra from Volcanic Columns." *Bulletin of Volcanology* 48:109–25.

Carey, S.N., H. Sigurdsson, C. Mandeville, and S. Bronto. 1996. "Pyroclastic Flows and Surges Over Water: An Example from the 1883 Krakatau Eruption." *Bulletin of Volcanology* 57:493–511.

Cas, R.A.F., and J.V. Wright. 1987. *Volcanic Successions: Ancient and Modern.* London.

Chester, D.K. 1988. "Volcanoes and Climate. Recent Volcanological Perspectives." *Progress in Physical Geography* 12(1):1–35.

———. 1993. *Volcanoes and Society.* London.

Chester, D.K., C. Dibben, and R. Coutinho. 1995. *Report on the Evacuation of the Furnas District, Sao Miguel, Azores, in the Event of a Future Eruption.* Commission for the European Communities, European Science Foundation Laboratory Volcano, Eruptive History and Hazard Open File Report 4. London.

Clapperton, C.M. 1977. "Volcanoes in Space and Time." *Progress in Physical Geography* 1(3):375–411.

Cogley, J.G., and A. Henderson-Sellers. 1984. "The Origin and Earliest State of the Earth's Atmosphere." *Review of Geophysics and Space Physics* 22(2):131–75.

Condie, K.C. 1982. *Plate Tectonics and Crustal Evolution.* 2nd ed. New York.

———. 1989. *Plate Tectonics and Crustal Evolution.* 3rd ed. New York.

Cotton, C.A. 1944. *Volcanoes as Landscape Forms.* Christchurch.

Cox, A., and R.B.H. Hart. 1986. *Plate Tectonics: How It Works.* Oxford.

Cox, K.G. 1989. "The Role of Mantle Plumes in the Development of Continental Drainage Patterns." *Nature* 342:873–7.

Crandell, D.R., and D.R. Mullineaux. 1978. *Potential Hazards from Future Eruptions of Mount St. Helens, Volcano, Washington.* United States Geological Survey Bulletin 1383-C. Washington, D.C.

Daly, R.A. 1911. *The Nature of Volcanic Action. American Academy of Arts and Sciences Proceedings* 47:47–122.

————.1933. *Igneous Rocks and the Depths of the Earth.* New York.

Dana, J.D. 1890. *Characteristics of Volcanoes.* New York.

Duncan, A.M., D.K. Chester, and J.E. Guest. 1981. "Mount Etna Volcano. Environmental Impact and Problems of Volcanic Prediction." *Geographical Journal* 147:164–79.

Duncan, A.M., C. Dibben, D.K. Chester, and J.E. Guest. 1996. "The 1928 Eruption of Mount Etna, Sicily, and the Destruction of the Town of Mascali." *Disasters* 20(1):1–20.

Eaton, J.P., and Murata, K.J. 1960. "How Volcanoes Grow." *Science* 132:925–39.

Eggers, A., J. Krause, H. Rush, and J. Ward. 1976. "Gravity Changes Accompanying Volcanic Activity at Peceya Volcano, Guatemala." *Journal of Volcanology and Geothermal Research* 1:229–36.

Fink, J.H., ed. 1990. "Lava Flows and Domes. Emplacement Mechanisms and Hazard Implications." *IAVCEI Proceedings in Volcanology* 2. Berlin.

Fisher, R.V., and H.U. Schmincke. 1984. *Pyroclastic Rocks.* Berlin.

Fiske, R., and W.T. Konoshita. 1969. "Inflation of Kilauea Volcano Prior to Its 1967–1968 Eruption." *Science* 165:341–9.

Forsyth, P.Y. 1988. "In the Wake of Etna, 44 B.C." *Classical Antiquity* 7(1):49–57.

Foxworthy, B.L., and M. Hill. 1982. *Volcanic Eruptions of 1980 at Mount St. Helens: The First 100 Days.* United States Geological Survey, Professional Paper 1249. Reston, VA.

Francis, P. 1983. "Giant Volcanic Calderas." *Scientific American* 248(6):46–56.

————. 1993. *Volcanoes: A Planetary Perspective.* Oxford.

Greeley, R. 1994. *Planetary Landscapes.* 2nd ed. London.

Guest, J.E., and R. Greeley. 1985. *Geology on the Moon.* London.

Guest, J.E., and A.M. Duncan. 1981. "Internal Plumbing of Mount Etna." *Nature* 290:584–6.

Guest, J.E., P. Butterworth, J. Murray, and W. O'Donnell. 1979. *Planetary Geology.* New York.

Guest, J.E., A.M. Duncan, P.D. Cole, J.L. Gaspar, G. Queiroz, N. Wallenstein, and T. Ferreira. 1994. *Preliminary Report on the Volcanic Geology of Furnas Volcano, São Miguel, The Azores.* Commission for the European Communities. European Science Foundation Laboratory Volcano, Eruptive History and Hazard Open File Report 4. London.

Hamilton, Sir W. 1772. *Observations on Mount Vesuvius, Mount Etna and Other Volcanoes of the Two Sicilies.* London.

Hamilton, W.B. 1988. "Plate Tectonics and Island Arcs." *Geological Society of America Bulletin* 100:1503–27.

Hammer, C.U. 1977. "Past Volcanism from Greenland Ice Sheet Impurities." *Nature* 270:482–6.

Hammer, C.U., H.B. Clausen, and W. Dansgaard. 1981. "Past Volcanism and Climate Revealed by Greenland Ice-Cores." *Journal of Volcanology and Geothermal Research* 11:3–10.

Handler, P. 1985. "Possible Associations between the Climatic Effects of Stratospheric Aerosols and Corn Yields in the United States." *Agricultural Meteorology* 35: 205–28.

————. 1986a. "Possible Associations between the Climatic Effects of Stratospheric Aerosols and Sea Surface Temperatures in the Eastern Tropical Pacific Ocean." *Journal of Climatology* 6:31–41.

———. 1986b. "Stratospheric Aerosols and the Indian Monsoon." *Journal of Geophysical Research* 91(D):14475–90.

———. 1989. "The Effect of Volcanic Aerosols on Global Climate." *Journal of Volcanology and Geothermal Research* 37:233–49.

Hardy, D.A., J. Keller, V.P. Galanopoulos, N.C. Flemming, and T.H. Druitt, eds. 1990. *Thera and the Aegean World III.* Vol. 2. *Earth Sciences.* London.

Hardy D.A., and A.C. Renfrew, eds. 1990. *Thera and the Aegean World III.* Vol.3. *Chronology.* London.

Hatch, F.H., A.K. Wells, and M.K. Wells. 1972. *Petrology of Igneous Rocks.* 13th ed. London.

Heiken, G., and K.H. Wohletz. 1985. *Volcanic Ash.* Berkeley, Calif.

Hess, H.H. 1962. "History of Ocean Basins" In *Petrologic Studies: A Volume in Honor of A.F. Buddington,* edited by Engle, A.E.J., H. L. James, and B. F. Leonard, 599–620. Boulder, Colo.

Hewitt, K. 1997. Regions of Risk: A Geographical Introduction to Disasters. Harlow Essex.

Hewitt, K., ed. 1983. *Interpretations of Calamity.* London.

Hoernes, R. 1893. *Erdbebenkurde.* Leipzig.

Hole, M.J. 1990. "Antarctic Volcanoes." *NERC News* (Natural Environmental Research Council, U.K.) 14 July: 4–6.

Hulme, G. 1974. "The Interpretation of Lava Flow Morphology." *Geophysical Journal of the Royal Astronomical Society* 39:361–83.

Jaggar, T.A. 1931. "Preparedness Against Disaster." *Volcano Letter* 338:2–4.

———. 1945. "Protection of Harbors from Lava Flows." *American Journal of Science* 243A:333–51.

———. 1949. *Steam Blast Volcanic Eruptions.* Hawaiian Volcano Observatory, Special Report 4. Honolulu.

Johnston, R.J. 1995. *Geography and Geographers: Anglo-American Human Geography Since 1945.* London.

Judd, J.W. 1888. *Volcanoes.* 4th ed. London.

Kasting, J.F., O.B. Toon, and J.B. Pollack. 1981. "How the Climate Evolved on the Terrestrial Planets." *Scientific American* 258(2):46–53.

Kilburn, C.R.J. 1981. "Pahoehoe and Aa Lavas: A Discussion and Continuation of the Model of Peterson and Tilling." *Journal of Volcanology and Geothermal Research* 11:373–82.

Kilburn, C.R.J., and G. Luongo. 1993. *Active Lavas: Monitoring and Modeling.* London.

Kokelaar, B.P. 1983. "The Mechanisms of Surtseyan Volcanism." *Journal of the Geological Society* 140:939–44.

———. 1986. "Magma-water Interactions in Subaqueous and Emergent Basaltic Volcanism." *Bulletin of Volcanology* 48:275–89.

Lamb, H.H. 1970. "Volcanic Dust in the Atmosphere; with a Chronology and Assessment of its Meteorological Significance." *Philosophical Transactions of the Royal Society of London* A266:425–533.

Latter. J.H. 1989a. "Preface." In *Volcanic Hazards, Assessment and Monitoring,* edited by J.H. Latter, v–viii. IAVCEI Proceedings in Volcanology 1. Berlin.

Latter, J.H., ed. 1989b. *Volcanic Hazards, Assessment and Monitoring,* IAVCEI Proceedings in Volcanology 1. Berlin.

Lopes, R., and J.E. Guest. 1982. "Lava Flows on Mount Etna, A Morphological Study." In *The Comparative Study of the Planets*, edited by A. Coradini and M. Fulchignoni, 441–59. Dordrecht.

Lough, J.M., and H.C. Fritts. 1987. "An Assessment of the Possible Effects of Volcanic Eruptions on North American Climate Using Tree-Ring Data, 1602 to 1900 A.D." *Climatic Change* 10:219–39.

Luhr, J.F., and T. Simkin, eds. 1983. *Paricutin: The Volcano Born in a Mexican Cornfield*. Phoenix.

Lyell, C. 1830. *Principles of Geology*. London.

Macdonald, G.A. 1958. "Barriers to Protect Hilo from Lava Flows." *Pacific Science* 12:258–77.

———. 1972. *Volcanoes*. Englewood Cliffs.

Marsh, B. 1984. "Mechanisms and Energetics of Magma Formation and Ascension." In *Explosive Volcanism: Inception, Evolution and Hazards*, no editor but published by the Geophysics Study Committee, National Academy Press, 67–83. Washington, D.C.

McBirney, A.R., and T. Murase. 1984. "Rheological Properties of Magmas." *Annual Review Earth and Planetary Science* 12:337–84.

McGuire, W.J. 1996. "Volcano Instability. A Review of Contemporary Themes." In *Volcanic Instability on the Earth and Other Planets*, edited by W.J. McGuire, A.P. Jones, and J. Neuberg, 1–23. Geological Society Special Publication 110. London.

McGuire, W.J., C.R.J. Kilburn, and J.B. Murray. 1995. *Monitoring Active Volcanoes: Strategies, Procedures and Techniques*. London.

McGuire, W.J., A.P. Jones, and J. Neuberg, eds. 1996. *Volcanic Instability on the Earth and Other Planets*. Geological Society Special Publication 110. London.

McWilliam, F. 1996. "Late Arrival at Waterloo." *The Geographical Magazine* LXVII (12):7.

Minakami, T. 1960. "Fundamental Research for Predicting Volcanic Eruptions. (Part 1) Earthquakes and Crustal Deformations Originating from Volcanic Activities." *Tokyo University Earthquake Institute Bulletin* 38:497–544.

Moore, J.G., K. Nakamuru, and A. Alcarez. 1966. "The 1965 Eruption of Taal Volcano." *Science* 151:955–60.

Mukherjee, B.K., K. Indira, and K.K. Dani. 1987. "Low Latitude Volcanic Eruptions and Their Effects on Sri Lankan Rainfall during the North East Monsoon." *Journal of Climatology* 7:145–55.

Murray, B.C., M.C. Malin, and R. Greeley. 1981. *Earthlike Planets*. San Francisco.

Nance, R.D., T.R. Worsley, and J.B. Moody. 1988. "The Supercontinent Cycle." *Scientific American* 259(1):72–9.

Neumann van Padang, M. 1934. "Haben bei den Ausbruchen des Slametvulkans Eruptionregen stattgefunden?" *Leidsche Geologische Medelingen* 6:79–97.

———. 1960. "Measures Taken by the Authorities of the Volcanological Survey to Safeguard the Population from the Consequences of Volcanic Outbursts." *Bulletin Volcanologique* 23:181–92.

Newell, R.E. 1981. "Introduction." *Journal of Volcanology and Geothermal Research* 11:1–2.

Newhall, C.G., and S. Self. 1982. "The Volcanic Explosivity Index (VEI): An Estimate of the Explosive Magnitude of Historical Volcanism." *Journal of Geophysical Research* 87(C):1231–8.

O'Hara, M.J., and R.E. Matthews. 1981. "Geochemical Evolution in an Advancing, Periodically Replenished, Periodically Tapped, Continually Fractionated Magma Chamber." *Journal of the Geological Society* (London) 138:237–77.

Orsi, G., S. De Vita, and M. Di Vito. 1996. "The Restless, Resurgent Campi Flegrei Nested Caldera (Italy). Constraints on Its Evolution and Configuration." *Journal of Volcanology and Geothermal Research* 74:179–214.

Peterson, D.W., and R.I. Tilling. 1980. "Transition of a Basalt Lava from Pahoehoe to Aa, Kilauea Volcano, Hawaii." *Journal of Volcanology and Geothermal Research* 7 (3/4):271–93.

Pieri, D.C., and S.M. Bologa. 1986. "Eruption Rate, Area and Length Relationships for Some Hawaiian Lava Flows." *Journal of Volcanology and Geothermal Research* 30:29–45.

Pinkerton, H. 1989. "Factors Affecting the Morphology of Lava Flows." *Endeavour* 11 (2):1987.

Pinkerton, H., and R.S.J. Sparks. 1978. "Field Measurements of the Rheology of Lava Flows." *Nature* 276:383–6.

Rampino, M., S. Self, and R.W. Fairbridge. 1979. "Can Rapid Climatic Change Cause Volcanic Eruptions?" *Science* 206:826–9.

Rampino, M.R., and R.B. Stothers. 1985. "Climatic Effects of Volcanic Eruptions." *Nature* 311:272.

Ringwood, A.E. 1975. *Composition and Petrology of the Earth's Mantle.* New York.

Rittmann, A. 1936. *Vulkane und ihre Tätigkeit.* Stuttgart.

Rowland, S.K., and G.P.L. Walker. 1987. "Toothpaste Lava. Characteristics and Origin of a Lava Structural Type Transitional Between Pahoehoe and Aa." *Bulletin of Volcanology* 49:631–41.

Ryan, M.P., ed. 1990. *Magma Transport and Ascent.* New York.

Rymer, H. 1995. "Microgravity Monitoring." In *Monitoring Active Volcanoes,* edited by B. McGuire, C. Kilburn, and J. Murray, 217–47. London.

Scandone, R. 1990. "Chaotic Collapse of Calderas." *Journal of Volcanology and Geothermal Research* 42:285–302.

Schmincke, H-U. 2004. *Volcanism.* Berlin; New York. Published by Springer.

Scrope, C.P. 1825. *Considerations on Volcanoes, the Probable Causes of Their Phenomena and Their Connection with the Present State and Past History of the Globe; Leading to the Establishment of a New Theory of the Earth.* London.

Self, S., and R.S.J. Sparks. 1978. "Characteristics of Pyroclastic Deposits Formed by the Interaction of Silicic Magma and Water." *Bulletin Volcanologique* 41:196–212.

Self, S., and R.S.J. Sparks, eds. 1981. *Tephra Studies.* Dordrecht.

Self, S., and J.V. Wright. 1983. "Large Wave-Forms from the Fish Canyon Tuff, Colorado." *Geology* 11:443–6.

Sharp, A.D.L., P.M. Davis, and P. Gray. 1980. "A Low-Velocity Zone beneath Mount Etna and Magma Storage." *Nature* 287:587–91.

Sheridan, M.F., and K.H. Wohletz. 1981. "Hydrovolcanic Explosions. The Systematics of Water-Pyroclast Equilibrium." *Science* 212:1387–9.

———. 1983. "Hydrovolcanism. Basic Considerations and Review." *Journal of Volcanology and Geothermal Research* 17:1–29.

Siebert, L. 1984. "Large Volcanic Debris Avalanches. Characteristics of Source Areas, Deposits and Associated Eruptions." *Journal of Volcanology and Geothermal Research* 22:163–97.

———. 1992. "Threats from Volcanic Avalanches." *Nature* 356:658–9.

Sigurdsson, H. 2000. *Encyclopedia of Volcanoes.* San Diego.

Sigurdsson, H., S. Carey, W. Cornell, and T. Pescatore. 1985. "The Eruption of Vesuvius in A.D. 79." *National Geographic Research* 1(3):332–87.

Sigvaldason, G.E. 1983. "International Conference on Lake Nyos Disaster, Yaounde, Cameroon 16–20 March 1987: Conclusions and Recommendations." *Journal of Volcanology and Geothermal Research* 39:97–107.

Sparks, R.S.J., and L. Wilson. 1976. "A Model for the Formation of Ignimbrites by Gravitational Column Collapse." *Journal of the Geological Society* (London) 132:441–51.

Sparks, R.S.J., S. Self, and G.P.L Walker. 1973. "Products of Ignimbrite Eruption." *Geology* 1:115–8.

Stommel, H., and E. Stommel. 1983. *Volcano Weather: The Story of 1816, the Year without a Summer.* Newport, R.I.

Stommel, H., and J.C. Swallow. 1983. "Do Late Grape Harvests Follow Large Volcanic Eruptions?" *Bulletin of the American Meteorological Society* 64:794–5.

Stothers, R.B. 1996. "The Great Dry Fog of 1783." *Climatic Change* 32:79–89.

Stothers, R.B., and M.R. Rampino. 1983a. "Historic Volcanism, European Dry Fogs and Greenland Acid Precipitation." *Science* 222:411–13.

———. 1983b. "Volcanic Eruptions in the Mediterranean Region Before A.D. 630 from Written and Archaeological Sources." *Journal of Geophysical Research* 88(B):6357–71.

Stuart, W.D., and M.J.S. Johnston. 1975. "Intrusive Origin of the Matsushiro Earthquake Swarm." *Geology* 3:63–7.

Symons, G., ed. 1888. *The Eruption of Krakatoa and Subsequent Phenomena.* Report of the Krakatoa Committee. London.

Tazieff, H., and J.C. Sabroux, eds. 1983. *Forecasting Volcanic Events, Developments in Volcanology 1.* Amsterdam.

Tedesco, D. 1995. "Monitoring Fluids and Gases at Active Volcanoes." In *Monitoring Active Volcanoes,* edited by B. McGuire, C.R.J. Kilburn, and J. Murray, 315–45. London.

Ui, T. 1983. "Volcanic Dry Avalanche Deposits: Identification and Comparison with Nonvolcanic Debris Stream Deposits." *Journal of Volcanology and Geothermal Research* 18:135–50.

van Andel, T.H. 1984. "Plate Tectonics at the Threshold of Middle Age." *Geologie en Mijnbouw* 63:337–41.

Vine, F.J., and D.H. Matthews. 1963. "Magnetic Anomalies Over Ocean Ridges." *Nature* 199:947–9.

Wadge, G., ed. 1994. *Natural Hazards and Remote Sensing.* London.

Wadge, G., and M.C. Isaacs. 1988. "Mapping the Volcanic Hazards from Soufriere Hills Volcano, Montserrat, West Indies, Using an Image Processor." *Journal of the Geological Society* (London) 145(4):541–53.

Walker, G.P.L. 1973. "Lengths of Lava Flows." *Philosophical Transaction of the Royal Society London* 274:107–18.

———. 1974. "Volcanic Hazards and The Prediction of Volcanic Eruptions." In *Prediction of Geological Hazards,* edited by B.M. Funnell, 23–41. Geological Society of London, Miscellaneous Paper 3. London.

———. 1981. "Generation and Dispersal of Fine Ash and Dust by Volcanic Eruptions." *Journal of Volcanology and Geothermal Research* 11:81–92.

———. 1982. "Volcanic Hazards." *Interdisciplinary Science Reviews* 7(2):148–57.

Wexler, H. 1952. "Volcanoes and Climate." *Scientific American* 186:74–80.

White, R.S., and D.P. McKenzie. 1995. "Mantle Plumes and Flood Basalts." *Journal of Geophysical Research* 100B:17543–85.

Wilson, C.J.N. 1986. "Pyroclastic Flows and Ignimbrites." *Science Progress* (Oxford) 70:171–207.

Wilson, J.T. 1965. "A New Class of Faults and Their Bearing on Continental Drift." *Nature* 207:343–7.

———. 1988. "Convection Tectonics. Some Possible Effects upon the Earth's Surface Flow from the Deep Mantle." *Canadian Journal of Earth Science* 25:1199–208.

Wilson, L. 1976. "Explosive Volcanic Eruptions III. Plinian Eruption Columns." *Geophysical Journal of the Royal Astronomical Society* 45:543–56.

———. 1980. "Relationship between Pressure, Volatile Content and Ejecta Velocity in Three Types of Volcanic Explosions." *Journal of Volcanology and Geothermal Research* 8:297–313.

Wilson, L., R.S.J. Sparks, T.C. Huang, and N.D. Watkins. 1978. "The Control of Eruption Column Heights by Eruption Energetics and Dynamics." *Journal of Geophysical Research* 83B:1929–36.

Wilson, L., H. Pinkerton, and R. Macdonald. 1987. "Physical Processes in Volcanic Eruptions." *Annual Review of the Earth and Planetary Sciences* 15:73–95.

Windley, B.F. 1977. *The Evolving Continents.* New York.

Wohletz, K.H. 1983. "Mechanisms of Hydrovolcanic Pyroclastic Formation. Grain Size, Scanning Electron Microscopy and Experimental Studies." *Journal of Volcanology and Geothermal Research* 17:31–63.

———. 1986. "Explosive Magma-Water Interaction. Thermodynamics, Explosive Mechanisms and Field Studies." *Bulletin of Volcanology* 48:245–64.

Wohletz, K.H., and R.G. McQueen. 1984. "Experimental Studies of Hydromagmatic Volcanism." In *Explosive Volcanism: Inception, Evolution and Hazards.* No editor. Published by the Geophysics Study Committee, National Academy Press. Washington, D.C.

2

Understanding Vesuvius and Preparing for Its Next Eruption

Roberto Santacroce, Raffaello Cioni, Paola Marianelli, and Alessandro Sbrana

The last eruption of Vesuvius occurred in March 1944. Since that time the volcano has been quiescent and there are no indications of a renewal of activity. Vesuvius, however, must be considered a very dangerous, active volcano. During its lifetime it has often experienced long rest periods, sometimes lasting centuries or tens of centuries, but its history suggests that the longer the preceding repose, the more violent the reawakening. Given the urbanization of the Vesuvian area (600,000 people live within 10 km of the summit crater, and the outskirts of Naples are only 15 km from the vent), an eruption today would have dreadful consequences.

This problem has been well presented to the Italian scientific community. Since its birth in 1983, the National Volcanological Group (GNV), the institution coordinating research and monitoring active Italian volcanoes, has promoted research to improve knowledge of Vesuvius structure, past behavior and present state, to develop monitoring, and to assess the potential hazard. Moreover, the GNV established institutional links with the State Department for Civil Defense, which in 1986 directly assumed the financial sponsorship of GNV's activities on Vesuvius and other active Italian volcanoes.

This chapter reviews the main results of recent volcanological and magmatological research on Vesuvius that has enabled the development of a general operational model of the volcano. This provides the basis for the eruptive scenario of the mid-term maximum expected event (MEE), which the Civil Defense Emergency Plan addresses.

The Eruptive History of Vesuvius and Its Mode of Operation

The volcanic activity in the Somma-Vesuvius area probably began 300,000–500,000 years ago, but available data allow a reliable reconstruction of the volcano's history only over the last 19,000 years (fig. 2.1). During this time interval the volcano showed great variability in both eruptive style and the composition of its erupted products. Three magmatic periods can be distinguished over the last 19,000 years. The oldest (19,000–ca. 10,000 B.P.) is characterized by the emission of slightly SiO_2-undersaturated lavas and pyroclastics (K-basalts to K-trachytes). This activity is dominated by two plinian eruptions, which were preceded by several centuries-long repose periods and which alternated with lava effusions and, possibly, minor explosive events. During the second period (ca. 10,000 B.P.–A.D. 79) three plinian eruptions occurred, alternating with long reposes and several subplinian and minor explosive events. Magma composition ranged from K-phonolitic tephrite to K-phonolite. The youngest period includes at least two subplinian eruptions (A.D. 472 and 1631), several other explosive or effusive events, and a long interval (1631–1944) of strombolian, semipersistent activity, frequently interrupted by violent, explosive-effusive eruptions. The magma composition ranged from leucititic tephrite to leucititic phonolite in this youngest period. The highly variable activity recorded by Vesuvius reflects the occurrence of irregularly spaced periods of open and obstructed conduit conditions.

Open Conduit Conditions

After the A.D. 1631 subplinian eruption, Vesuvius was characterized by nearly continuous activity, indicating open conduit conditions, which persisted until 1944. In this period, 18 strombolian cycles can be distinguished (Alfano and Friedlander 1929; Arnò et al. 1987), separated by rest periods with a maximum duration of seven years and closed by powerful explosive and lava eruptions (final eruptions). Within each of these cycles minor, mainly effusive eruptions frequently occurred (intermediate eruptions).

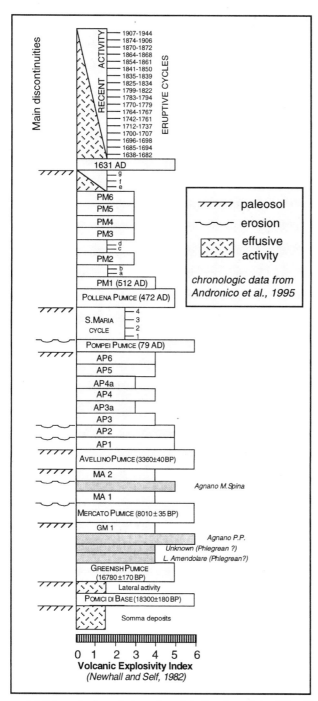

Fig. 2.1. Schematic chronologic section of the Vesuvius activity. (After Cioni et al. 1995a)

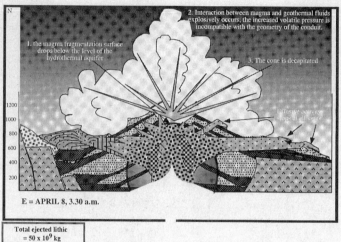

E = APRIL 8, 3.30 a.m.

Total ejected lithic
= 50 x 10^9 kg

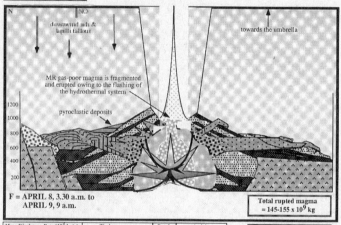

F = APRIL 8, 3.30 a.m. to
APRIL 9, 9 a.m.

Total rupted magma
= 145-155 x 10^9 kg

Total ejected lithic
= 130-140 x 10^9 kg

Mass Discharge Rate [10^3 kg/s]		Timing	Batch	Activity
mass	magma			
4,000	2,000	8.4, 3.30 to 2.00 pm	MR	lapilli & ash fallout
1,900	1,000	8.4, 2.00 pm to 9.4, 9.00 am	MR	ash fallout

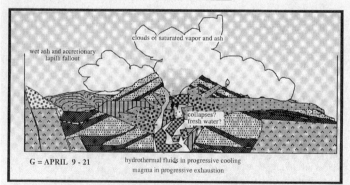

G = APRIL 9 - 21   hydrothermal fluids in progressive cooling
magma in progressive exhaustion

Mean Discharge Rate [10^3 kg/s]		Timing	Batch	Activity	Total erupted magma = 110 x 10^9 kg	Total ejected lithic = 80-90 x 10^9 kg
mass	magma					
200	1200	April 9 to 21	MR	ash fallout		

The final eruptions have been interpreted (Santacroce 1983; Civetta and Santacroce 1992; Santacroce et al. 1994) as episodic events causing the nearly total emptying of the shallow plumbing system. The following quiescence reflects the time needed to recharge the system, restoring a continuous magma column up to the surface and renewing persistent strombolian conditions. The intermediate eruptions likely result from the periodic arrival of fresh magma batches into a full plumbing system. The consequent magma overflow results in either summit or lateral lava effusions. These overflows provide a rough idea of the frequency of new magma batches and of their volume. As an order of magnitude, volumes of $5-10 \times 10^6$ m^3 and eruption frequency of 20–40 per 100 years are implied.

The 1874–1906 Cycle and the April 1906 Eruption

The open conduit behavior of Vesuvius can be illustrated by the penultimate cycle of its recent history. The cycle began in January 1874 after about 20 months of quiescence with a quiet resumption of strombolian activity at the Central Crater. It was characterized by intense effusive, mainly lateral, activity resulting in the emplacement of a series of lava ramparts and cumulo-domes around the Vesuvius cone. Most of the lava erupted between 1881 and 1904, during five long periods of continuous quiet effusions. The volume of lava erupted between 1874 and the April 1906 eruption was estimated at 40×10^6 m^3 (Imbò 1949).

Fig. 2.2A. After repeated magma pulses, from 1872 a large volume of magma accumulated at a very shallow depth forming a high-enthalpy hydrothermal system. Repeated mixing with new magma and continuous crystal settling produced a stratified body which, at different times, injected fractures and formed a series of dome-like structures around the volcano, as examples of type 1 ("intermediate") eruption.

Fig. 2.2B. At the end of this phase in 1904, a crystal-rich magma (MR) remained in the reservoir. Because of its high viscosity, a new batch of low viscosity magma (MI) was able to rise up without mixing and erupted at Central Crater in May 1905.

Fig. 2.2C. In April 1906 a new batch (M2) entered the system and pressed the MR body, whose large phenocrysts form a filter at the mouths of fractures in the conduit, outward. Fractions of filter-press differentiated MR are injected into reactivated fractures. Moderate mixing occurs between contiguous portions of MI and M2.

Fig. 2.2D. High lava fountains eject MI magma until its exhaustion and reach their peak when the gas-rich head of the M2 body is involved. Once the ejection of M2 is completed, portions of MR are also fountained. During this stage a maximum effusion rate of MR magma through all lateral vents occurs.

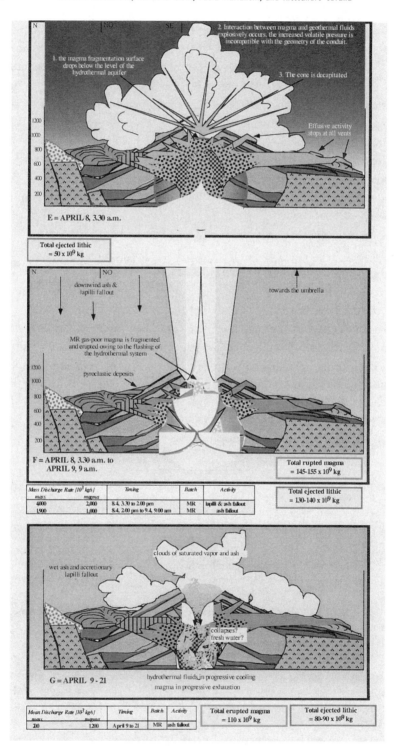

This cycle was closed by the 1906 eruption. Because of the availability of detailed contemporary descriptions and the variability of the recorded phenomena, this eruption remains a classic in volcanology. Every volcanologist would like to be able to describe an eruption with the same clarity and vividness as Mercalli (1906) or Perret (1924), and many textbooks use "Vesuvius 1906" as the example of how greatly the eruptive style of a volcano can change during a single event lasting for several days. Recent papers provide detailed information on the deposits and discuss the dynamics of this eruption (Bertagnini et al. 1991; Mastrolorenzo et al. 1993; Santacroce et al. 1993). The last of these papers focuses on relationships between eruption dynamics and petrogenetic processes. The hypothesized sequence of events is illustrated by figure 2.2.

The eruption began early on 4 April with the opening of a system of fractures along the southern slopes of the cone. The first vent opened at 1200 m.a.s.l. but in the next two days lava was emitted from vents at progressively lower elevations. On the morning of 6 April lava poured out from a vent at 600 m.a.s.l. Early in the afternoon of 7 April the eruption dynamics changed. The magma level in the conduit rose rapidly and higher and higher lava fountains were produced at the Central Crater. The fountains reached their climax in the night of 7–8 April. At the same time there was a spectacular resurgence of effusive activity from new vents; lavas poured rapidly from both the new and the previously opened vents. On 8 April, at about 3:30 a.m., the activity radically changed again. The lava fountaining abruptly ceased, and following a series of violent explosions, the upper portion of the Vesuvius cone was torn asunder, "like the falling of the petals of a flower" (Perret 1924), and was blown in all directions. This phase was immediately followed by the rising of a high, sustained eruption column, which continued until the morning of 9

Fig. 2.2E. As a result of the vigorous drainage, the magma column descends in the conduit below the surface of the intersection with the hydrothermal aquifer; the juvenile gas pressure of MR magma is low and unable to prevent the inflowing of hydrothermal fluids that suddenly depressurized with the explosive destruction of the upper part of the cone.

Fig. 2.2F. The formation of a high eruption column follows with lapilli and ash fallout. The lava emission stops. The flashing of the hydrothermal aquifer was the main cause of this phase since it provided an enormous quantity of hot gases to interact with MR, incrementing its capability of being explosively erupted.

Fig. 2.2G. Because of considerably lowered fluid temperature and high water-magma ratio, low steam clouds are produced, laden with prevalently juvenile ash. Their rapid cooling leads to the condensation and fallout of muddy ash and accretionary lapilli. This state of slow cooling continues until magma exhaustion.

April, when the eruption entered its final phase, characterized by very low eruptive clouds and ash fallout. By 21 April the eruption was effectively over.

Based on petrochemical features and isotopic data (Santacroce et al. 1993), three different magma bodies, M1, M2, and MR, in the 1906 eruption can be identified All data are coherent in suggesting that:

1. M1 and M2 magma bodies represent the two last magma arrivals (May 1905 and April 1906 respectively) in the eruptive system of Vesuvius. About 15–20% of M2 lapilli resulted from mixing between the mafic tail of the M1 magma body and the salic head of the M2 body.

2. The conspicuous MR magma body represents a crystal-enriched body that developed at a very shallow depth after repeated intrusions of tephritic magma and mixing, fractionation and extrusions of the tephritic-phonolitic cumulo-domes emplaced around the cone between 1881 and 1904. As a consequence, a hydrothermal system was present below Vesuvius in 1906.

3. Most of the MR body was explosively erupted by the flashing of this hydrothermal system, which provided an enormous quantity of hot fluids to interact with MR magma.

4. The 1906 lava flows generated by a filter differentiation process of MR magma were induced by concentrations of large clinopyroxene phenocrysts at the mouths of fractures in the conduit. Their Sr-isotopic signature results from mixing, fractionation, and cumulo-domes extrusions of all magma batches that supplied Vesuvius after 1872, the final eruption immediately preceding the 1906 event, and prior to the arrival of the M1 feeding unit.

Although knowledge of other eruptions of the period 1631–1944 is less complete than that for the 1906 cycle, several facts may be generalized to illustrate the open conduit behavior of Vesuvius (Civetta and Santacroce 1992; Santacroce et al. 1994, 1995):

1. Feeding occurs in relatively small mafic batches, called deep feeding units (DFU), such as the M2 of the 1906 eruption.

2. During strombolian cycles the shallow plumbing system is full

of magma and each arrival of a new DFU induces the emission of a portion of the resident magma body, while the freshly arrived melt mixes with the remaining magma. The intermediate eruptions result from the emission of hybridized differentiated magmas produced by repeated mixing and crystal fractionation of DFUs of different age.

3. In these conditions the DFUs cannot maintain their individuality as erupted products. The M2 batch of 1906 was erupted in less than three hours and this minimal residence time was critical for the preservation of its relatively primitive composition. Any attempt at the study of magmas of Vesuvius must recognize that only a small part of the erupted product represents deep magma batches unaffected by modifying processes at shallow depths.

4. A hydrothermal system forms because of the long residence of a conspicuous mass of magma at very shallow depth.

5. Most final eruptions have a violent phreatomagmatic final phase that involves fluids from this shallow hydrothermal system, as indicated by the recurrent occurrence of cocoa-colored lapilli containing abundant hydrothermalized lithics (1872, 1906, 1944). The mass of magma during final eruptions is generally significantly higher than that of intermediate eruptions. The juvenile material erupted during phreatomagmatic phases generally consists of mafic, crystal-rich lapilli and ash suggesting the involvement in the eruption of highly porphyritic magmas which are remnants of previous mixing and fractionation processes. Both the phreatomagmatic phase and the nature of the juvenile material are evidence of the nearly complete emptying of the shallow plumbing system induced by the unusual dynamics of the final phases of the eruption. Any final eruption leaves the plumbing system clear and open for subsequent magma batches as the quiet resumption of strombolian activity characterizing the beginning of each new cycle indicates.

6. Volume estimates for 1631–1872 are unreliable since available data refer to lava flows only, but the homogeneous nature of erupted magmas is strongly suggestive of a steady magma supply rate characterizing the entire 1631–1944 interval.

7. The present 51-year period of quiescence departs from the 1631–1944 pattern of activity in which the maximum length of repose between cycles is seven years (Carta et al. 1981).

Obstructed Conduits: Plinian to Subplinian Magma Chambers and Their Emptying

When a conduit is obstructed, a magma chamber forms and grows until an eruption is initiated. During Vesuvius' history eruptions ending obstructed periods had varying magnitudes reflecting the partial emptying of chambers of various sizes and depths. Whatever the size of the eruption, the deposits are characterized by the presence of significant geochemical and isotopic gradients indicating that the magma reservoirs were compositionally zoned (fig. 2.3). As a first approximation, with the exception of the Subplinian Greenish Pumice eruption (at present poorly studied), the higher the degree of chemical evolution of the erupted products, the older the age of the chamber (i.e., the greater the length of repose preceding the eruption) and the larger the magnitude of the eruption.

To investigate the nature of chamber formation and magma evolution and the eruption dynamics, the A.D. 79 products were studied in detail (Civetta et al. 1991; Cioni et al. 1995b). Three main phases can be distinguished in the eruption: a phreatomagmatic opening phase, a plinian main phase, and a caldera-forming phase with phreatomagmatic surge and flow deposit emplacement. Eight eruptive units are recognized in the deposits of the different phases (EU1 to EU8 in fig. 2.4). The plinian deposits, both fall and minor flows, range from the early phonolitic white pumice to the late tephritic-phonolitic gray pumice. The upper phreatomagmatic flow units exhibit larger variations, with both gray and white pumice clasts and more abundant mafic crystals in the gray pumice.

White pumice results from the withdrawal of magma from the top of the chamber and is characterized by moderate compositional and isotopic layering. Sanidine is the main liquidus phase with minor melanitic garnet, Fe-salitic pyroxene or K-pargasitic amphibole, nepheline, and titaniferous magnetite. The temperature was between 850–900°C based on the homogenization temperature of the glass inclusions in the sanidine and leucite crystals.

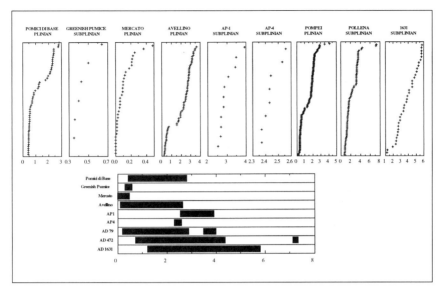

Fig. 2.3. MgO variations recorded by the deposits of selected plinian and subplinian eruptions of Vesuvius. The vertical variations shown by the upper diagrams are only indicative of the actual depositional sequence.

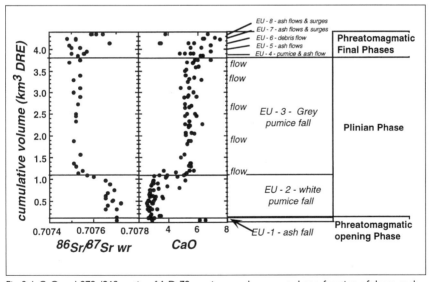

Fig. 2.4. CaO and 87Sr/86Sr ratio of A.D. 79 pumice samples reported as a function of dense rock equivalent cumulative erupted volume. Volume proportions after Sigurdsson et al. (1985) and Civetta et al. (1991); distinction of different eruption units (EU) after Cioni et al. (1992a). (Redrawn after data from Cioni et al. 1995b)

Gray pumice includes a complex phenocryst paragenesis consisting of three separate assemblages:

1. A low-temperature salic assemblage identical to white pumice, as confirmed by the isotopic ratio of the sanidine and phonolitic glass inclusions.
2. A mafic cumulitic assemblage consisting of diopside, olivine, and phlogopite, with lower values of the $^{87}Sr/^{86}Sr$ ratio (0.7071–0.7074). The compositions of glass inclusions and their homogenization temperatures indicate crystallization at 1130–1160°C from K-basaltic to K-tephritic melts.
3. Relatively rare minerals bearing glass inclusions with intermediate temperature and composition.

The gray pumice results, therefore, from a mixture of three components: phonolitic "white" melts with a high $^{87}Sr/^{86}Sr$ ratio (salic end member or SEM), mafic cumulates with a low $^{87}Sr/^{86}Sr$ ratio (cumulitic end member or CEM), and a crystal-poor gray magma (mafic end member or MEM).

The MEM composition has been calculated by considering sanidine and diopside + phlogopite as indicators of the MEM and CEM included in the gray pumice. The lower portion of the Pompeian magma chamber was therefore occupied by a homogeneous, phonolitic-tephritic, gray magma, which was never erupted without being largely mixed. No unambiguous gray magma liquidus phases were found, and this was taken as an indication of its substantially overheated state. The gray magma had a high temperature (possibly around 1050°C), very low viscosity (5–10 × 10² poises) and a density of 2500–2600 kg/m³, which is slightly higher than that of the white magma (2400–2450 kg/m³). These features are consistent with the establishment of a physical discontinuity separating the white body from the gray one. The gray-white mixing was essentially syneruptive as suggested by variations in magma discharge rate that are closely linked to the extent of the mixing (Sigurdsson et al. 1990; Cioni et al. 1990, 1992a, 1992b). The inferred pre-A.D. 79 arrangement of the Vesuvian chamber is shown in figure 2.5. Figure 2.6 summarizes the reconstructed sequence of events and the subsurface processes inferred to have induced that sequence.

The pre-eruptive arrangement of the Pompeian chamber can now be completed by discussing briefly the white to gray transition and the modality

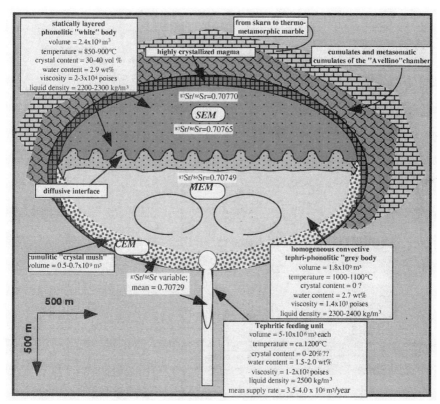

Fig. 2.5. Sketch of the Vesuvius magma chamber before the A.D. 79 Pompeii plinian eruption, assuming its nearly complete emptying during the eruption. (After Cioni et al. 1995b)

of magma supply. Following the ideas of Turner (1985), the white-gray boundary was probably characterized by the initial formation of a diffusive interface with crystallization of the gray magma within a limited volume beneath the contact. When gray and white liquids reached equal density, the interface broke down and mixing occurred. Complete hybridization of various types of physical mingling depends on the viscosities of the magmas after they come into thermal equilibrium (Sparks and Marshall 1986). We calculated that 25–30% of crystals formed from gray magma before conditions for mixing were reached. At 900°C gray residual liquid and white magma have close viscosities (0.4–0.5×10^5 poises, fig. 2.7) and a very short time is needed for blending (Huppert et al. 1984, 1986; Campbell and Turner 1986; Furman and Spera 1985). In our opinion, the fractionation of the gray magma and the subsequent white and gray mixing occurred at two

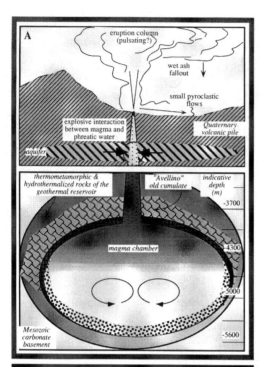

Fig. 2.6A. A.D. 79, first phase: phreatomagmatic opening, EU1 deposition (accretionary lapilli-bearing whitish ash fallout), 24 August, early afternoon. The conduit opens through phreatomagmatic explosion(s) within shallow aquifer(s). A purely phreatic trigger is possible. Low, vapor-saturated clouds form with eastward fallout of whitish ash.

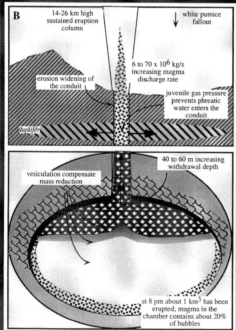

Fig. 2.6B. A.D. 79, second phase: uninterrupted sustained eruption column EU2 deposition (white pumice fallout), 24 August, 1 to 8 p.m. The conduit widens, the magma discharge rate increases as well as the juvenile gas pressure. An eruption column forms, whose height increases with time, depth of magma withdrawal, and discharge rate. The chamber maintains its volume. At 8 p.m. the column is 26 km high, and depth of magma withdrawal is far from the diffusive interface. White pumice is dispersed southeastward. Within the chamber about 3–3.5 km³ of magma remains. The compositional layering is again substantially stable.

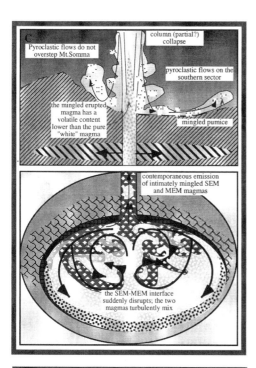

Fig. 2.6C. A.D. 79, second phase: first column instability, EU2fl deposition (pumice and ash flow deposits), 24 August, about 8 p.m. The increasing depth of bubble nucleation induces instability until disruption of the boundary interface. Because of the quite similar densities of two magmas, the layering overturns and magmas turbulently mix. During the transition from a nearly static layering to a turbulent agitation of the whole chamber, the discharge rate suddenly drops and the column collapses.

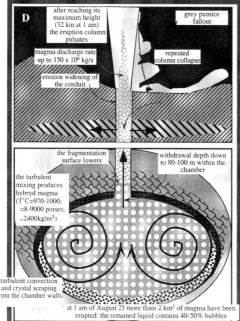

Fig. 2.6D. A.D. 79, second phase: pulsating eruption column, EU3 + EU3fl deposition (gray pumice fallout and pumice flow), 24–25 August, ca. 8 p.m. to early morning. The column newly rises reaching its maximum elevation, discharge rate, and depth of magma extraction at about 1 a.m. Phonotephritic, gray, mixed pumice covers wide areas southeastward. In the chamber, mixing proceeds until complete hybridization. From 1 a.m. the discharge rate reduces and partial collapses of the column repeatedly occur, originating pyroclastic flows that reach Herculaneum and Oplontis.

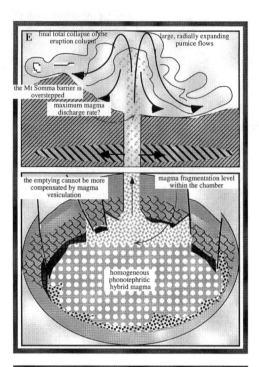

Fig. 2.6E. A.D. 79, end of the second phase: final destabilization of the column, EU 3fl deposition (large pumice flow), 25 August, ca. 8 a.m. onward. The fragmentation level possibly descends in the chamber because of the emptying not compensated by increasing vesiculation. The discharge rate suddenly increases, inducing column total collapse and large, radially expanding pumice flows. Ravages extend to Herculaneum, Pompeii, and Ottaviano areas. The initial failure of the magma chamber walls can be hypothesized.

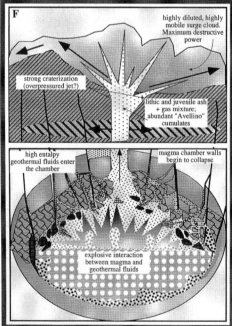

Fig. 2.6F. A.D. 79, third phase: magma chamber collapse, explosive interaction between geothermal fluids and magma, EU4 + EU5 deposition (dry surge and flow), 25 August, morning. The magma chamber walls fail and the geothermal system flashes, fragmenting the chamber shell and the reservoir rocks. Hydrothermal fluids explosively interact with magma. A juvenile-lithic gas and particle mixture reaches the surface, probably as an overpressured jet, craterizing the vent. A radially expanding, terrific, base surge-like explosion wave originates. Effects extend as far as 15 km from the vent, razing Pompeii and Stabiae.

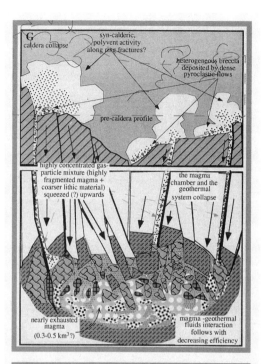

Fig. 2.6G. A.D. 79, end of the third phase: EU6 and EU7 deposition (mass flow, surge, landslide), 25 August. Most of the magma has been withdrawn. The plumbing system collapses, inducing caldera sinking, accompanied by the emplacement of dense, heterogeneous pyroclastic flows, poor in juvenile material (EU6), probably erupted through ring fractures driving the caldera collapse. Another base surge-like explosion occurs, probably related to the final destabilization of the geothermal system (not shown in the figure).

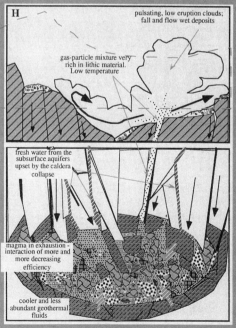

Fig. 2.6H. A.D. 79, final phases: low, pulsating eruption clouds, EU8 deposition (wet pyroclastic flow and mud hurricanes), 25 August, long duration. The falling final phases mark the progressive exhaustion of the capability of magma to interact with cooler and proportionally more abundant fluids, both geothermal phreatic. The deposits are fine-grained, muddy, and lithic-rich. They result from pulsating explosions produced by low, dense, frequently collapsing clouds. The length of this phase in unknown.

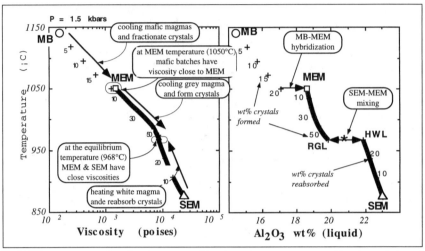

Fig. 2.7. Temperature vs. viscosity plots summarizing the main processes controlling the evolution of the Pompeiian magma chamber and the emission of the gray pumice: *left*, of magmas (liquid and crystals); *right*, of Al2O3 content (liquids). *MB*, mean of mafic magma batches feeding the Pompeiian chamber; *MEM, CEM*, and *SEM*, as in figs. 2.9–2.10; *RGL*, residual liquid after crystallization of 55wt% solid; *HWL*, "heated white" liquid formed from SEM crystals resorbed. Numbers indicate wt% of crystals formed or reabsorbed. (After Cioni et al. 1995b)

different temporal and spatial scales: (1) slowly and quietly on the white-gray boundary layer throughout the life of the Pompeian magma chamber (while both white and gray magmas were progressively changing in compositions, and with repeated episodes of breakdown of the diffusive interface to create the static layering of the white magma); and (2) quickly and turbulently inside the chamber during the eruption, once the partial emptying of the chamber and the increased magma discharge rate created conditions for the simultaneous emission of the white and gray bodies (figs. 2.6 C and D).

Magma Supply to Plinian and Subplinian Chambers

Diopside crystals of Pompeii pumice contain primary melt inclusions, homogeneous within single crystals but different from crystal to crystal, whose composition ranges from K-basalts to K-tephrite. Given the assumptions that (1) the temperature of homogenization (T_{hom}) of the melt inclusion is the (minimal) temperature of crystallization of the host mineral, and (2) after homogenization and quenching, the composition of the included glass is representative of the magma from which the host mineral crystallized, then the most primitive compositions are considered as indicative of the variability of melts having supplied the Pompeian chamber (Cioni et al. 1995b; Marianelli et al. 1995a, 1995b). The periodic input of dense and hot magma into a chamber whose bottom is occupied by the resident gray magma substantially repeats, at each new magma arrival, the situation discussed at the white-gray boundary in which crystallization of the feeding magma occurs before reaching equilibrium temperature and mixing with the gray magma (fig. 2.7).

The frequent periodic arrival of hot mafic magma batches was driving the chamber, providing heat for its maintenance and mass for its growth. These batches have an overall moderately variable composition, similar to that of mafic batches feeding Vesuvius during periods of open conduit conditions, and their temperature exceeds 1140°C.

Glass inclusions in diopside were studied in pumice samples from other plinian and subplinian eruptions (Marianelli et al. 1995a, 1995b). Within the statistical validity of the available data set, their compositional range can be considered as representative of the variability of mafic melts, having supplied Vesuvius during the recharge periods preceding the sampled eruptions. Within an overall basaltic compositional spectrum, a general increase in the silica-undersaturation degree with decreasing age of the eruption can be observed from Avellino to Pollena, fitting the general pattern shown by erupted products well.

The presence of a large overheated mass is evidence of the young, growing stage of the A.D. 79 chamber. A comparison with older plinian events indicates that some resulted from the emptying of much more mature magma chambers located at similar depths. This could suggest an external trigger of the A.D. 79 eruption, inducing its emptying ahead of the time expected for an undisturbed internal evolution. During the history of Vesuvius, eruptions interrupting obstructed periods with chambers located at different depths were probably repeatedly triggered by either internal or external factors. The possible maximum size of these chambers increases with depth, while the aspect ratio decreases (fig. 2.8). Available data suggest that highly evolved compositions, close to thermal minima, could be reached only by deeper, larger, longer-lived, externally undisturbed magma chambers. It is likely that shallower chambers within the volcano's sedimentary cover are structurally prevented from reaching plinian sizes (of the order of cubic km). Most probably their life cannot exceed a few centuries.

After their onset, the eruptions commonly proceed with the rise of an eruption column whose dynamics, duration and evolution are widely varying

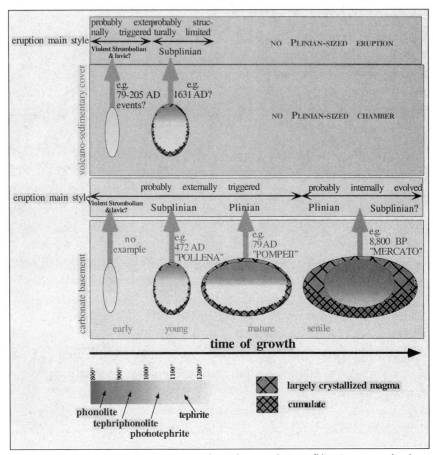

Fig. 2.8. General speculative scheme suggesting the evolution with time of Vesuvius magma chambers.

as a function of chamber size, shape, and layering, and the different processes acting within it. The A.D. 79 example cannot be generalized, however, and the plinian-type deposits of each eruption need a specific and detailed study. This magmatic phase determines the extent of magma withdrawal such that, at the end of the phase, it leads to either the preservation or the destabilization and collapse of the magma chamber.

In the first case, the eruption progressively weakens with the decreasingly volatile content of the magma. After repeated phreatomagmatic pulses of declining energy, related to medium to moderate magma-water interaction in the conduit, the end of the eruption leaves a significant amount of magma in the chamber.

In the second case, the collapse of the chamber induces the flashing of the hydrothermal system with extremely effective interaction between magma and hydrothermal fluids. Likewise for open conduit conditions, this hydrothermo-magmatic phase (and its phreatomagmatic tail) should induce the nearly total exhaustion of stored magma. The end of the eruption leaves a plumbing system to be restored and the renewal of activity could follow either obstructed or open conduit paths.

Vesuvius' Mode of Operation

The main elements of the volcanic plumbing system, (the state of the conduit, deep magma supply rate, the depth, age, size, and shape of the magma chamber, associated geothermal system and phreatic aquifers) can display a variety of conditions whose combinations and interactions drive the state of the volcano and the nature of its eruptions. In spite of this apparent complexity, however, a relatively simple general operational model of Vesuvius can be proposed (fig. 2.9). In either open or obstructed conduit conditions only four states can be recognized; these are conceptually equivalent but of greatly differing scale.

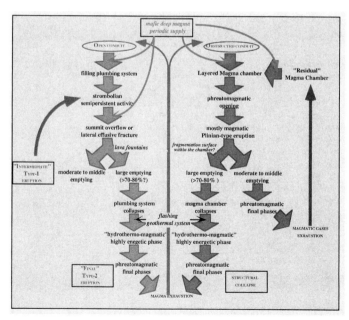

Fig. 2.9. General scheme of the behavior of Vesuvius. (Modified after Santacroce et al. 1995)

The Scenario of the Expected Eruption and the Emergency Plan

The previous pages summarize recent scientific results indicating that the 1944 eruption marked the transition from open to obstructed conduit conditions and argue that, in the last 2,000–3,000 years there have been no major differences, except for the depth of magma storage, and in the magma supply processes in open and obstructed conduit conditions. Vesuvius is therefore to be considered broadly as a steady-state volcano, fed by the periodic arrival of K-tephritic magma batches whose varying behaviors result from the size of the magma reservoir and the extent of its emptying. These factors are controlled in their turn by the depth of the obstruction of the conduit and the dynamics of triggering and emptying.

The volume of magma that entered the Vesuvian system after 1944 should be roughly on the order of $2 \times 10^8 \, m^3$. Such a volume of magma, if totally ejected during a single explosive event, could result in a subplinian eruption of relatively low magnitude. The last eruption of this kind in A.D. 1631 had a similar magnitude although it has probably been underestimated

Table 2.1. Sequence of Events of the Subplinian MEE

Eruption Phase	Phenomena	Duration	Affected Area (km²)
Phreatomagmatic opening	Repeated explosions Moderate to strong earthquakes Ballistic ejection of blocks (2–3 km from the vent) Lee-side ash fallout (ca.10 km from the vent)	Minutes to hours	10–20
Sustained eruption column	Formation of a 12–20 km high eruption column Lee-side lapilli and ash fallout (roof collapse at 10–30 km from the vent) Ballistic ejection of blocks and bombs (3–5 km from the vent) Continuous strong tremors	Hours	150–200
Pyroclastic flow emplacement	Column destabilization and collapse(s) Pyroclastic flows and ash cloud surges emplacement Possible structural collapse of the upper portions of the cone Strong isolated earthquakes Landslides Moderate tsunami waves	Hours	50
Phreatomagmatic vaning	Repeated explosions due to magma-water interaction in the conduit Ash and mud fallout; mud hurricanes Heavy rain; mud flows; floods Isolated earthquakes	Days to months (?)	50–100

(Rosi et al. 1993; Rolandi et al. 1993). Such an eruption has been taken as the reference event for the present maximum expected eruption of Vesuvius. The scenario of the eruptive phenomena of this mid-term maximum expected event (MEE) results from field and historical data (table 2.1). It was included in the final report of a technical scientific commission created in 1991 by the Department of Civil Defense to "establish the guidelines for the assessment of risk related to an eruption in the Vesuvius area (Presidenza Del Consiglio dei Ministri, Dipartimento Della Protezione Civile 1992)," and was last updated in 1995 (Barberi et al. 1995).

By combining the areal distribution of the A.D. 1631 products (Rosi et al. 1993) with the results of computer-assisted hazard mapping for MEE plinian fallout and pyroclastic flow emplacement (Macedonio et al. 1988a, 1988b, 1990; Barberi et al. 1990), a hazardous area of about 2,000 km^2 must be connected to the MEE (Santacroce 1990; Luongo and Santacroce 1992). Within this area two zones are distinguished (fig. 2.10) based on the type and size of phenomena potentially affecting them:

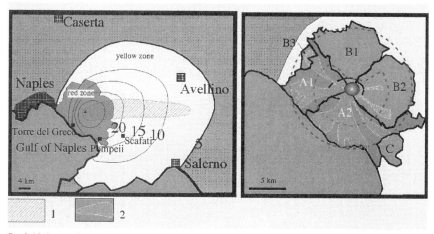

Fig. 2.10. Limit of hazardous zones related to a subplinian maximum expected event of Vesuvius. *Left*, the Red Zone includes the 18 municipalities of the circumvesuvian area, while the Yellow Zone is defined by the 5% isoprobability curve to have more than 100 kg/m^2 of ash and lapilli fall deposit in case of a subplinian event with magnitude of 0.2 km^3 (Barberi et al. 1990). *Right*, the Red Zone is included within the area expected to be affected by pyroclastic flows and surges due to column collapses (collapse height: 300 m [inner dotted line] and 1000 m [outer dotted line]) (Macedonio et al. 1988b; Santacroce 1990). A, B, and C define subzones of the Red Zones to be evacuated in the order A-B-C. The areas affected by pyroclastic fall (1) and flow (2) deposits during the A.D. 1631 eruption (Rosi et al. 1993) are reported for comparison.

1. The Red Zone (about 250 km²) could be subject to nearly total destruction over wide areas due to pyroclastic flow, surge emplacements, and very heavy ballistic fallout. During the A.D. 1631 eruption about 20% of this zone was devastated by pyroclastic flows.
2. A Yellow Zone (about 1800 km²) that could be affected by heavy (>200 kg/m²) ash and lapilli fallout, as well as by mud fall and flows. In A.D. 1631, 10–15% of this area was severely damaged.

The Eruption Precursors

A main problem in defining the MEE scenario concerns the symptoms indicating that an eruption is approaching, the eruption's precursors. The historic record is, obviously, totally qualitative and mainly refers to the period 1631–1944 during which the volcano was characterized by open conduit conditions. Most of this information is probably not relevant to the present state of the volcano. The hypothesized precursors were therefore defined from the chronicles of the A.D. 1631 eruption (in Rolandi et al. 1993; Rosi et al. 1993), as well as from recent experiences of eruptions interrupting long rest periods (e.g., 1980 St. Helens, 1991 Pinatubo, 1994 Rabaul). In A.D. 1631 macroscopic precursors, including conspicuous uplift of the floor of the Vesuvius crater, ground shaking, and lowering of the piezometric level in wells, were observed at least 15 days before the eruption. (This is a very critical and delicate point since the expected sequence of precursors determines the alert levels and the emergency plan. To improve the capability of recognizing and interpreting any sign of an anomalous state of the volcano, the monitoring network has been greatly improved. Cooperative research programs involving a large number of Italian and foreign scientists are increasing the knowledge of Vesuvius and the capability of modeling and forecasting its future behavior.

The Monitoring System

The Osservatorio Vesuviano (OV) has been charged, since its birth in 1841, with volcano surveillance through the management of the monitoring networks. These consist of (Osservatorio Vesuviano 1995):

1. A seismic network of 10 stations (1 three-component) in which the signals are radioed to the Surveillance Center, sampled, and stored;

2. geometric leveling with 287 benchmarks forming 15 closed circuits, which have a total extension of about 220 km and are measured once per year;

3. planimetric leveling with 21 benchmarks and 60 measured base lines on the medium-high slopes of the volcano, which are measured once per year;

4. a GPS network of 21 benchmarks, connected to the Campi Flegrei network and including EDM networks of both areas;

5. a tiltmetric network currently consisting of one automatic station (two others will be installed in the near future), a marigraphic network, and three tide gauges;

6. a gravimetric network in which there is continuous registration of data from a gravimetric station at OV and periodic measurements of the gravimetric network (with 20 benchmarks);

7. geochemical sampling of fumeroles and water wells.

The Emergency Plan

The eruptive scenario was the basic document for the establishment of the National Emergency Planning of the Vesuvian Area (the Plan) which, following the guidelines of the 1992 document, was prepared by an ad hoc Commission (Presidenza Del Consiglio dei Ministri, Dipartimento Della Protezione Civile 1995). As part of the Plan, the OV is responsible for issuing eight levels of scientific alerts (table 2.2), determined on the basis of instrumental (seismicity, ground deformation, fluid geochemistry, and gravimetry) and observational data. An exercise simulating a limited emergency at Vesuvius (alert level 3) was successfully carried out in June 1996 as a first attempt to verify the efficacy of the Plan.

The Plan is a complex document providing procedures for the organization of civil defense during an emergency. It contains an evacuation plan, based on the MEE, and includes guidelines for establishing value and vulnerability maps of the region, encouraging the education of the population, establishing links between the scientific community and national and local civil defense institutions, and adjusting the Plan according to eventual

Table 2.2. Scientific Alert Levels

Level	Alert State	Volcano State	Civil Defense Main Actions
0, No alert	Low	Typical background values	None
1, Attention	Medium	Departure from background values of one monitored indicator	Population is alerted
2, Attention	High	Departure from background values of one monitored indicator suggesting a possible pre-eruptive state	Prefecture provides logistic support to the scientific community
3, Pre-alarm	Very high	Departure from background values of more than one monitored indicator suggesting a possible pre-eruptive state	Cabinet declares the State of Emergency The Civil Defense model of intervention is activated
4, Alarm	Maximum	Several indicators are coherent with a pre-eruptive state	Red Zone is evacuated (outside Campania region)
5, Waiting	Maximum	Data indicate pre-eruptive conditions; situation probably irreversible	Civil Defense and scientific operators leave the Red Zone
6, Eruption in progress	Maximum	Eruption in progress	That part of Yellow Zone affected by heavy fallout is evacuated (within Campania region)
7, After the eruption	Maximum	Eruption is over; attention has to be paid to possible late phenomena (mudflows, gas emission)	The State Department of Civil Defense defines modalities of return of population. The State of Emergency is revoked

structural interventions in the area and modifications to the expected eruption scenarios.

The management of the plan requires a permanent establishment of scientists, technicians, and administrators charged with promoting initiatives to mitigate the risk and modifying the Plan as necessary. This staff, the Commissione incaricata di provvedere all'aggiornamento dei piani di emergenza dell'area flegrea e dell'area vesuviana connessi a situazioni di emergenza derivanti dal rischio vulcanico, was created in February 1996 by the State Secretary for Civil Defense.

The Italian scientific community is fully conscious of the complexity of the problem of Vesuvius. The Plan was a necessary technical instrument for mitigating the volcanic risk in the Vesuvius area. Its existence is a successful first step on this road and it offers scope for changes and improvements. The framework for managing the problem of Vesuvius has been developed and the technical and juridical instruments now exist to extend the present emergency management plan to a more complex emergency prevention and risk mitigation plan. The Department of Civil Defense, the local civil authorities, and the scientific community are now in a position to realize actual interventions through specific laws and extraordinary, long-term, large financial interventions by the national and regional governments.

ACKNOWLEDGMENT

This paper was written after a lecture given by one of us (R.S.) in Cuma at a symposium organized in 1995 by Tufts University. We would very much like to thank Professor David Chester for the critical review of the manuscript.

REFERENCES

Alfano, G.B., I. Friedlander. 1929. "La Storia Del Vesuvio Illustrata Dai Documenti coevi." *Ulm. A.D. Donau, K. Holm*, 1–69. Napoli.

Andronico, D., G. Calderoni, R. Cioni, A. Sbrana, R. Sulpizio, R. Santacroce. 1995. "Geological Map of Sommo-Vesuvius Volcano." *Periodico Di Mineralogia* 64:77–8.

Arnò, V., C. Principe, M. Rosi, R. Santacroce, A. Sbrana, and M.F. Sheridan. 1987. "Eruptive History." In *Somma-Vesuvius,* edited by R. Santacroce, 53–103. CNR Quaderni de la Ricerca Scientifica 114. Roma.

Barberi, F., G. Macedonio, M.T. Pareschi, and R. Santacroce. 1990. "Mapping the Tephra Fallout Risk: An Example from Vesuvius (Italy)." *Nature* 344:142–4.

Barberi, F., C. Principe, M. Rosi, and R. Santacroce. 1995. *Scenario dell'evento eruttivo massimo atteso al Vesuvio in caso di riattivazione a breve-medio termine (aggiornamento al 20.1.1995).* Confidential Report, CNR, Gruppo Nazionale per la Vulcanologia. Roma.

Bertagnini, A., P. Landi, R. Santacroce, and A. Sbrana. 1991. "From Magmatic to Phreatomagmatic Activity through the Flashing of a Shallow Depth Hydrothermal System: The 1906 Eruption of Vesuvius." *Bulletin of Volcanology* 53:517–32.

Campbell, I.H., and J.S. Turner. 1986. "The Influence of Viscosity on Fountains in Magma Chambers." *Journal of Petrology* 27:1–30.

Carta, S., R. Figari, G. Sartoris, E. Sassi, and R. Scandone. 1981. "A Statistical Model from Vesuvius and Its Volcanological Implications." *Bulletin of Volcanology* 44(2):129–51.

Cioni, R., D. Andronico, G. Calderoni, D.J. Donahue, P. Marianelli, R. Santacroce, A. Sbrana, and R. Sulpizio. 1995a. *An Updated Chronostratigraphic Scheme of the Last 19,000 Years of Vesuvius Magmatic and Eruptive History.* AGU Fall Meeting, suppl. to *Eos,* Nov.7, 1995 (abstract).

Cioni, R., L. Civetta, P. Marianelli, N. Metrich, R. Santacroce, and A. Sbrana. 1995b. "Compositional Layering and Syneruptive Mixing of a Periodically Refilled Shallow Magma Chamber: The A.D. 79 Plinian Eruption of Vesuvius." *Journal of Petrology* B4 36(3):739–76.

Cioni, R., P. Marianelli, and A. Sbrana. 1990. "L'eruzione Del 79 D.C.: Stratigrafia Dei Depositi Ed Impatto Sugli Insediamenti Romani Nel Settore Orientale E Meridionale Del Somma Vesuvio." *Rivista di studi Pompeiani* 4:179–98.

Cioni, R., P. Marianelli, and A. Sbrana. 1992a. "Dynamics of the A.D. 79 Eruption: Stratigraphic, Sedimentologic and Geochemical Data on the Successions of the Somma-Vesuvius Southern and Eastern Sectors." *Acta Vulcanologica,* Marinelli 2:109–24.

Cioni, R., A. Sbrana, and R. Vecci. 1992b. "Morphologic Features of Juvenile Pyroclasts from Magmatic and Phreatomagmatic Deposits of Vesuvius." *Journal of Volcanology and Geothermal Research* 51:61–78.

Civetta, L., R. Galati, and R. Santacroce. 1991. "Magma Mixing and Convective Compositional Layering within the Vesuvius Magma Chamber." *Bulletin of Volcanology* 53:287–300.

Civetta, L., and R. Santacroce. 1992. "Steady-State Magma Supply in the Last 3400 Years of Vesuvius Activity?" *Acta Vulcanologica*, Marinelli 2:147–60.

Furman, T., and F.J. Spera. 1985. "Commingling of Acid and Basic Magma and Implications for the Origin of I-Type Xenoliths, I Field and Petrochemical Relations of an Unusual Dyke Complex at Eagle Lake, Sequoia National Park, California, USA." *Journal of Volcanology and Geothermal Research* 24:151–78.

Huppert, H.E., R.S.J. Sparks, and J.S. Turner. 1984. "Some Effects of Viscosity on the Dynamics of Replenished Magma Chambers." *Journal of Volcanology and Geothermal Research* 89:6857–77.

Huppert, H.E., R.S.J. Sparks, J.A. Whitehead, and M.A. Hallworth. 1986. "The Replenishment of Magma Chambers by Light Inputs." *Journal of Geophysical Research* 91:6113–22.

Imbò, G. 1949. "L'attività Eruttiva Vesuviana E Relative Osservazioni Nel Corso Dell'intervallo Intereruttivo 1906–1944 Ed In Particolare Del Parossismo Del Marzo 1944." *Ann. Osserv. Vesuviano, Napoli*, 185–380. 5ª serie, vol. unico celebrativo del primo centenario dell'Osservatorio Vesuviano. Napoli.

Luongo, G., and R. Santacroce. 1992. *Relazione Finale del Gruppo Informale di Lavoro 'Pericolosit.' Commissione incaricata di stabilire le linee guida per la valutazione del rischio connesso ad eruzione nell area vesuviana.* Confidential Report. Department of Civil Defense. Rome.

Macedonio G., M.T. Pareschi, and R. Santacroce. 1988a. "A Numerical Simulation of the Plinian Fall Phase of 79 A.D. Eruption of Vesuvius." *Journal of Geophysical Research* 93 B12:14817–27.

———. 1988b. "Simulazione Della Massima Eruzione Attesa In Caso Di Riattivazione Del Vesuvio." *Bollettino GNV* 1988:349–67.

———. 1988c. "Volcanic Hazard from Tephra Fallout and Flowage during the Next Eruption of Vesuvius." *Proceedings of the Kagoshima International Conference on Volcanoes*, 487–90. Kagoshima.

———. 1990. "Renewal of Explosive Activity at Vesuvius: Models for the Expected Tephra Fallout." *Journal of Volcanology and Geothermal Research* 40:327–42.

Marianelli, P., R. Cioni, and R. Santacroce. 1995a. "Melt Inclusions in Ca-Mg-Rich Clinopyroxene from Tephritic to Phonolitic Pyroclasts. A Clue to the Understanding of the Feeding History of the Vesuvius Magma Chambers." AGU Fall Meeting, suppl. to *Eos*, Nov.7, 1995 (abstract).

Marianelli, P., N. Metrich, R. Santacroce, and A. Sbrana. 1995b. "Mafic Magma Batches at Vesuvius: A Glass Inclusion Approach to the Modalities of Feeding Potassic Strato-Volcanoes." *Contributions on Mineralogy and Petrology* 120:159–69.

Mastrolorenzo, G., R. Munno, and G. Rolandi. 1993. "Vesuvius 1906: A Case Study of Paroxysmal Eruption and Its Relation to Eruption Cycles." *Journal of Volcanology and Geothermal Research* 58:217–37.

Mercalli, G. 1906. "La Grande Eruzione Vesuviana Cominciata Il 4 Aprile 1906." *Mem. Pont. Accad. Nuovi Lincei* 24:1–34.

Osservatorio Vesuviano. 1995. *La Sorveglianza Delle Aree Vulcaniche Napoletane.* Napoli.

Perret, F.A. 1924. *The Vesuvius Eruption of 1906. Study of a Volcanic Cycle.* Carnegie Inst. Pub. 339. Washington, D.C.

Presidenza Del Consiglio Dei Ministri, Dipartimento Della Protezione Civile. 1992. *Relazione Della Commissione Incaricata Di Stabilire Le Linee Guida Per La Valutazione Del Rischio Connesso Ad Eruzione Nell'area Vesuviana.* Confidential Report. Rome.

———. 1995. *Pianificazione Nazionale d'Emergenza dell'Area Vesuviana.* Official Report, Department of Civil Defense. Rome.

Rolandi G., A.M. Barrella, and A. Borrelli. 1993. "The 1631 Eruption of Vesuvius." *Journal of Volcanology and Geothermal Research* 58:183–201.

Rosi M., C. Principe, and R. Vecci. 1993. "The 1631 Eruption of Vesuvius Reconstructed from the Review of Chronicles and Study of Deposits." *Journal of Volcanology and Geothermal Research* 58:151–82.

Santacroce R. 1983. "A General Model for the Behavior of the Somma-Vesuvius Volcanic Complex." *Journal of Volcanology and Geothermal Research* 17:237–48.

———. 1990. *Evento Massimo Atteso Nel Caso Di Ripresa A Medio-Breve Termine Dell'attivita' Eruttiva Del Vesuvio.* Confidential Report, GNV and Department of Civil Defense. Rome.

Santacroce R., A. Bertagnini, L. Civetta, P. Landi, and A. Sbrana. 1993. "Eruptive Dynamics and Petrogenetic Processes in a Very Shallow Magma Reservoir: The 1906 Eruption of Vesuvius." *Journal of Petrology* 34(2):383–425.

Santacroce R., R. Cioni, L. Civetta, P. Marianelli, N. Metrich, and A. Sbrana. 1994. "How Vesuvius Works." *Atti dei Covegni Lincei, "Large Explosive Eruptions,"* 112:185–96.

Santacroce, R., R. Cioni, M. Rosi, and A. Sbrana. 1995. "A Model of Operation of Vesuvius Based on Geological and Petrological Data." AGU Fall Meeting, suppl. to *Eos*, Nov.7, 1995 (abstract).

Sigurdsson, H., W. Cornell, and S. Carey. 1990. "Influence of Magma Withdrawal on Compositional Gradients during the A.D. 79 Vesuvius Eruption." *Nature* 345:519–21.

Sparks, R.S.J., and L.A. Marshall. 1986. "Thermal and Mechanical Constraints on Mixing Between Mafic and Silicic Magmas." *Journal of Volcanology and Geothermal Research* 29:99–124.

Turner, J.S. 1985. "Multicomponent Convection." *Ann. Rev. Fluid Mech.* 17:11–44.

3

Eruptive Activity of Etna before A.D. 1600, with Particular Reference to the Classical Period

Angus M. Duncan, David K. Chester, and John E. Guest

Mount Etna, Sicily, is one of the few volcanoes in the world that is continuously active (Chester et al. 1985). The frequent reference to eruptions of Etna in classical texts dating back to the colonization by the Greeks suggests that the current pattern of continuous eruptive behavior extends back for at least 2,500 years. The oldest eruption described is probably that of 693 B.C. and though there is no evidence to substantiate it, legend has it that the Sicans were driven from eastern Sicily by a large eruption of Etna prior to the first settlement by the Greeks.

Despite the hazard from volcanic eruptions, the lower slopes of Etna have been densely populated from early times. Then as now, people were presumably attracted by the fertile volcanic soils and the supply of water from the springs that issue from the base of the volcanic pile. Indeed Catania and Naxos, two of the early Greek settlements in Sicily, are situated at the foot of the volcano. The communities that were established on the flanks of the volcano clearly adjusted to its eruptive behavior, and Etna became something of a tourist attraction during Roman times (Finley et al. 1986). Catania, which was established in 729 B.C., has been engulfed in part by lava three times in its history but has remained an important settlement and is now the second city of Sicily with a population of over 400,000. This is in contrast to the development of communities in classical times around Vesuvius. Though it had been recognized that Vesuvius was probably volcanic in origin (Sigurdsson

Fig. 3.1. Vent area of the 1983 flank eruption of Mount Etna showing a typical effusive discharge of lava from the base of the fissure system.

et al. 1985), prior to the eruption of A.D. 79 it was not regarded as a potentially active volcano and the eruption came as a catastrophic surprise to the communities of Pompeii and Herculaneum. These towns were utterly destroyed by volcanic activity and were not re-established. Vesuvius is a relatively small volcano, with a height of 1180 m.a.s.l. and a diameter of only about 14 km. Villages and small towns are clustered on the lower slopes, particularly on the western flank, most being located less than 8 km from the current crater. This, taken together with the violent nature of much of the activity of Vesuvius, makes it a very hazardous volcano. Eruptions on Etna, on the other hand, are typically effusive (fig. 3.1) with mild explosive activity restricted to the vent areas. In addition, Etna is a large volcano, around 3000 m.a.s.l. in height with an area of 1750 km². Much of the activity takes place well away from areas of habitation. Only large eruptions with vents at low altitude that send lava down to the lower slopes or the relatively rare more explosive eruptions will have had an impact on the local community.

The purpose of this chapter is to examine the records of eruptions of Etna in early historic times, to assess how the attitude of the community has developed, and from this information, together with geological data, build a picture of the eruptive behavior of the volcano from around 700 B.C. up to A.D. 1600.

Records of Eruptive Behavior of Etna Up to A.D. 1500

Even prior to the colonization of Sicily by the Greeks, around 734 B.C., there is evidence that volcanism influenced the local mythology. The Sicels had cults involving subterranean processes associated with volcanic manifestations. There was a temple to the Sicel goddess, Hybla, next to the mud volcano at Paternò, at the southwest margin of Etna (Freeman 1892; Maniscalco, this volume) and there was a temple to the fire god, Hadranus, near Adrano. These Sicel legends became incorporated into subsequent Greek mythology.

Pindar (*Pythian Odes* 1.13–28) makes one of the earliest references to an eruption of Etna, probably concerning the eruption of 474/479 B.C. (Rodwell 1878; Chester et al. 1985). There is some ambiguity in relating early records to specific eruptions. Legend has it that Empedocles took his life by jumping into the summit crater; there is no evidence to support this myth and the Torre del Filosofo, a building just south of the summit cone which is named after him, was probably the site of a tower built when Hadrian ascended the volcano. Thucydides (3, 116) refers to several early eruptions, the first of which is considered to be ca. 693 B.C., when vents opened up on the southern flank sending down a flow of lava which partly destroyed Catania (Tanguy 1980; Romano and Sturiale 1982; Stothers and Rampino 1983; Chester et al. 1985). It is probably during this eruption that the famous incident involving the *fratelli pii* occurred. It is recorded that as the lavas entered Catania two youths, Anapias and Amphinomus, carried their aged parents on their shoulders through the flaming streets to safety; a temple was erected in their honor.

Diodorus Siculus (14.59.3; cf. Stothers and Rampino 1983) reports a lava flow that entered the sea north of Catania in 394/396 B.C. This eruption formed a cone, Mt. Gorna, near Trecastagni and the lava flowed east, entering the sea at Santa Maria la Scala (Romano and Sturiale 1982; Chester et al. 1985). This lava may have cut through the eastern coastal route of the island, causing the Carthaginian general Himilco to detour west around the volcano on his march from Messina to Syracuse. Other sources imply that it was the lava from Mt. Moio, a cone on the northern periphery of Etna, that caused the detour of the Carthaginian army. The lavas from Mt. Moio are, however, prehistoric in age and the Greek settlement at Naxos is actually built on top of the distal part of this flow.

It appears that volcanic activity increased after 141 B.C., leading up to the major eruption of 122 B.C. (Lucr. 6.639–646). Major explosive activity from the summit craters deposited ash in a southeasterly direction and lava that erupted from near Trecastagni flowed toward the north of Catania. Thick accumulation of ash on roofs in Catania led to collapse of buildings and considerable damage. In response to the eruption, the Roman Authorities granted the inhabitants of Catania immunity from taxes for 10 years (Rodwell 1878).

An eruption of Etna is reported at the onset of the civil war between Pompey and Caesar in 49 B.C. and this was followed by a major explosive event occurring at the time of Caesar's assassination in 44 B.C. (Chester et al. 1985; Forsyth 1988; Chester et al. 2000). Stothers and Rampino (1983) suggest that the solar halo witnessed at the time of Caesar's death, the hazy conditions, and the resulting crop failure may have been caused by volcanic aerosols injected into the atmosphere by this explosive eruption. Vergil (*Geo.* 1.466–73) states: "After the death of Caesar. . .how often we saw Etna flooding out from her burst furnaces, boiling over the Cyclopean fields and whirling forth balls of flame and molten stones" (quoted in Stothers and Rampino 1983, 6359). The tenor of nearly contemporary accounts indicates that this was a large eruption by Etnean standards. According to Pliny the Elder: "Etna. . . .is so hot that it belches out sands in a ball of flame over a space of 50 to 100 [Roman] miles" (Stothers and Rampino 1983, 6359). Ash falls from Etnean eruptions are rarely deposited more than 20 km from the volcano, so that a distance of up to 150 km (equivalent to 100 Roman miles) would support the interpretation that this was a large eruption.

In A.D. 40, Suetonius (*Caligula* 51, from Stothers and Rampino 1983) refers to an explosion from Etna that caused Caligula to flee from the region, but the nature of this eruptive event is unclear. The eruption of A.D. 252/3 was the next major phase of activity to be recorded. This was a substantial flank eruption in which a cone, Mt. Peloso, was formed 2 km north of Nicolosi (Romano and Sturiale 1982), and the lava flowed south, threatening Catania. The inhabitants brought out the veil of the recently martyred St. Agatha and paraded it in front of the advancing lava. This was the first recorded appearance of St. Agatha in her role of protecting the local community from the destructive forces of the volcano, a custom that has continued to the present day (Chester et al. 1985).

The last record of an eruption during Roman times is a reference in a fragment of Olympiodorus's *History*, quoted by Photius of activity by Etna in the early fifth century. Uchrin (1990) suggests that this eruption may have been the cause of the darkness in A.D. 417 described by Marcellinus (*Chronicon*). A summary of the major eruptions of Etna during the classical period is provided in table 3.1.

Over the next 600 years there are few references to eruptive activity of Etna. This probably reflects the political and cultural environment of the so-called Dark Ages, during which there was a lack of educated observers who could have left a written record, rather than a period of calm in the activity of the volcano. Reference to an eruption in A.D. 812 may have been made only because Charlemagne was in Messina at the time. After A.D. 1100, accounts of eruptions become more common and include reference to a large earthquake associated with the volcano that destroyed Catania in A.D. 1169 and killed several hundred people (Rodwell 1878; Chester et al. 1985). The increase in written accounts no doubt reflects the development of an educated ecclesiastical community that included men such as Henry Aristippus, an Archdeacon of Catania in the 12th century, a scholar and scientist with an interest in the volcanology of Etna (Norwich 1970). In the 15th and 16th centuries a more complete record of flank eruptions is available in the literature. Major flank eruptions are noted in A.D. 1408, 1444, 1446, 1536, 1537, 1566 and 1579.

Activity of Etna Volcano 700 B.C. to A.D. 1500

Information from the historical records of the classical period are insufficient to enable a detailed picture of the eruptive behavior of the volcano to be established. The Romans and Greeks did not make detailed objective observations of the volcano and its behavior. Although Etna is a large volcano, persistent activity at the summit and indeed most flank eruptions are unlikely to have had much impact on the urban communities which were concentrated on the southern and eastern flanks. Some events, such as the one that frightened Caligula, were probably recorded only because someone famous was in the area. The fact that substantial lava flows reached the foot of the volcano in ca. 693 B.C., 396 B.C., 122 B.C., and A.D. 252/253 suggests that for much of this time Etna was behaving in a fashion comparable to that which was seen later in the 17th century A.D. (Hughes et al. 1990).

Coltelli et al. (1995a), in a detailed study of the pyroclastic deposits on the southern and eastern flanks of Etna, quote a radiocarbon date of 2180 ± 60

Table 3.1. Summary of documented eruptive activity of Etna from ca. 700 B.C. through to mid-fifth century A.D. (From Chester et al. 2000)

Date	Documented eruptive activity	Comment	References in Ancient Authors	Modern summaries of ancient activity
c. 693 B.C.	Eruption on south flank. The main vent was probably Mt Monpilieri, 1 km south of Nicolosi. Other vents reported at Campo Pio, 6 km north of Catania. Lava invaded the city of Catania (established in 729 B.C.).	Eruption famous for the story of the fratelli pii, the two brothers who carried their parents away from the advancing lava.	Thucydides 3, 116	Chester, et al. 1985; Romano and Sturiale 1982; Stothers and Rampino 1983
c. 479/475 B.C.	The vent area was probably on SSE flank.		Thucydides 3, 116, Pindar Pythian Odes, I, III	Chester, et al. 1985; Stothers and Rampino 1983
425 B.C.	A substantial eruption.	6th year of Peloponnesian war.	Thucydides 3, 116	Chester, et al. 1985; Romano and Sturiale 1982; Stothers and Rampino 1983
396 B.C.	A flank eruption built up the cone of Mt Gorna 3.5 km N of Trecastagni. Lava flows entered the sea just N of Acireale.	It is recorded that the lava flows prevented the Carthaginian General, Himilco, from marching along the coast from Messina to Syracuse.	11	Chester, et al. 1985; Romano and Sturiale 1982; Stothers and Rampino 1983
135 B.C.	Lava and ashes erupted. Eruptions also reported in 140 and 126 B.C.		III	Stothers and Rampino 1983
122 B.C.	Major explosive activity from summit craters with the deposition of ash in a SE dispersal direction. Lava was erupted from a vent near Trecastagni, Mt. Trigona.	Reports that the thick accumulation of ash destroyed roofs in Catania. Roman authorities granted the inhabitants of Catania immunity from taxes for 10 years.	Lucretius 6. 639-646, Orosius 5.18	Chester, et al. 1985; Romano and Sturiale 1982; Stothers and Rampino 1983
49 & 44 B.C.	An eruption was reported in 49 B.C. at the outset of the civil war between Pompey and Caesar. A large eruption was reported at the time of Caesar's death in 44 B.C.	Dimming of the sun and hazy conditions reported in Italy at that time have been attributed to this eruption (III).	Vergil Georgics 1. 466-473	Chester, et al. 1985; Romano and Sturiale 1982; Stothers and Rampino 1983
36 B.C.	Report of an eruption.		Appian Civil Wars 5. 117	Chester, et al. 1985; Stothers and Rampino 1983
32 B.C.	Stream of lava reported which did damage.	During civil war.	Dio Roman History 50. 8.3	Stothers and Rampino 1983
?A.D. 70	Report of an eruption.		Suetonius Caligula	Chester, et al. 1985; Stothers and Rampino 1983
A.D. 252/3	Flank eruption, the lava nearly reached Catania.	It is alleged that the flow stopped when the veil of St. Agatha was brought to the flow front.	Suetonius Caligula	Chester, et al. 1985; Romano and Sturiale 1982; Stothers and Rampino 1983
A.D. 417	Suggestion that darkening of the sun in A.D. 417 described by Marcellinus (9) may correlate with an eruption of Etna reported by Olympiodorus (10) ca. A.D. 420.		Marcellinus Chronicon, Olympiodorus in Photius, Library	Stothers and Rampino 1983

for a paleosol immediately below one of their youngest layers, FG, and correlate it with the 122 B.C. eruption. This eruption is classified as plinian by Coltelli et al. (1995a) and is one of the most explosive events to occur at Etna during the last 5,000 years. It is likely that the eruptive column would have extended to a height of more than 10 km above the volcano. A map (adapted from Coltelli et al.1995a) showing the distribution of the pyroclastic fall deposit from the 122 B.C. eruption is shown in figure 3.2. It can be seen from the distribution that more than 10 cm of ash would have been deposited in Catania. By comparison, the 1979 eruption, which was one of the more explosive in recent years and produced a substantial eruptive column (fig. 3.3) with a dispersal to the southeast, deposited only 3 mm of ash on Catania, causing minimal disruption except closure of the airport for a short period of time. Such explosive eruptions are often accompanied by heavy rainfall and the ash becomes waterlogged, increasing its density. During the 1991 eruption of Mt. Pinatubo in the Philippines, for example, over one third of the buildings in the town of Castillejos suffered partial or total collapse as a consequence of ash fall of a thickness of 15 to 20 cm (Spence et al. 1996). It is not surprising then that the ash fall from the 122 B.C. eruption of Etna led to the damage in Catania, requiring the support from the Roman authorities discussed above.

Another pyroclastic layer identified by Coltelli et al. (1995b) is indicative of a significant explosive eruption. It is younger than the 122 B.C. eruption but is overlain by deposits of an eruption with a radiocarbon date of 980 ± 60 B.P. Coltelli et al. (1995b) suggest it may be first century A.D. in age and tie in with historic records of ash fall on Taormina and Catania between A.D. 38 and 40. This deposit may, however, have resulted from the major explosive eruption of 40 B.C., at the time of Caesar's death.

The fact that there appear to be no historic records of the explosive eruption whose deposits Coltelli et al. (1995b) date at 980 ± 60 B.P. bears witness to the lack of written documentation after the collapse of the Roman Empire in the west and before the re-emergence of scholastic activity in the middle ages following the Norman conquest in the 11th century A.D. In the middle ages, although there are a number of accounts of eruptions, there is insufficient detail to enable a full picture of the eruptive behavior of the volcano to be developed.

In the 17th century A.D., Etna behaved in a more vigorous fashion than has been the case during the 19th and 20th centuries, with a mean effusion rate of lava of 1.19 m^3s^{-1} (Hughes et al. 1990). Large volume flank eruptions

sent several lava flows down to the base of the volcanic pile partially
engulfing Catania with lava in A.D. 1669. Following the major 1669 eruption, there was collapse in the summit region of the volcano. Since 1750
Etna has behaved in a broadly steady-state fashion (Guest and Duncan
1981) characterized by persistent activity at the summit craters, at times

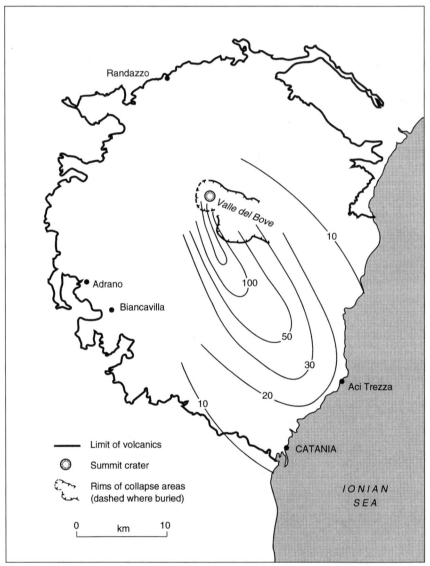

Fig. 3.2. Isopach map (contour map showing thickness of deposit in cm) of the pyroclastic-fall
deposit of 122 B.C. eruption. (After Coltelli et al. 1995a)

Fig. 3.3. View of the pyroclastic plume from the 1979 eruption of Etna. This was a relatively minor explosive event but gives a minimum impression of how the volcano would have looked during an explosive eruption such as that of 122 B.C. or 44 B.C.

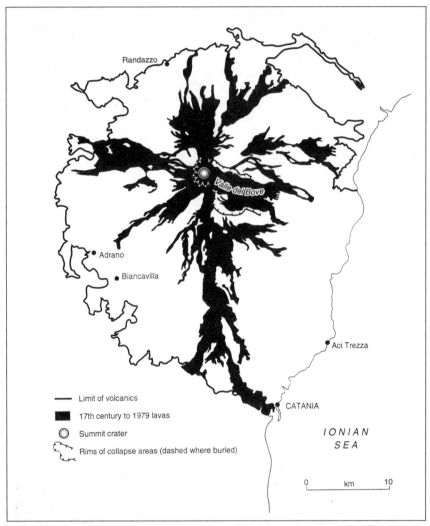

Fig. 3.4. Map showing the distribution of lavas younger than A.D. 1600 on Mount Etna. This gives a good impression of the rate of resurfacing of the volcano by lava over a 400-year period.

involving low effusion rate discharge of lavas, around 0.18 m^3s^{-1}, punctuated every few years by flank eruptions with higher effusion rate emission of lava. Only once during this period has lava caused significant damage to property, the destruction of the town of Mascali in 1928 (Duncan et al. 1996; Chester et al., this volume). The coverage of Etna by flows younger than A.D. 1600 shown in figure 3.4 gives a clear impression of the rate of resurfacing by lava of the volcano over a 400-year period, a time span which incorporates phases of both high and low average effusion rates. It is reasonable to assume that, based on the available historical and geological data, a broadly similar rate of resurfacing occurred during classical times.

Conclusion

Dominated by the bulk of Etna and confronted by its frequent activity, the inhabitants of eastern Sicily have since earliest times attempted to explain the volcanic phenomena. The indigenous Sicels developed a cult involving subterranean forces and their mythological interpretations of the volcanic phenomena were inherited by the early Greek settlers. Subsequently, philosophers began to seek more rational explanations of the natural phenomena. Lucretius proposed that the volcano was hollow underneath with basaltic caverns that penetrated to the sea and allowed water to percolate to the depth of the volcano's throat. Wind and air were heated in the caverns, and in turn heated the surrounding rocks until a sulfur flame rose and forced itself out, scattering its ashes and rolls of smoke and causing pitchy blackness. The poet Ovid (*Met.* 15.343) attributed the activity of Etna to its many air passages that breathed flame and would continue to do so until its fuel was exhausted. Although contemptuous of the myths surrounding volcanic phenomena, the philosophers based their interpretation on speculation and musing, demonstrating little interest in objective observation, and as a consequence showed little understanding. The Scottish geologist, Sir Archibald Geikie, however, argued in his Williams Memorial Lecture at John Hopkins University in 1896 that, "the speculations of the philosophers who began to observe the operation of natural processes and who, though their deductions were often about as unscientific as the myths for which they are substituted, may yet be claimed the earliest pioneers of geology" (Geikie 1905, 5).

It was not until the Renaissance that Etna became the subject of more analytical study. Cardinal Bembo provides a broad description of the geography of the volcano in A.D. 1495 (*De Aetna Petri Bembi*). An eyewitness description of the eruption of A.D. 1536 is contained in a published work by Antonio Filoteo (Rodwell 1878). From A.D. 1600 to the present day there is an almost complete record of flank eruptions. It is tempting to equate the pattern of activity provided by the historic records prior to A.D. 1600 with the actual pattern of the eruptive behavior of the volcano over that time, and although there has been variability in the eruptive behavior of Etna (Duncan and Guest 1982; Hughes et al. 1990), it is likely that the variability in historic records reflects in part political and sociological factors. Eruptions tend to have been recorded only if they had a major impact on the community or important people were in the area and there were literate people available to provide written accounts. If eruptions occurred in remote parts of the volcano or during periods when the local inhabitants did not have the means or tradition for making written accounts, then records of the activity will not have been preserved. Notwithstanding these factors, Etna has one of the best historical records of any active volcano, and over the last 25 years these data have contributed to our understanding of the volcano and its eruptions.

REFERENCES

Chester, D.K., A.M. Duncan, J.E. Guest, and C.R.J. Kilburn. 1985. *Mount Etna: Anatomy of a Volcano.* London.

Chester, D.K., A.M. Duncan, J.E. Guest, P.A. Johnston, and J.L.L. Smolenaars. 2000. "Human Response to Etna Volcano During the Classical Period." In *The Archaeology of Geological Catastrophes,* edited by W.G. McGuire, D.R. Griffiths, P.L. Hancock, and I.S. Stewart, 179–88. Geological Society, Special Publications 171. London.

Coltelli, M., P. Del Carlo, and L. Vezzoli. 1995a. "A Plinian Eruption of Basaltic Composition in the Historical Activity of Mt. Etna." *Period. Mineral. Roma* 64:145–6.

———. 1995b. "Stratigraphy of the Holocene Mt. Etna Explosive Eruptions." *Period. Mineral. Roma* 64:14–13.

Duncan, A.M., and J.E. Guest. 1982. "Mount Etna: Variations in its Internal Plumbing." *Geophysical Surveys* 5:213–27.

Duncan, A.M., C. Dibben, D.K. Chester and J.E. Guest. 1996. "The 1928 Eruption of Mount Etna Volcano, Sicily, and the Destruction of the Town Of Mascali." *Disasters* 20:1–21.

Finley, M.I., D. Mack Smith, and C.J.H. Duggan. 1986. *A History of Sicily.* London.

Forsyth, P.Y. 1988. "In the Wake of Etna, 44 B.C." *Classical Antiquity* 7:49–57.

Freeman, E.A. 1892. *Sicily. Phoenician, Greek and Roman. (The Story of Nations,* Vol. 31). London.

Giekie, A. 1905. *The Founders of Geology.* 2nd ed. London.

Guest, J.E., and A.M. Duncan. 1981. "Internal Plumbing of Mount Etna." *Nature* 290:584–6.

Hughes, J.W., J.E. Guest, and A.M. Duncan. 1990. "Changing Styles of Effusive Eruption on Mount Etna since A.D. 1600." In *Magma Transport and Storage,* edited by M.P. Ryan, 385–406. Chichester.

Norwich, J.J. 1970. *The Kingdom in the Sun.* London.

Rodwell, G.F. 1878. *Etna: A History of the Mountain and Its Eruptions.* London.

Romano, R., and C. Sturiale. 1982. "The Historical Eruptions of Mount Etna (Volcanological Data)." In *Mount Etna Volcano, A Review Of The Recent Earth Sciences Studies,* edited by R Romano, 75–97. Memorie della Società Geologica Italiana 23.

Sigurdsson, H., S. Carey, W. Cornell, and T. Pescatore. 1985. "The Eruption of Vesuvius in A.D. 79." *National Geographic Research* 1:332–87.

Spence, R.J.S., A. Pomonis, P.J. Baxter, A.W. Coburn, M. White, and M. Dayrit. 1996. "Building damage caused by the Mt. Pinatubo eruption of June 14–15, 1991. In *Fire and Mud: Eruptions and Lahars of Mount Pinatubo, Philippines,* edited by C.G. Newhall and R.S. Punongbayan, 551–556. Seattle.

Stothers, R.B., and M.R. Rampino. 1983. "Volcanic Eruptions in the Mediterranean before A.D. 630 from Written and Archaeological Sources." *Journal of Geophysical Research* 88:6357–71.

Tanguy, J.-C. 1980. "L'Etna étude petrologique et paleomagnetique implications volcanologique." Ph.D. diss., Université Pierre et Marie Curie, Paris.

Uchrin, G. 1990. "Olympiodorus's Eruption of Mount Etna. A Possible Date of A.D. 417." *Eos* 71, no. 11 (1990): 329, 334.

— 4 —

The Campi Flegrei Nested Caldera (Italy): A Restless, Resurgent Structure in a Densely Populated Area

❖

Giovanni Orsi, Sandro de Vita, Mauro Di Vito, and Roberto Isaia

The Campi Flegrei caldera (CFc) is located at the northeastern corner of the Phlegraean Volcanic District (PVD), which includes the city of Napoli, Campi Flegrei (CF), the volcanic islands of Procida and Ischia, and the northwestern part of the Gulf of Napoli (fig. 4.1). The magmatism of this district is related to the extensional tectonism that affected the Tyrrhenian margin of the Apennines thrust belt generating northwest–southeast- and northeast–southwest-trending normal and vertical faults (Ippolito et al. 1973; D'Argenio et al. 1973; Finetti and Morelli 1974; Bartole 1984). As a consequence of this tectonism the large graben of the Campanian Plain was formed and disjointed by a number of smaller horst and graben structures (Carrara et al. 1973; Finetti and Morelli 1974), and a framework enabling magma ascent to the surface was established. The CFc is inhabited by 1.5 million people. In the past 30 years it has shown signs of unrest with two bradyseismic events that have generated a maximum net uplift of 3.5 m around the town of Pozzuoli (Barberi et al. 1984). The intense urbanization and the very active short-term deformations make the volcanic risk very high. In an area of such high risk, it is of critical importance to understand the volcano's evolution and its relationship to short- and long-term deformational history to enable effective forecasting of the future behavior of the system. The aim of this chapter is to outline the volcanological and deformational history of the CFc.

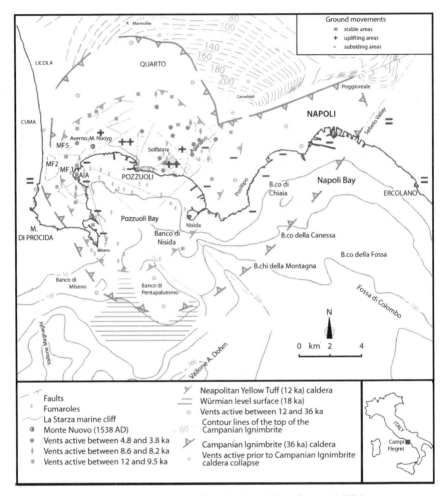

Fig. 4.1. Structural sketch map of the Campi Flegrei caldera. (After Orsi et al. 1996)

Morphological and Structural Outlines

The CFc includes both subaerial and submerged parts (fig. 4.1) whose morphology is very complex, largely resulting from constructive and destructive volcanic and volcano-tectonic events that occurred alternately and sometimes coevally. Variations in the relationship between sea- and earth-surface levels have also contributed to the present morphological setting. The subaerial part of the CFc comprises the CF and the city of Napoli. The horseshoe-shaped CF surrounds Pozzuoli Bay and its center is characterized by a rugged morphology consisting of many tuff-rings and tuff-cones, sur-rounded to the west, north, and east by lowlands. The submerged part of the caldera includes northwestern Napoli Bay and Pozzuoli Bay. It is bordered on the southeast by a line that connects the Vallone A. Dohrn Canyon to the Sebeto Valley inland (fig. 4.1; De Bonitatibus et al. 1970; Colantoni et al. 1972; Segre 1972; De Pippo et al. 1984; Crane et al. 1985). Level surfaces, generated by sea-level stands, occur only outside the depression of Pozzuoli Bay. The deepest among these surfaces occurs at 120–150 m.b.s.l. and is cor-related with the level surface generated during the Würmian regression (Pescatore et al. 1984) between 18,000 and 14,000 B.P. (Shackleton and Hopdike 1973). The Roman coastline is located at about 10 m.b.s.l. (Günter 1903; Segre 1972; De Pippo et al. 1984).

The structural setting of the area results from deformational events related to either regional tectonism or volcano-tectonics. The regional tectonism has produced normal and vertical faults that trend mostly northeast–southwest and northwest–southeast, with a subordinate trend north–south (fig. 4.1). Well-defined northeast–southwest trending faults are the Vallone A. Dohrn Canyon-Sebeto Valley, and the Camaldoli-Poggioreale features. Morphological and seismic data show northwest–southeast trending faults at Fossa di Colombo, along the northeastern slope of Banco di Pentapalummo, and southwest of Banchi della Montagna (Segre 1972; De Pippo et al. 1984; Crane et al. 1985). Faults trending north–south are also shown by seismic and mor-phological data at Vallone Magnaghi Canyon and along the Baia-Banco di Miseno alignment inland (Segre 1972; Finetti and Morelli 1974; Crane et al. 1985).

Volcanic History

Since the 19th century, many scientists have investigated the geological his-tory of the subaerial part of the CFc (Johnston Lavis 1889; Dell'Erba 1892; De Lorenzo 1904; Rittmann 1950) and more recent studies have shed light on its evolution over the last 50,000 years (fig. 4.2) (Scherillo 1953, 1955; Scherillo and Franco 1960, 1967; Rosi et al. 1983; Di Girolamo et al. 1984; Rosi and Sbrana 1987; Barberi et al. 1991; Dvorak and Berrino 1991; Dvorak and Gasparini 1991; Orsi et al. 1996). The caldera is composed mostly of volcanic rocks ranging in composition from latite, trachyte, and alkali-trachyte to peralkaline phonolite and rare trachybasalts (Armienti et al.

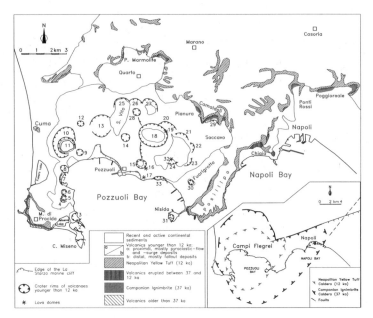

Fig. 4.2. Geological sketch map of the Neapolitan-Phlegraean area. *ML*, Miliscola; *Smi*, San Martino islet; *TG*, Torregaveta; *CU*, Cuma; *SS*, San Severino; *PM*, Punta Marmolite; *TL*, Trefola; *TF*, Torre di Franco; *VR*, Verdolino; *PR*, Ponti Rossi; *SA*, SantíArpino; *MR*, Moiariello; *MS*, Montesanto; *Smh*, San Martino hill; *EC*, Monte Echia; *TM*, Trentaremi; *CR*, Coroglio; *VL*, Villanova. Location of vents is indicated by numerals on the map: *1*, Capo Miseno; *2*, Punta Pennata; *3*, Bacoli; *4*, Bellavista; *5*, Fondi di Baia I; *6*, Fondi di Baia II; *7*, Baia; *8*, Mofete; *9*, Monte Nuovo; *10*, Archiaverno; *11*, Averno; *12*, Fondo Riccio; *13*, Gauro; *14*, Cigliano; *15*, Solfatara; *16*, Accademia; *17*, Monte Olibano; *18*, Astroni; *19*, Caprara; *20*, Sartania; *21*, Pigna San Nicola; *22*, Monte Sant'Angelo; *23*, Grotta del Cane; *24*, Agnano-Monte Spina; *25*, Montagna Spaccata; *26*, Pisani; *27*, San Martino; *28*, Senga; *29*, Minopoli; *30*, Santa Teresa; *31*, Nisida; *32*, Cupola di Monte Spina; *33*, La Pietra. (After Orsi et al. 1996).

1983, 1984; Di Girolamo et al. 1984; Rosi and Sbrana 1987; Villemant 1988; Civetta et al. 1991). Subordinate marine clastic sediments are also present. Seismic investigations have contributed to the understanding of the geological and structural setting of the submerged part of the caldera (De Bonitatibus 1970; Latmiral et al. 1971; Finetti and Morelli 1974; Pescatore et al. 1984; Fusi et al. 1991; Fevola et al. 1993).

Geological, petrological, and geophysical data suggest the existence of a magma reservoir beneath the CF (Armienti et al. 1983, 1984; Di Girolamo et al. 1984; Barberi et al. 1978; Rosi and Sbrana 1987; Villemant 1988; Civetta et al. 1991) located at a shallow depth (4–5 km; Berrino et al. 1984; Ortiz et al.1984; Ferrucci et al. 1992). The magmatic system is still active as testified by the last eruption which occurred in 1538 A.D. at Monte Nuovo (Di Vito et al. 1987), the recent bradyseismic episodes in 1969–72 and 1982–84 (Casertano et al. 1977; Barberi et al. 1984, 1989), and the widespread fumarolic and thermal springs activity.

The morphological depression of the CF was interpreted by Rosi et al. (1983) and Rosi and Sbrana (1987) and Barberi et al. (1991) as the result of a caldera collapse during the eruption of the Campanian Ignimbrite (CI; Di Girolamo 1970; Barberi et al. 1978; Fisher et al. 1993; Civetta et al. 1997; Rosi et al. 1996), which occurred 37,000 B.P. (Deino et al. 1992, 1994). Other researchers, however, interpret the depression as a caldera related to the Neapolitan Yellow Tuff (NYT) eruption (12,000 B.P.; Orsi and Scarpati 1989; Orsi et al. 1991a, 1992, 1995; Scarpati et al. 1993; Wohletz et al. 1995; Lirer et al. 1987; Scandone et al. 1991). Orsi et al. (1992 and 1996) demonstrated that the CF depression and the area of the city of Napoli are parts of a nested caldera complex resulting from collapses related to both the CI and NYT eruptions. Furthermore, they interpreted the recent unrest episodes as related to an ongoing resurgence inside the youngest caldera.

The geological and deformational history of the CF can be reconstructed using the CI, the NYT, and the related calderas as markers.

Volcanism Older than 37,000 B.P.

Rocks older than CI are exposed only in the scarps bordering the CF and along sea cliffs (fig. 4.2). They are mostly alkalitrachytic in composition and include the lava domes of Punta Marmolite (47,000 B.P.) and Cuma (37,000 B.P.; Cassignol and Gillot 1982), the pyroclastic deposits of the Tufi di Torre Franco Unit (>42,000 B.P.; Alessio et al. 1973), and the remnant of the Monte Grillo tuff cone (fig. 4.2). The products of at least 10 eruptions older than the CI, interbedded with paleosols, have been found along the scarps bordering the Quarto Plain on the northeast and correlated with those found in drill cores in the areas of Ponti Rossi, Poggioreale, Chiaiano, and Secondigliano, inside the city of Napoli (Orsi et al. 1996).

Campanian Ignimbrite

The CI (fig. 4.2) is the largest pyroclastic deposit of the Campanian area and ranges in composition from trachyte to phonolitic-trachyte. It covers an area of about 30,000 km^2 with an estimated volume of erupted magma of about 150 km^3 (Civetta et al. 1997). Attribution of pyroclastic deposits exposed along the margin of the CF depression to the CI is debated in the literature (Lirer et al.1991; Perrotta and Scarpati 1994; Rosi et al. 1996; Civetta et al. 1997; Orsi et al. 1996). The vent for the eruption was located north of Napoli, along a northwest–southeast trending fracture (Di Girolamo 1970; Barberi et al. 1978; Di Girolamo et al. 1984), in the depression of Acerra (Scandone et al. 1991), and in the CF (Rosi et al. 1983, 1996; Rosi and Sbrana 1987; Barberi et al. 1991; Fisher et al. 1993; Orsi et al. 1992, 1996; and Ort et al. 1997). On the basis of stratigraphic position, textural characteristics and petrological and isotope data, the breccia deposits exposed along the Camaldoli-Poggioreale alignment were also attributed to the CI by Rosi et al. (1996) and Civetta et al. (1997) (fig. 4.2).

Campanian Ignimbrite Caldera
The area collapsed in response to the CI eruption (fig. 4.1) has been recently defined by Orsi et al. (1996). The high-angle scarps bordering the CF depression to the north result from the morphological evolution of the CI caldera-fault scarps and are unconformably mantled by volcanics younger than CI. The distribution of the upper surface of the CI suggests that the Camaldoli-Poggioreale scarp resulted from partial reactivation of an earlier fault system during the caldera collapse. The southeastern structural boundary of the caldera is submerged and follows the northeast–southwest trend delineated by the Vallone A. Dohrn Canyon and the Sebeto Valley. The Sebeto Valley also marks the border between the subsiding area of the caldera and the stable Vesuvian area (fig. 4.1). The southern boundary is marked by the alignment of the submerged vents of the Pentapalummo and Miseno volcanoes, both younger than CI and likely located inside the caldera. The western boundary is exposed only in the two heights of Monte di Procida and Cuma. The caldera covers an area of about 230 km^2. Considering an average downthrown of about 700 m (Barberi et al. 1991), the collapsed volume is on the order of 160 km^3, which is in good agreement with the estimated volume of the CI (150 km^3 DRE; Civetta et al. 1997).

Volcanism between 37,000 and 12,000 B.P.
After the CI and before the NYT eruptions, volcanism generated edifices and deposits that presently can be found only at the periphery of the sub-aerial portion of the CFc and at the southern edge of Pozzuoli Bay (fig. 4.2). On land these deposits are exposed at Vallone del Verdolino, Pianura, Monte

di Procida, Posillipo, along the scarp bordering the Quarto plain to the north and northeast, and in the city of Napoli (fig. 4.2). They were generated mostly by hydromagmatic eruptions and subordinately by dome-forming eruptions. The sedimentological and morphological characteristics of the exposed rocks indicate that the vents for these eruptions were located inside the CI caldera.

Interpretation of seismic profiles (Pescatore et al. 1984; Fusi et al. 1991) across Pozzuoli Bay suggests that the Pentapalummo volcano overlies the CI, and that both are unconformably molded by the Würmian surface (18,000–14,000 B.P.; Shackleton and Hopdike 1973). Furthermore, the Miseno volcano, which is not overlain by the CI, is also molded by the Würmian surface. This implies that the age of both the Pentapalummo and Miseno volcanoes must be bracketed between 37,000 and 18,000–14,000 B.P.

Neapolitan Yellow Tuff

The NYT eruption, the second largest eruption in the Campanian area, was phreatoplinian-to-phreatomagmatic with a very complex history (Orsi et al. 1991a, 1992, 1995; Wohletz et al. 1995). The volume of erupted magma, ranging in composition from alkali-trachyte to latite, was about 40 km^3, and the area covered by the tuff was about 1,000 km^2, including the bays of Napoli and Pozzuoli (fig. 4.2). In these areas, the deposits related to the NYT eruption are included in the lowermost of two superimposed layers of sediments overlying the slopes of the Pentapalummo volcano (Orsi et al. 1996). These two layers are characterized by variable internal textures and are separated by a level surface that only occurs to the north of the alignment of banks (Pescatore et al. 1984). The lower layer has an age bracketed between 18,000–14,000 and 9,000–6,500 B.P. (Buccheri and Di Stefano 1984; Carbone et al. 1984).

Neapolitan Yellow Tuff Caldera

During the NYT eruption a caldera began to collapse and, although it is well constrained by the sedimentological and chemical characteristics of the tuff, the only inland morphological feature that can be correlated to its rim is the high-angle western slope of the Posillipo hill, which likely represents the morphological evolution of a caldera-fault scarp (fig. 4.1; Orsi and Scarpati 1989; Orsi et al. 1991a, 1992, 1995; Scarpati et al. 1993; Wohletz et al. 1995).

The structural boundary of the caldera was reconstructed by Orsi et al. (1996) mainly on the basis of gravimetric and magnetic data (Barberi et al. 1991), distribution of vents younger than 12,000 B.P., distribution of dated level surfaces in the submerged portion of the CF (Pescatore et al. 1984; Fusi et al. 1991), and interpretation of boreholes. The alignments of positive magnetic anomalies demonstrated by Barberi et al. (1991) have been interpreted as the product of intrusions along the marginal faults of the NYT caldera. All eruptive vents younger than 12,000 are located inside this area (fig. 4.1). The vents along the Averno-Capo Miseno alignment show that the western margin of the NYT caldera follows a north–south trending feature, likely related to a regional fault system.

The structural boundary of the NYT caldera borders Pozzuoli Bay to the south. The abrupt interruption of the Würmian level surface (18,000–14,000 B.P., Shackleton and Hopdike 1973) and its downthrown north of the Pentapalummo bank support the interpretation that the depression of Pozzuoli Bay was formed during the NYT caldera collapse (Orsi et al. 1996) (fig. 4.1). The bay is bordered to the south by scarps cut into the Pentapalummo deposits and buried by sediments that include the NYT. The age of the scarps is therefore compatible with that of the NYT and very likely formed during the NYT caldera collapse. The Banco di Nisida volcano, which has been dated as younger than 9,000 B.P. (Pescatore et al. 1984), likely grew inside the NYT caldera toward its southern margin. All the available data demonstrate that the caldera collapse occurred by means of both reactivation of preexistent structures and generation of new faults, which disjointed the caldera floor in a number of differentially displaced blocks. The caldera covers an area of about 90 km^2, but deep drillings in the San Vito area show that the collapse is of about 600 m (Agip 1987). Extrapolating this value to the whole caldera floor, the volume of the collapse is of about 54 km^3, in agreement with the estimated volume of magma extruded during the NYT eruption.

Volcanism Younger than 12,000 B.P.

The results of recent stratigraphical, structural and radiocarbon (AMS) geochronological investigations allowed Di Vito et al. (1999) to define the timing of volcanic and deformational events in the past 12,000 years. The authors defined three epochs of activity: 12,000–9,500 B.P.; 8,600–8,200 B.P.; and 4,800–3,800 B.P. These epochs were separated by two periods of quiescence that lasted 1,000 and 3,500 years, respectively, during which two widespread paleosols formed. The last eruption occurred in A.D. 1538.

Epoch I started soon after the NYT caldera collapse and lasted 2,500 years. The floor of the caldera, except its northern sector, was invaded by the sea, which at that time was about 60 m lower than its present level (Labeyrie et al. 1976). During this epoch, 34 eruptions occurred with a mean frequency of one eruption every 70 years.

All the eruptions of this epoch were explosive, varying from magmatic to phreatomagmatic, according to the vent position with respect to the coastline. Most of the eruption vents were located along the submerged structural margin of the caldera (fig. 4.1), and the eruptions were mostly hydromagmatic, forming zeolitized tuff cones. Magmatic to phreatomagmatic eruptions took place mostly within the Soccavo area, in the northeastern sector of the caldera (fig. 4.2). The pyroclastic deposits of these eruptions are exposed in the northeastern sector of the caldera floor and over an area of a few kilometers outside its rim to the north and east. The fallout deposits of the Pomici Principali Tephra, the product of the highest magnitude eruption of this epoch, were dispersed up to 50 km east of the eruption vent. The lack of pyroclastic deposits of Epoch I in the center of the caldera is due to their reworking in a shallow sea environment, as testified by the occurrence of marine sediments with compatible ages and stratigraphic position. These deposits show monotone sedimentological characteristics, although sea level was rising during their deposition, implying that the caldera floor was also uplifted. This is further demonstrated by the emersion of the La Starza marine terrace that overlies the La Starza block shortly before 8,600 B.P.

A quiescent period, which lasted 1,000 years, followed this epoch of intense volcanic activity. During this quiescence, a thick and widespread paleosol formed in the emerged portion of the caldera floor.

During Epoch II, which started with the Fondi di Baia eruption at 8,600 B.P., six low-magnitude eruptions took place, with a mean frequency of one eruption every 65 years. All the eruption vents of this epoch were located along the northeastern structural margin of the NYT caldera, except for the Fondi di Baia eruption vent, which was located in the western sector (fig. 4.1). The eruptions were explosive, both magmatic and phreatomagmatic, and most of the deposits from these eruptions were distributed over the emerged part of the caldera floor. During this epoch the La Starza block and the Fuorigrotta and Agnano areas partially emerged.

A quiescent period lasting 3,500 years, followed Epoch II. During this quiescence the sea level rose, invaded the area presently occupied by the Fuorigrotta, Agnano, San Vito, and Toiano plains, and partly eroded the

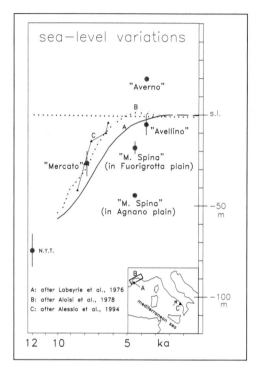

Fig. 4.3. Sea level variations in the past 12,000 years compared with present day elevation of the base of the pyroclastic deposits of the Vesuvian Avellino and Mercato; the Phlegraean Averno, Agnano-Monte Spina and Neapolitan Yellow Tuff eruptions; and the overlying coastal marine sediments. (After Orsi et al. 1996)

Fig. 4.4. Plots of the net vertical displacement of surfaces formed at sea level between the present and the time of their formation. Crosses show measured surfaces along a west–east profile reported in insert. (After Orsi et al. 1996)

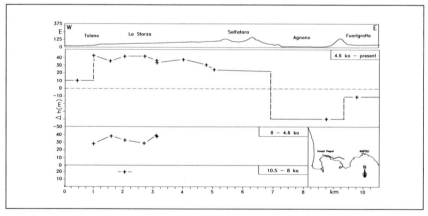

volcanoes formed around the plains. Contemporaneously a thick and widespread paleosol formed in the emerged portion of the CFc.

During Epoch III 16 explosive and four effusive eruptions occurred, with a mean frequency of one eruption every 50 years. The eruption vents were located in the northeastern sector of the NYT caldera (fig. 4.1). Only two eruptions took place in the northwestern sector of the caldera, in the same area in which the Monte Nuovo eruption, the last of the caldera activity, later occurred (A.D. 1538). The explosive eruptions varied from magmatic to phreatomagmatic and produced fall and flow deposits that were mostly dispersed in the northeastern portion of the CFc and within a few kilometers of the caldera rim. Only the Agnano-Monte Spina eruption (de Vita et al. 1999), the highest magnitude event of this epoch, produced pyroclastic-fall deposits distributed to the northeast up to 45 km from the vent area and pyroclastic flows which reached 14 km from the caldera rim. The magmas that erupted in the CFc over the past 12,000 years have ranged in composition from trachybasalt to latite, trachyte, alkali-trachyte, and phono-trachyte.

Deformational History

The floor of the NYT caldera has been deformed by an ongoing resurgence. Structural features such as faults and displacement of blocks are evidence of long-term deformations, but two bradyseismic events occurring in 1970–72 and 1982–84 provided the opportunity to monitor short-term deformations and permitted investigation of the relationships between long- and short-term deformations.

Long-Term Deformations

Resurgence inside the NYT caldera began at least 10,000 B.P. The most uplifted part of the caldera floor is the La Starza block, composed of a marine terrace that includes two sequences of marine sediments, each of which is overlaid by continental deposits dated at 8,600 and 4,600 B.P., respectively (Di Vito et al. 1999). As sea level has been almost constantly rising in the past 10,000 years, the two continental deposits testify to two periods of ground uplift at a rate higher than the sea level rise.

A comparison of the present depth of surfaces separating coastal marine sediments from overlying pyroclastic deposits of known age emplaced in a subaerial environment, and the sea level at the time of their formation has allowed Orsi et al. (1996) and Di Vito et al. (1996) to estimate the cumulative long-term vertical displacement of the area including each single surface (fig. 4.3). The results show that the resurgence of the center of the NYT caldera has not been homogeneous. Instead, it occurs through a simple-shearing mechanism (Orsi et al. 1991b) that produces differential vertical displacement of a number of blocks (fig. 4.4). Furthermore, in the periphery of the caldera floor there are blocks that are significantly less uplifted than those in the center, or are subsiding. Compiling of all the results (fig. 4.1) shows that in the past 12,000 years the area due east of the Sebeto Valley has been stable while the area due west has been subsiding. A general subsidence has also affected both the area between the Posillipo coast and the Agnano plain, and the coast between Averno and Capo Miseno. The uplifted part shows clear evidence of brittle disjointing.

The structural lineaments active in the CFc during the past 12,000 years are mainly northeast–southwest, northwest–southeast, and subordinately north–south trending faults. These faults, as well as those related to the caldera collapse, are likely part of regional lineaments repeatedly reactivated through time. Although the caldera floor is deformed, the conditions for magma to rise to the surface were not established in its southwestern part corresponding to its rise in Pozzuoli Bay. The vents' distribution suggest that during Epochs I and II volcanism was influenced by the caldera lineaments, while in Epoch III it was highly controlled by the resurgence of the La Starza block. During Epoch I, the magma rose to the surface mainly through the marginal faults of the NYT caldera, while in Epoch II the magmas reached the surface only through the northeastern sector of this fault system. During Epoch III, most of the vents were located in the northeastern sector of the resurgent block, near the active margin of the NYT caldera during Epoch II and the apex of this resurgence occurred just before Epoch III.

Short-Term Deformations

Short-term vertical deformations have been detected in the CF in recent times. The occurrence of the Roman coastline at about 10 m.b.s.l. and of numerous Roman and medieval remains below sea level is evidence that the area has generally subsided in the past 2,000 years (Günter 1903; De Pippo et al. 1984). The A.D. 1538 Monte Nuovo eruption was preceded by a slow ground-uplift that became faster a few days before the eruption and localized in the area in which the vent opened (Rolandi et al. 1985). The maximum ground uplift was estimated by Parascandola (1947) at 7 m. Since the Monte Nuovo eruption, the area subsided until roughly 1969, when a new uplift took place. Between 1969 and mid-1972 the CF was affected by the first monitored positive bradyseismic event. The maximum uplift was 1.7 m and was detected in the area of the town of Pozzuoli (Corrado et al. 1977). This uplift was accompanied by seismicity with epicenters concentrated in the northern part of Pozzuoli Bay and in the area between Averno and Agnano. Between mid-1972 and late 1974, the ground subsided 0.22 m, while for the next eight years there was no significant change in ground elevation and there was almost no seismicity. At the beginning of 1982, a new, intense uplift occurred and lasted until late 1984, generating an uplift of 1.8 m (Barberi et al, 1984). The seismicity from 1983 to the end of 1984 was very intense and most of the epicenters were located between Solfatara and Monte Nuovo, although many were also in the northern part of Pozzuoli Bay. The hypocenters, located at a depth of 0.5 to 4 km (Aster et al. 1990), were in the most uplifted sectors of the resurgent block and along its southern marginal faults in the Bay of Pozzuoli. Since late 1984 the ground has generally subsided, with small, scattered uplifts. The subsidence has not been accompanied by earthquakes, but seismicity has been related to the small uplifts. Between late 1988 and April 1989, a minor episode of uplift (with a maximum of 7.5 cm) occurred near Pozzuoli. This episode generated a maximum vertical deformation around the town of Pozzuoli and was accompanied by intense seismicity.

Conclusion

The CFc is suitable for investigating the relationships between regional tectonics as well as volcano-tectonics and volcanism. Both structural setting and deformational history of the caldera show that, in an area affected by tectonic features generated by the regional stress field, the deformations produced in response to a local stress field tend to follow the preexisting features. This relationship can be demonstrated for both CI and NYT calderas. In particular, during the collapse of the CI caldera, northeast–southwest trending regional faults were partially reactivated and formed its eastern boundary. The fault systems bordering the resurgent block inside the NYT caldera show similar relationships with regional tectonic features. The orientation and kinematics of these systems constrain the area distribution of the vents active during resurgence. During Epochs I and II, the eruption vents were located along the structural boundary of the NYT caldera. In Epoch III the eruption vents were located only along the structural boundaries of the resurgent block generated by a tensional stress regime, where the conditions for magma to rise to the surface did not form (fig. 4.5); this explains the absence of volcanism in the Bay of Pozzuoli.

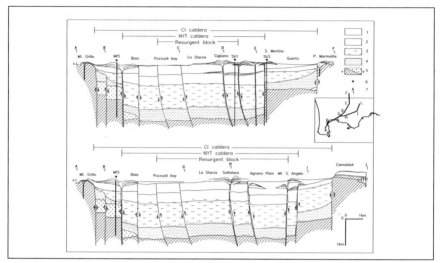

Fig. 4.5. Geological cross-sections of the Campi Flegrei caldera. Their location is reported in insert (after Orsi et al., 1996). *1*, volcanic and marine sediments younger than 12,000 B.P.; *2*, Neapolitan Yellow Tuff (12,000 B.P.); *3*, volcanic and marine sediments emplaced between 37,000 and 12,000 B.P.; *4*, Campanian ignimbrite (37,000 B.P.); *5*, rocks older than 37,000 B.P. a: pyroclastics, b: lavas; *6*, location of deep boreholes; *7*, markers along profiles.

The short-term deformation likely results from the interplay of a fragile and a ductile component. Arrival of new magma generates an increase in both the pressure and the temperature of the magmatic system. The pressure increase results in a vertical stress applied to the roof rocks of the magma chamber. Under such conditions, these rocks are fractured and faulted at variable depth, as testified by the occurrence of earthquakes and the location of their hypocenters. Fracturing of the rocks above the magma chamber allows an increase in both heat and volatile transfer toward the surface. This transfer generates an increase in both the pressure and temperature of the shallow geothermal system, which causes the ductile component of the deformation. When the heat transfer ends, the related decompression of the geothermal system causes the ground subsidence. During the phases of subsidence of a bradyseismic event, the deformation is only ductile and without seismicity. After each bradyseismic event the ductile component of the deformation is partially recovered, while the fragile component is permanent. The long-term deformation likely results from the summation of many short-term deformational events.

REFERENCES

Agip, 1987. *Modello geotermico del sistema flegreo (Sintesi)*. San Donato.

Alessio, M., F. Bella, S. Improta, G. Belluomini, C. Cortesi, and C. and B. Turi. 1971. "University of Rome Carbon-14 Dates IX." *Radiocarbon* 13(2):395–411.

———. 1973. "University of Rome Carbon-14 Dates X." *Radiocarbon* 15(1):165–78.

Alessio, M., L. Allegre, F. Antonioli, G. Belluomini, S. Improta, L. Manfra, and M. Preite. 1994. "La Curva di Risalita del Mare Tirreno Negli Ultimi 40 Ka Tramite Datazioni di Speleotemi Sommersi e Date Archeologiche." *Atti del Convegno dei Lincei GEOSUB* 1994. Palinuro (abstract).

Aloisi, J.C., A. Monaco, N. Planchais, J. Thommeret, and Y. Thommeret. 1978. "The Holocene Transgression in the Golfe Du Lion, Southwestern France: Palaeogeographic and Palaeobotanical Evolution." *Geogr. Phys. Quat.* 32(2):145–62.

Armienti, P., F. Barberi, H. Bizouard, R. Clocchiatti, F. Innocenti, N. Metrich, M. Rosi, and A. Sbrana. 1983. "The Phlegraean Fields: Magma Evolution within a Shallow Chamber." *Journal of Volcanology and Geothermal Research* 17:289–311.

Armienti, P., F. Barberi, and A. Innocenti. 1984. "A Model of the Phlegraean Fields Magma Chamber in the Last 10,500 Years." *Bulletin of Volcanology* 47:349–59.

Aster, R.C., R.P. Meyer, G. De Natale, A. Zollo, M. Martini, E. Del Pezzo, R. Scarpa, and G. Iannaccone. 1990. "Seismic Investigation of the Campi Flegrei Caldera." In *Volcanic Seismology*, edited by P. Gasparini, R. Scarpa and K. Aki, 462–83. Heidelberg.

Barberi, F., M. Carapezza, F. Innocenti, G. Luongo, and R. Santacroce. 1989. "The Problem of Volcanic Unrest: The Phlegraean Fields Case History." *Atti del Convegno dei Lincei* 80:387–405.

Barberi, F., E. Cassano, P. La Torre, and A. Sbrana. 1991. "Structural Evolution of Campi Flegrei Caldera in Light of Volcanological and Geophysical Data." *Journal of Volcanology and Geothermal Research* 48(1–2):33–49.

Barberi, F., G. Corrado, F. Innocenti, and G. Luongo. 1984. "Phlegraean Fields 1982–1984: Brief Chronicle of a Volcano Emergency in a Densely Populated Area." *Bulletin of Volcanology* 47(2):175–85.

Barberi, F., F. Innocenti, L. Lirer, R. Munno, T. Pescatore, and R. Santacroce. 1978. "The Campanian Ignimbrite: A Major Prehistoric Eruption in the Neapolitan Area (Italy)." *Bulletin of Volcanology* 41(1):1–22.

Bartole, R., 1984. "Tectonic Structures of the Latian-Campanian Shelf (Tyrrhenian Sea)." *Bollettino di Oceanografia Teorica e Applicata* 2:197–230.

Berrino, G., G. Corrado, G. Luongo, and B. Toro. 1984. "Ground Deformation and Gravity Change Accompanying the 1982 Pozzuoli Uplift." *Bulletin of Volcanology* 47(2):187–200.

Buccheri, G., and E. Di Stefano. 1984. "Contributi Allo Studio Del Golfo Di Pozzuoli. Pteropodi e Nannoplancton Calcareo Contenuti in Tre Carote: Considerazioni Ambientali e Biostratigrafiche." *Mem. Soc. Geol. It.* 27:181–93.

Carbone, A., L. Lirer, and R. Munno. 1984. "Caratteri Petrografici dei Livelli Piroclastici Rinvenuti in Alcuni Gravity Cores nel Golfo di Pozzuoli e nel Golfo di Napoli." *Mem. Soc. Geol. It.* 27:195–204.

Carrara, E., F. Iacobucci, E. Pinna, and A. Rapolla. 1973. "Gravity and Magnetic Survey of the Campanian Volcanic Area, S. Italy." *Bollettino di Geofisica Teorica ed Applicata* 15(57):39–51.

Casertano, L., A. Oliveri, and M.T. Quagliariello. 1977. "Hydrodynamics and Geodynamics in the Phlegraean Fields Area of Italy." *Nature* 264:161–4.

Cassignol, C., and P.Y. Gillot. 1982. *Range and Effectiveness of Unspiked Potassium-Argon Dating: Experimental Ground Work and Applications in Numerical Dating and in Stratigraphy*. New York.

Civetta, L., E. Carluccio, F. Innocenti, A. Sbrana, and G. Taddeucci. 1991. "Magma Chamber Evolution under the Phlegraean Field during the Last 10 Ka: Trace Element and Isotopic Data." *European Journal of Mineralogy* 3:415–28.

Civetta, L., G. Orsi, L. Pappalardo, R.V. Fisher, G.H. Heiken, and M. Ort. 1997. "Geochemical Zoning, Mixing, Eruptive Dynamics and Depositional Processes—The Campanian Ignimbrite, Campi Flegrei, Italy." *Journal of Volcanology and Geothermal Research* 75:183–219.

Colantoni, P., M. Del Monte, A. Fabbri, P. Gallignani, R. Selli, and L. Tomadi. 1972. "Ricerche Geologiche nel Golfo di Pozzuoli." In *Relazione Sui Rilievi Effettuati Nell'area Flegrea Nel 1970–71*, edited by L. Versino, 26–76. CNR Quaderni de la Ricerca Scientifica 83. Roma.

Corrado, G., I. Guerra, A. Lo Bascio, G. Luongo, and F. Rampoldi. 1977. "Inflation and Microearthquake Activity of Phlegraean Fields, Italy." *Bulletin of Volcanology* 40 (3):169–88.

Crane, W., E. Bonatti, J. Labrecque, and R. Bell. 1985. *Bay of Naples Geophysical Profiles*. R/V Conrad C 2508, L-DG0, Tech. Rep.

D'Argenio, B., T.S. Pescatore, and P. Scandone. 1973. "Schema Geologico dell' Appenino Meridionale." *Accademia Nazionale dei Lincei (Quaderni)* 183:49–72.

De Bonitatibus, A., G. Latmiral, L. Mirabile, A. Palumbo, E. Sarpi, and A. Scalera. 1970. "Rilievi Sismici Per Riflessione: Strutturali, Ecografici (Fumarole) e Batimetrici nel Golfo di Pozzuoli." *Bollettino della Società dei Naturalisti* X, 79:97–115.

Deino, A.L., G.H. Courtis, and M. Rosi. 1992. "40Ar/39Ar Dating of Campanian Ignimbrite, Campanian Region, Italy." *International Geological Congress, Kyoto, Japan, 24 Aug.–3 Sept.:* 633 (abstract).

Deino, A.L., G.H. Courtis, J. Southon, F. Terrasi, L. Campajola, and G. Orsi. 1994. "14C and 40Ar/39Ar Dating of the Campanian Ignimbrite, Phlegraean Fields, Italy." *ICOG 77* (abstract).

Dell'Erba, L. 1892."Considerazioni sulla Genesi del Piperno." *Atti Acc. Sc. Fis. Mat.* 5:1–22.

De Lorenzo, G. 1904. "The History of Volcanic Action in the Phlegraean Fields." *Quarterly Journal of the Geological Society* 9.

De Pippo, T., A. Di Cara, M. Guida, T. Pescatore, and P. Renda. 1984. "Contributi allo Studio del Golfo di Pozzuoli: Lineamenti Di Geomorfologia." *Mem. Soc. Geol. It.* 27:151–9.

de Vita, S., G. Orsi, L. Civetta, A. Carandente, M. D'Antonio, T. Di Cesare, M. Di Vito, R.V. Fisher, R. Isaia, E. Marotta, M. Ort, L. Pappalardo, M. Piochi, and J. Southon. 1999.

"The Agnano-Monte Spina Eruption (4.1 ka) in the Resurgent, Nested Campi Flegrei Caldera (Italy)." *Journal of Volcanology and Geothermal Research* 91(2–4):269–301.

Di Girolamo, P. 1970. "Differenziazione Gravitativa e Curve Isochimiche nella 'Ignimbrite Campana.' (Tufo Grigio Campano auct.)." *Rendiconti della Società Italiana di Mineralogia e Petrologia* 26:1–45.

Di Girolamo, P., M.R. Ghiara, L. Lirer, R. Munno, G. Rolandi, and D. Stanzione. 1984. "Vulcanologia e Petrologia dei Campi Flegrei." *Bollettino della Società Geologica Italiana* 103:349–413.

Di Vito, M.A., S. de Vita, and G. Orsi. 1996. "Processi deformativi a lungo termine nella caldera dei Campi Flegrei, desunti da dati di perforazioni." *Archeologia e Vulcanologia in Campania,* "Arte Tipografica, Napoli":29–38.

Di Vito, M.A., R. Isaia, G. Orsi, J. Southon, S. de Vita, M. D'Antonio, L. Pappalardo, and M. Piochi. 1999. "Volcanic and Deformational History of the Campi Flegrei Caldera in the Past 12 ka." *Journal of Volcanology and Geothermal Research* 91(2–4):221–46.

Di Vito, M.A., L. Lirer, G. Mastrolorenzo, and G. Rolandi. 1987. "The Monte Nuovo Eruption (Campi Flegrei, Italy)." *Bulletin of Volcanology* 49:608–15.

Dvorak, J.J., and G. Berrino. 1991. "Recent Ground Movement and Seismic Activity in Campi Flegrei, Southern Italy: Episodic Growth of a Resurgent Dome." *Journal of Geophysical Research* 96:2309–23.

Dvorak, J.J., and P. Gasparini. 1991. "History of Earthquakes and Vertical Movement in Campi Flegrei Caldera, Southern Italy: Comparison of Precursory Events to the A.D. 1538 Eruption of Monte Nuovo and Activity since 1968." *Journal of Volcanology and Geothermal Research* 48:77–92.

Ferrucci, F., A. Hirn, G. De Natale, J. Virieux, and L. Mirabile. 1992. "P-SV Conversions at a Shallow Boundary beneath Campi Flegrei Caldera (Italy): Evidence for the Magma Chamber." *Journal of Geophysical Research* 97:15351–59.

Fevola, F., N. Fusi, and L. Mirabile. 1993. "Rilievi di Sismica Monocanale Ad Alta Risoluzione: Aspetti Dell'evoluzione Geomorfologica del Golfo di Napoli." *Annali Istituto Universitario Navale di Napoli* 60:61–71.

Finetti, I., and C. Morelli. 1974. "Esplorazione Sismica a Riflessione Dei Golfi di Napoli e Pozzuoli." *Bollettino di Geofisica Teorica ed Applicata* 16 (62/63):175–222.

Fisher, R.V., G. Orsi, M. Ort, and G. Heiken. 1993. "Mobility of a Large-Volume Pyroclastic Flow Emplacement of the Campanian Ignimbrite, Italy. *Journal of Volcanology and Geothermal Research* 56:205–20.

Fusi, N., L. Mirabile, A. Camerlenghi, and G. Ranieri. 1991. "Marine Geophysical Survey of the Gulf of Napoli (Italy): Relationships between Submarine Volcanic Activity and Sedimentation." *Mem. Soc. Geol. It.* 47:95–114.

Giudicepietro, F. 1993. *La Dinamica Recente Dell'area Vulcanica Flegrea.* Ph.D. diss., University Federico II-Napoli.

Günter, R.T. 1903. *The Submerged Greek and Roman Foreshore Near Naples.* Oxford.

Ippolito, F., F. Ortolani, and M. Russo. 1973. "Struttura Marginale Tirrenica Dell'appennino Campano: Reinterpretazione di Dati di Antiche Ricerche di Idrocarburi." *Mem. Soc. Geol. Ital.* 12:227–50.

Johnston Lavis, H.F. 1889. *Report of Committee Appointed For the Investigation of the Volcanic Phenomena of Vesuvius and Its Neighbourhood.* London.

Labeyrie, J., G. Lalou, A. Monaco, and J. Thommeret. 1976. *Chronologie des niveaux eustatiques sur la côte de russillon de 33.000 ans B.P. a nous jours.* Paris.

Latmiral, G., A.G . Segre, M. Bernabini, and L. Mirabile. 1971. "Prospezioni Sismiche Per Riflessione Nei Golfi di Napoli e Pozzuoli ed Alcuni Risultati Geologici." *Bollettino della Società Geologica Italia* 90:163–72.

Lirer, L., G. Luongo, and R. Scandone. 1987. "On the Volcanological Evolution of Campi Flegrei." *Eos, Trans. Am. Geophys. Union* 68:226–34.

Lirer, L., Rolandi, G., and Rubin, M. 1991. "14C Age of the 'Museum Breccia' (Campi Flegrei) and its Relevance for the Origin of the Campanian Ignimbrite." *Journal of Volcanology and Geothermal Research* 48:223–7.

Orsi G., L. Civetta, A. Aprile, M. D'Antonio, S. de Vita, G. Gallo, and M. Piochi. 1991a. "The Neapolitan Yellow Tuff: Eruptive Dynamics, Emplacement Mechanism and Magma Evolution of a Phreatoplinian-To-Plinian Eruption." In *Large Ignimbrite Eruptions of the Phlegraean Fields Caldera: The Neapolitan Yellow Tuff and The Campanian Ignimbrite,* edited by G. Orsi and M. Rosi, 76–115. Napoli.

Orsi, G., L. Civetta, M. D'Antonio, P. Di Girolamo, and M. Piochi. 1995. "Step-filling and Development of a Three-Layers Magma Chamber: The Neapolitan Yellow Tuff Case History." *Journal of Volcanology and Geothermal Research* 67:291–312.

Orsi, G., M. D'Antonio, S.de Vita, and G. Gallo. 1992. "The Neapolitan Yellow Tuff, A Large-Magnitude Trachytic Phreatoplinian Eruption: Eruptive Dynamics, Magma Withdrawal and Caldera Collapse." *Journal of Volcanology and Geothermal Research* 53:275–87.

Orsi, G., S. de Vita, and M.A. Di Vito. 1996. "The Restless, Resurgent Campi Flegrei Nested Caldera (Italy): Constraints on Its Evolution and Configuration." *Journal of Volcanology and Geothermal Research* 74(3–4):179–214.

Orsi, G., G. Gallo, and A. Zanchi. 1991b. "Simple Shearing Block Resurgence in Caldera Depressions. A Model from Pantelleria and Ischia." *Journal of Volcanology and Geothermal Research* 47:1–11.

Orsi, G., and C. Scarpati. 1989. "Stratigrafia e Dinamica Eruttiva del Tufo Giallo Napoletano." *Boll. GNV* 2:917–30.

Ort, M.H., G. Orsi, L. Pappalardo, R.V. Fisher. Forthcoming."Emplacement Processes in a Far-Traveled Dilute Pyroclastic Current: Anisotropy of Magnetic Susceptibility Studies of the Campanian Ignimbrite." *Bulletin of Volcanology.*

Ortiz, R., V. Aràba, M. Astiz, and A. Valentin. 1984. "Magnetotelluric Survey in the Bradyseismic Area of Campi Flegrei." *Bulletin of Volcanology* 47:239–46.

Parascandola, A. 1947. *I Fenomeni Bradisismici Del Serapeo Di Pozzuoli.* Napoli.

Perrotta, A., and C. Scarpati. 1994. "The Dynamics of the Breccia Museo Eruption (Campi Flegrei, Italy) and the Significance of Spatter Clasts Associated with Lithic Breccias." *Journal of Volcanology and Geothermal Research* 59:335–55.

Pescatore, T., G. Diplomatico, M.R. Senatore, M. Tramutoli, and L. Mirabile. 1984. "Contributi allo Studio del Golfo di Pozzuoli: Aspetti Stratigrafici e Strutturali." *Mem. Soc. Geol. It.* 27:133–49.

Rittmann, A. 1950. "Sintesi Geologica dei Campi Flegrei." *Bollettino della Società Geologica Italiana* 69:117–77.

Rolandi, G., M.A. Di Vito, and G. Díalessio. 1985. "Il Sollevamento del Suolo Durante la Fase Preeruttiva del M. Nuovo." *Rendiconti dell'Accademia della Scienze Fisiche e Matematiche (Napoli).* Serie IV, Vol. LII/1:15–34.

Rosi, M., and A. Sbrana. 1987. *Phlegrean Fields.* CNR Quaderni de la Ricerca Scientifica 114:1–175. Roma.

Rosi, M., A. Sbrana, and C. Principe. 1983. "The Phlegrean Fields: Structural Evolution, Volcanic History and Eruptive Mechanisms." *Journal of Volcanology and Geothermal Research* 17:273–88.

Rosi, M., L. Vezzoli, P. Aleotti, and M. De Censi. 1996. "Interaction between Caldera Collapse and Eruptive Dynamics during the Campanian Ignimbrite Eruption, Phlegraean Fields, Italy." *Bulletin of Volcanology* 57:541–54.

Scandone, R., F. Bellucci, L. Lirer, and G. Rolandi. 1991. "The Structure of the Campanian Plain and the Activity of the Neapolitan Volcanoes." *Journal of Volcanology and Geothermal Research* 48(1–2):1–31.

Scarpati, C., P. Cole, and A. Perrotta. 1993. "The Neapolitan Yellow Tuff—A Large Volume Mutiphase Eruption from Campi Flegrei, Southern Italy." *Bulletin of Volcanology* 55:343–56.

Scherillo, A. 1953. "Sulla Revisione del Foglio Napoli della Carta Geologica D'Italia." *Bollettino del Servizio Geologico de Italia* 75:808–26.

Scherillo, A. 1955. "Petrografia Chimica dei Tufi Flegrei 2) Tufo Giallo, Mappamonte, Pozzolana." *Rendiconti dell'Accademia della Scienze Fisiche e Matematiche (Napoli)* 22:317–30.

Scherillo, A., and E. Franco. 1960. "Rilevamento Stratigrafico del Territorio Comunale di Napoli." *Bollettio della Società dei Naturalisti* 69:255–62.

Scherillo, A., and E. Franco. 1967. "Introduzione alla Carta Stratigrafica del Suolo di Napoli." *Atti dell'Accademia Pontaniana* 16:27–37.

Segre, A.G. 1972. *La Carta Batimetrica N. 1256 I.I. Del Golfo Di Pozzuoli.* Genova.

Shackleton, N.J., and N.D. Hopdike. 1973. "Oxygen Isotope and Palaeomagnetic Stratigraphy of Equatorial Pacific Core V28-238: Oxygen Isotope Temperature and Ice Volumes on a 105 Year Scale." *Quaternary Research* 3:39–55.

Villemant, B.1988. "Trace Element Evolution in the Phlegraean Fields (Central Italy): Fractional Crystalization and Selective Enrichment." *Contribution on Mineralogy and Petrology* 98:169–83.

Wohletz, K., G. Orsi, and S. De Vita. 1995. "Eruptive Mechanisms of the Neapolitan Yellow Tuff Interpreted from Stratigraphic, Chemical and Granulometric Data." *Journal of Volcanology and Geothermal Research* 67:263–90.

PART II

RESPONSES IN HISTORIC
AND PREHISTORIC TIMES

— 5 —

Responses to Eruptions of Etna
from the Classical Period to 1900

◈

David K. Chester, Angus M. Duncan, and John E. Guest

In the literature on the management of natural hazards it has become customary to relate the responses and adjustments made by societies following disasters to their levels of economic development (White 1973; Burton et al. 1978; Whittow 1987; Chester 1993). For most of human history people have lived in folk or preindustrial societies, and many still live in them. Following a disaster, these societies will recover by harmonizing their responses with nature, rather than employing technological solutions to manage and control it, and responses to disasters in such cultures typically show many or all the features listed in table 5.1. With the onset of economic development, all changes. When disaster strikes a modern technological or industrial society, emphasis is placed on shifting the burden of losses from the individual, family, and isolated community to the society, nation, and international agency. Loss sharing becomes important through aid transfers and insurance, and technology assumes a central position in reducing the threat from subsequent events. Responses involve control over nature, a narrowing in the range of adjustments, high costs, and inflexibility. Finally, there is a characteristic postindustrial response (table 5.1). Incorporating the best of the pre- and postindustrial responses, this represents a future "ideal" and it is doubtful whether any society has yet reached this stage in its disaster planning, though and with respect to volcanic hazard reduction, Iceland, the United States and Japan come close to it (Chester 1993, 237).

Table 5.1. Type of Society

	Folk or preindustrial society	Modern technological or industrial society	Comprehensive or post-industrial society
Characteristics identified by White (1973)	1. A wide range of adjustments 2. Action is by individuals or small groups 3. Emphasis is on harmonization with, rather than technological control over, nature 4. Low capital requirements 5. Responses vary over short distances 6. Responses are flexible and easily abandoned if unsuccessful	1. A narrow range of adjustments 2. Action requires co-ordinated action by government 3. Emphasis on technological control over, rather than harmonization with, nature 4. High capital requirements 5. Responses tend to be uniform 6. Responses are inflexible and difficult to change	Combines features of the pre- and postindustrial responses
Characteristic identified by other writers	7. Losses are perceived as inevitable. The mindset of the inhabitants is dominated by notions of supernatural punishment or vengeance 8. Responses continue over time periods ranging from hundreds to thousands of years	7. Losses may be reduced by government action, science, technology, and economic development 8. Rarely observed anywhere until the mid-19th century	Understanding both the nature of the hazard threat and the cultural detail of a society are vital considerations if disaster vulnerability is to be fully understood

For a given society the three stages shown in table 5.1 may be sequential but not necessarily so, because features of more than one type of response may be seen at the same time amongst different groups and regions within the same country or society (White 1973).

In Sicily, the industrial phase (table 5.1) of hazard management is less than 90 years old. Much has been written on the responses of the Italian state to the frequent flank eruptions which have occurred on Mount Etna (fig. 5.1) since 1900 (Chester et al. 1985 and references; Gruppo Nazionale per il Volcanologia (GNV) 1990; Chester 1993; Duncan et al. 1996; Chester et al. 1999). Although Italian unification occurred in 1860, it was only after the 1909 Messina earthquake that civil defense planners, scientists, and technologists became actively involved in disaster management in Sicily. In the present century major flank eruptions of Etna, which have either threatened or caused significant destruction, have occurred 12 times (in 1910, 1911, 1923, 1928, 1947, 1950–1951, 1971, 1979, 1981, 1983, 1991–1993, and 2001). Running roughly parallel with this sequence—but with some exceptions—is a history of progressively greater state involvement with managing

Fig. 5.1. Map showing the location of places referred to in the text and in tables 5.2 and 5.3. (After Chester et al. 1985, 353)

eruptions and mitigating their consequences. Although the effectiveness of some of these state sponsored initiatives, particularly those before the 1983 eruption, have been questioned in terms of their effectiveness (Duncan et al. 1996 and references; Chester et al. 1999), they have all to varying degrees involved the application of science, technology, civil defense, and planning as tools to reduce losses and allow recovery to take place.

With some exceptions (e.g., Chester et al. 1985 and older works by Rodwell 1878; vön Waltershausen 1880; Hyde 1916), relatively little has been written about the character of preindustrial responses to Etna's flank eruptions, despite this being the dominant coping strategy from the classical era until ca.1900. It is the responses during this period that are the focus of the present chapter. Not only did the people of Etna respond in ways which were typically preindustrial, but some of these characteristics form a legacy that still influences the ways in which policy makers and local inhabitants act when faced with potential or actual losses.

Preindustrial Beliefs About Etna

Although flank eruptions are known on Etna from ca. 693 B.C. and possibly even from ca. 1500 B.C., the historical record only becomes complete after A.D. 1500 (Duncan et al., this volume). Until the 17th century, only the briefest details are available (Gemmellaro 1828; Rodwell 1878; vön Waltershausen 1880; Romano and Sturiale 1982; Chester et al. 1985), but evidence suggests that following eruptions action was taken by individuals and small groups, and only isolated instances of outside assistance are recorded. Rome, for example, granted a 10-year moratorium on taxes to the inhabitants of Catania in response to the damage caused by air-fall ashes from the 122 B.C. eruption (Rodwell 1878, 82). Paradoxically, the only other well-documented instance of external aid from this period produced an effect completely contrary to its intention. Following the catastrophic eruption of A.D. 1669, which destroyed much of Catania, to at least five large towns and 14 small villages, the Spanish Viceroy sent money and troops. The troops promptly restored order, but rumors spread that the authorities only provided aid because they wished to steal the sacred veil of the local Saint Agatha, which was thought to have the power to halt lava flows (Mack-Smith 1968). It is also reported that troops were used during the 1874, 1879, 1883 and 1892 eruptions. Their primary remit was the maintenance of law and order (*The Times* [London]. 7 September 1874, 6 June 1879, 23 March 1883), although in 1883 they were used to prevent people from congregating in churches because of the strong risk of volcanic earthquakes (*The Times* [London]. 27 March 1883, 2 April 1883), and in

1892 they assisted in the distribution of bread and the strictly limited financial aid made available by the central government (*The Times* [London]. 21 July 1892, 26 July 1892).

The system of beliefs held by those suffering losses is fundamental to any understanding of preindustrial responses both generally (Burton et al. 1978; Warrick 1979) and on Etna. During the classical period, writers espoused a variety of views on what caused Etna's eruptions (Chester et al. 1985; Duncan et al. this volume) but regardless of whether they interpreted eruptions in terms of a religious, mythological or "scientific" *weltanschauung,* they held that, losses could not be predicted and were inevitable (Chester et al. 1985, 355). The course of an eruption could be affected, if at all, only through divine appeasement. Lucilius Junior, writing in the first century of the present era, notes that people offered incense to the gods who they believed controlled the mountain and its eruptions (Hyde 1916). In christian times this fatalistic attitude was grafted on to a theodicy which held that loss had to be accepted because it was an expression of God's punishment and vengeance. All that could be done by suffering humanity was to appeal to God to prevent the disaster and then plan recovery from it. Although in the European Enlightenment more sophisticated theodicies became available, especially from the Lutheran Gottfried Wilhelm Leibniz and his successors, these insights had little impact on rural Catholic Sicily, which clung to theodicies first articulated by the Church fathers, especially Augustine and Irenaeus (Chester 1998), who emphasized that natural calamities were a punishment for sinfulness and that human good—in terms of self-sacrifice and public service—could emerge from even the worst catastrophe. From the 16th century on there was a renaissance in scientific approaches to the study of volcanoes and of Etna, which had lain dormant since the classical era, and significant contributions were made by a distinguished international cast of scientists. Major contributions were made by the natural philosopher Giovanni Alfonso Borelli and the Syracusan aristocrat Francesco D'Arezzo in the 17th century (Middleton 1982). Sir William Hamilton laid secure observational foundations for the study of the volcanoes of the Italian south in the 18th century and has rightly been called the person who made "the first note-worthy contribution" to volcanology (Bullard 1976, 16), while in the 19th century study of Etna was central to volcanological advances made by such luminaries as Elie de Beaumont, L. vön Buch, C. Gemmellaro, G. Gemmellaro, Sir Charles

Lyell, George Poulett-Scrope, and W. Sartorius vön Waltershausen (Middleton 1982; Chester et al. 1985) and although their impact on the developing sciences of geology, igneous petrology, and volcanology has been incalculable, their influence was negligible on the people of Etna who continued to accept divine explanations.

A theodicy based on a vengeful God meant that virtually all eruptions became associated with a well developed liturgy of propitiation. As early as A.D. 252, when lava was approaching Catania (fig. 5.1), the people of the city rushed to the tomb of St. Agatha, who had been martyred the previous year, and carried her veil to the flow front. It was claimed that this halted the flow and saved Catania (vön Waltershausen 1880). Following the veil's "success" it was used on many subsequent occasions, most notably in the large eruption of A.D. 1669, when it was claimed that its efficacy prevented the whole of Catania being destroyed. Even as late as 1886, when Nicolosi (fig. 5.1) was threatened, the veil is still recorded as being in regular use (Hyde 1916).

Another aspect of traditional theodicies is that tragedy may lead to human good and heroic acts, and many such instances are recorded in the preindustrial era. An early legend chronicled by Seneca involved two brothers, the *fratelli pii.* These were the brothers Anapias and Amphinomus who carried their parents on their shoulders through the blazing streets of Catania while the lava parted in front of them. Much later, in A.D. 1669, Diego Pappalardo and some fellow citizens of Catania attempted to divert a lava flow that threatened their city. This caused civil unrest because the diverted flow placed the city of Paterno at risk (fig. 5.1). Such diversions were declared illegal and were not attempted again until 1983. These stories are now part of both recorded history and folklore.

Notwithstanding liturgies of propitiation, major losses occurred frequently (table 5.2), but because flank eruptions produce relatively slow moving lava flows, few people have been killed directly by eruptions. One of the few instances of deaths caused by a lava flow occurred in 1843 when at least 36 people were reportedly killed by a steam explosion as they watched a flow enter a pond (Chester et al. 1985). It has often been reported that during an eruption in A.D. 1169 an estimated 15,000 people were killed in Catania alone, but this eruption is of doubtful veracity, and it seems certain that these deaths were actually caused by earthquakes (Romano and Sturiale 1982, 81).

In spite of a widespread belief in their inevitability, eruptions in the preindustrial era brought forth responses that were more subtle and sophisticated than is commonly supposed. Following a flank eruption of Etna there are normally two types of closely related loss that the inhabitants must face: loss of housing and loss of agricultural land.

Loss of Housing

Tables 5.2A and 5.2B summarize the losses that occurred to the principal settlements of Etna between A.D. 1300 and 1900. The settlement geography of the Etna region was typical of Sicily, with rural settlement comprising isolated farmsteads being very rare. Most people lived in large agro-towns, commuting to their fields daily (King and Strachan 1978). On Etna the vast majority of the population worked on scattered family plots, sometimes as small as 2 ha. The most intensively worked area was the *corona*, the immediate vicinity of the village (Chester et al. 1985, 38–64), and land use intensity decreased in all directions with increasing distance from both the agro-town and from Catania, the principal city and port of the region. Given

Table 5.2A

Date	Settlement Destroyed
1408	Trecastagni and Pedara
1537	Nicolosi
1646	Several small villages (unnamed) on north the north flank of the volcano
1669	Belpasso (12 March), S. Pietro Clarenza (13 March), Mascalucia (13 March), Comporotondo (13 March), possibly S. Giovanni di Gelermo (15 March), Misterbianco (25 March), most of Catania (12–23 April), and 14 smaller villages
1689	Several small villages in the vicinity of Macchia

Table 5.2B

Date	Outskirts of Settlements Affected
1371 or 1381	Catania
1444	Catania
1536	Randazzo (lava approached to within 1.5 km)
1566	Linguaglossa
1595	Adrano
1607 or 1610	Adrano (lava approached to within 1.5 km)
1651–1653	Bronte
1792	Zafferana (losses in suburbs)
1811	Milo
1832	Bronte (lava approached to within 2 km)
1843	Bronte (lava breached road 2.8 km to the south)
1852–1853	Zafferana (lava approached to within 0.5 km of town center)
1879	Passopisciaro (between Randazzo and Linguaglossa)
1883	Nicolosi
1886	Nicolosi (lava approached to within 0.5 km)
1892	Nicolosi

this settlement geography, the loss of a village was catastrophic because it included most of the housing for the community and much of its premium agricultural land. Even a near miss could be very serious because the highly valued *corona* land could be sterilized.

As figure 5.1 shows, losses in the period from A.D. 1300 to 1900 were not randomly distributed, but were highly concentrated in the southwestern through the eastern sectors of the volcano, being particularly severe in the south and southeast. Although data are fragmentary, it seems that this pattern of losses was little different in the centuries leading up to A.D. 1300. The 693 B.C. and 425 (or 424) B.C. eruptions both affected Catania, the latter event damaging only part of the city. The 396 (or 394) B.C. eruption almost destroyed Acireale, and eruptions in 122 B.C., A.D. 40 and A.D. 252 (or 253) seriously affected Catania (Rodwell 1878; Romano and Sturiale 1982). It has been argued that large flank eruptions in remote areas may not have been noted because of a lack of literate observers (Wadge 1977), but two other factors are more likely to have been responsible for this southern and eastern bias in the pattern of recorded losses. First, throughout history the southern and eastern flanks have been agriculturally favored regions and today 70% of the population of the region lives on the 40% of the land area represented by these sectors. Secondly, geological evidence implies that most flank eruptions occurred in these same sectors of the volcano (Anon 1979; Duncan et al. 1981).

Although families and communities had little option but to bear the losses when disaster struck, there is plentiful evidence to suggest that communities were able to recover quickly. Nicolosi (fig. 5.1), for example, was totally destroyed by lava in A.D. 1537, but was a thriving community when struck by an earthquake in A.D. 1633 and was probably rebuilt again by the time of the A.D. 1669 eruption (Chester et al. 1985, 350).

The means by which families and communities recovered from eruptions are not known in detail, but valuable information may be gleaned from historical records. Some elements of long established preindustrial strategies of coping have lingered into recent centuries and provide additional insights. Sicilian society is based on a combination of extended families and client relationships, especially that of godparents (King 1973), and coping with disasters through family networks was long established and important. During the 1928 eruption that destroyed the town of Mascali on the eastern flank of the volcano, for instance, most of the displaced people were accommodated with relations in other villages (Duncan et al. 1996, 12). Following the 1883 eruption, press reports indicate that many people in Biancavilla, Belpasso, Nicolosi, and Borello left their villages to live elsewhere, presumably with relations, leaving those without alternative accommodation to make do with makeshift dwellings and tents (*The Times* [London]. 23 March 1883; 27 March 1883; 2 April 1883). Although the distinction between those families able to live elsewhere and those forced to "live in the fields" suggests a marginalization of the poor or those without extended family members living close by, it should not be forgotten that many farmers possessed permanent shelters on their family plots that were normally used for storage and as venues for siestas during the summer (C. Dibben, personal communication), but in an emergency, these shelters could be easily brought into service as temporary family homes. The description "living in the fields" which appears in many press accounts from the 19th century may not, therefore, be so suggestive of rural distress as it appears at first sight. With the exception of Nicolosi, no village was seriously threatened in 1883 (table 5.2); all survived and were quickly reoccupied. Similar spontaneous evacuations occurred in 1843 and 1886 (*The Times* [London]. 20 December 1843; 28 May 1886).

Peasant agriculture involves maximizing family security rather than profit and one feature of this system in Sicily is that landholding was and is fragmented. As a consequence, it is highly unlikely that an individual family would lose all of its land—owned or rented—in a single eruption. Chalmers Clapperton (1972) reported that as recently as the 1971 eruption, after several decades of major agricultural change on Etna, farmers successfully spread their losses because they held land in fragmented holdings. Another aspect of security is pastoralism, and while high altitude pastoralism has declined on Etna in recent decades, in the preindustrial era it was an important source of additional income for many peasant farmers (Cumin 1938), who often worked their land on a part-time basis. These high level pastures were owned by large landowners and by the Church and leased to members of an extended family on a seasonal basis.

It is a popular belief that people panic in the face of disasters, but recent research has cast considerable doubt on this opinion (e.g., Quarentelli and Dynes 1972; Drabek 1986), and there is plentiful evidence from the preindustrial era on Etna to counter it. Apprehension and even fear were commonly noted (*The Times* [London]. 18 April 1883), but many 19th-century records show that people were usually calm and approached the inevitability of losses with equanimity (e.g., *The Times* [London]. 29 May 1886; 13 July

1892). Normal day-to-day activities continued unabated as people plied their trades and tended their crops (*The Times* [London]. 18 April 1883). Perhaps the most significant sign of calm was the clear sense that family and community were capable of recovery, provided action was taken both to minimize losses and to provide mutual assistance. During the 1843, 1852, 1863, and 1883 eruptions, villagers carefully removed and stored all that could be salvaged from their dwellings (*The Times* [London]. 20 December 1843; 2 October 1852; 1 August 1863; 27 March 1883), and in 1892 local relief committees were established in several villages (*The Times* [London]. 18 July 1892). In short, the preindustrial response on Etna was aimed at rapid recovery and survival of family and village community.

Table 5.3 shows that between A.D. 1400 and 1900 more than 35 towns and villages suffered from the effects of flank eruptions, some on more than one occasion. Despite high and frequent losses, abandonment of an area never occurred, the universal response being to rebuild a town or village, either on the same site or as close to it as possible. This response was not without its practical difficulties. When an earthquake destroyed a settlement no sterilization of land occurred, rubble was quickly cleared, and rebuilding could commence. In the case of land inundated by lava, rebuilding was extremely difficult because only rudimentary earth moving techniques were available. The substrate, which is composed of solid—sometimes hot—rock, would also not be suitable building land for some time. It was reported that following the A.D. 1669 eruption, lava took eight months to cool and peasant farmers were able to boil water on it for a considerable period of time (Rodwell 1878; King 1973).

In its long history, Catania has been destroyed by volcanic eruptions several times and twice by earthquakes, but its site has never been abandoned. Chester et al. (1985, 352–3) argue that since Catania was never wholly destroyed by lava, the city was able to continue functioning. Even in its semi-ruined state it held better locational advantages than any alternative site, and it remained the principal port of the Etna region (fig. 5.1).

With the exception of low intensity rough grazing, lava flows had little agricultural value for centuries until weathering converted them into agriculturally useful soils, but could be built over without reducing the productive agricultural land area of a community (see below). Even when settlements were not destroyed, land sterilized by lava was frequently used to accommodate urban expansion. Following each damaging eruption, Catania rebuilt over land sterilized by lava (Blunt 1968), and such land had the distinct advantage of being much cheaper than the premium agricultural land of either the city's corona or of surrounding villages. In smaller towns and villages, the picture varied (Chester et al. 1985, 354). In those settlements which were destroyed, devastation was invariably either total or nearly so, and the usual decision was to rebuild the town or village as close as possible to the original site, maximizing any locational advantages, particularly communication (see table 5.3). Not all relocations were successful; in the case of Belpasso, which was totally destroyed in A.D. 1669, the new site was found to be unsuitable and a third village had to be constructed (table 5.3).

Table 5.3

Eruption	Settlement	Rebuilding/Location
1408	Trecastagni Pedara	Both towns destroyed and relocated nearby
1536	Randazzo	A near miss. A small settlement was subsequently built on the flow
1537	Nicolosi	Destroyed and rebuilt on same site
1566	Linguaglossa	A near miss. The town was eventually expanded over the flow
1595	Adrano	A near miss. Later a settlement was built on this flow
1607 or 1610	Adrano	A near miss. Later a settlement was built on this flow
1646	Northern flank villages	The village of Passopisciaro was built on this flow
1651–1653	Bronte	A near miss. The town expanded over the flow
1669	Nicolosi	Destroyed by volcanic earthquake and rebuilt on same site
	Belpasso	Destroyed and rebuilt on a new site (Mezzocampo), but the air was unhealthy. The present site, 1 km from flow, was chosen in 1695
	S. Pietro Clarenza	Destroyed and relocated
	Mascalucia	Destroyed and relocated
	Camporotondo	Destroyed and relocated
	S. Giovanni di Gelermo	Destroyed and relocated
	Misterbianco	Destroyed and relocated
	14 small hamlets	Some were relocated. The fate of others is uncertain
1689	Macchia	The outskirts of this village and several other villages were destroyed. The town expanded and the lava flow is now intensively settled
1792	Zafferana	The outskirts were destroyed and there was little subsequent settlement on flow
1811	Milo	A near miss. There was little subsequent settlement on this flow
1832	Bronte	A near miss. There was little subsequent settlement on this flow
1843	Bronte	A near miss. There was little subsequent settlement on this flow
1852–1853	Zafferana	A near miss. The village expanded over the flow
1879	Passopisciaro other villages	A near miss. The village expanded over the flow
1886	Nicolosi	A near miss. There was little subsequent settlement on this flow
1892	Nicolosi	A near miss. There was little subsequent settlement on this flow

Loss of Agricultural Land

The most productive agricultural land on Etna is found below 1,000 m in the so-called *regione piedmontese* (Milone 1960; Rochefort 1961; Duncan et al. 1981) and, even with the security afforded to peasant farmers by fragmented landholdings and high altitude pastoralism, any loss of agricultural land in this region was very serious. Not surprisingly, incursions of lava in these areas caused considerable distress in the preindustrial era as has been documented and commented upon by many observers (Ferrara 1818; Rodwell 1878; vön Waltershausen 1880; Hyde 1916). Research carried out by the authors (Chester et al. 1985, 346) indicates that even when weathering rates are at their highest (on low altitude flows of the relatively well-watered southern flanks), lava flows may remain sterile for at least 150 years, are only capable of sustaining rough grazing by livestock after 200 years, and require many hundreds of years before major cash crops may be grown (James et al. 2000). Calculations indicate that between A.D. 1500 and 1900 some 8% of the total land area of the regione piedmontese was effectively sterilized by lava.

Lava will be recolonized by natural processes. As lichens and mosses are succeeded over the centuries by higher order grasses and eventually by trees, in the preindustrial era peasant agriculturalists harmonized with and assisted this process. Once grasses were established, so was pastoralism and later hardy tree crops having both an economic and subsistence value—almonds, figs, and pistachios—were planted (King 1973, 161). Land use maps and aerial photographs indicate that farmers had an accurate perception of agricultural potential. Pyroclastic materials, although of limited occurrence on Etna, weather to produce soils much more quickly than lavas. In the vicinity of the high altitude village of Nicolosi (fig. 5.1) it appears that vines have been established for a considerable time on pyroclastic materials dating from the A.D. 1669 eruptions, while lavas of a similar age are even today fit only for grazing livestock. Recolonization was not without innovation and the introduction three centuries ago of the South American prickly pear cactus (*Opuntia ficus-indica*) whose powerful root system helped to break lava flows, gave farmers a new technique in their quest to assist natural processes (Duncan et al. 1996, 10).

Conclusion

Reviewing the record of human responses to the frequent flank eruptions shows that all the features listed in table 5.1, as being typical of a preindustrial society were evidenced at some time in the Etna region. As mentioned earlier some aspects of the preindustrial response were more sophisticated than is commonly supposed and the following are particularly noteworthy:

1. The general lack of panic shown by the majority of inhabitants;
2. the development of planned strategies of salvage and evacuation;
3. the use made of extended family structures;
4. the security afforded by land-fragmentation and seasonal employment;
5. the highly refined way in which farmers worked with and assisted natural processes of recolonization; and
6. the perception of the relative recolonization potential of pyroclastic materials as opposed to lava flows.

Some aspects of this preindustrial model of coping survived well into the 20th century and some features of it are still found. Liturgies of propitiation have been evident in most twentieth century eruptions—even in those which have occurred during the past 20 years—and the story of Monsignor Nicotra, who in 1928 offered his life to God in exchange for the salvation of the village of S. Alfio, is a powerful and oft repeated tale in many an Etnean village. S. Alfio was saved, but Nicotra died four months later. The 1928 eruption was transitional, in the sense that it showed an interesting overlap between a characteristic preindustrial and a more typical industrial response. S. Alfio was at the time a remote village and the Monsignor's actions—so typical of a preindustrial society—should be seen in the light of this isolation. In contrast, the town of Mascali, which was almost totally destroyed in 1928, was more integrated into the rapidly modernizing Italian state, being located near to the coast and astride the main rail and road routes of eastern Sicily. Although liturgies of propitiation were in evidence, the main feature of the response was state intervention on a large scale. This included rebuilding the town to a high standard at some distance from the flow front (Duncan et al. 1996). Politically, this action represented an exercise in centralized fascist power by the government of Benito Mussolini for propaganda and prestige (Chester et al. 1999).

Evacuation and salvage of all that can be removed from a dwelling is still practiced, in part because this represents a strong tradition, but also because insurance is very rare, especially in the domestic sector, because of its high cost and poor availability (Chester et al. 1985, 362; C. Dibben, personal communication). In most other respects, responses today are typically industrial and many indigenous strategies of coping, which were maintained for such a long period, are a thing of the past. Technology transfer, applied science, and the centralized management of disasters represent the contemporary *zeitgeist* on Etna as it does in the rest of Italy and the developed world.

REFERENCES

Anon. 1979. *Carta Geologica del Monte Etna* (scale 1:50,000). Rome.

Blaikie, P., T. Cannon, I. Davis, and B. Wisner. 1994. *At Risk: Natural Hazards, People's Vulnerability and Disasters.* London.

Blunt, A. 1968. *Sicilian Baroque.* London.

Bullard, F.M. 1976. *Volcanoes of the Earth.* Austin.

Burton, I., R.W. Kates, and G.F. White. 1978. *The Environment and Hazard.* New York.

Chester, D.K. 1993. *Volcanoes and Society.* London.

Chester, D.K. 1998. "The Theodicy of Natural Disasters." *Scottish Journal of Theology* 51(4):485–505.

Chester, D.K., A.M. Duncan, J.E. Guest, and C.R.J. Kilburn. 1985. *Mount Etna: The Anatomy of a Volcano.* London.

Chester, D.K., A.M. Duncan, C. Dibben, J.E. Guest, and P.H. Lister. 1999. "Mascali, Mount Etna Region, Sicily: An Example of Fascist Planning during the 1928 Eruption and Its Continuing Legacy." *Natural Hazards* 19:29–46.

Clapperton, C.M. 1972. "Patterns of Physical and Human Activity on Mount Etna." *Scottish Geographical Magazine* 88:160–7.

Cumin, G. 1938. "Le pastorizia Etnea." *Revista Geographica Italiana* 45:9–21.

Drabek, T.E. 1986. *Human System Responses to Disaster: An Inventory of Sociological Findings.* New York.

Duncan, A.M., D.K. Chester, and J.E. Guest. 1981. "Mount Etna Volcano: Environmental Impact and Problems of Volcanic Prediction." *Geographical Journal* 147:164–79.

Duncan, A.M., C. Dibben, D.K. Chester, and J.E. Guest. 1996. "The 1928 Eruption of Mount Etna Volcano, Sicily, and the Destruction of the Town of Mascali." *Disasters* 20:1–20.

Ferrara, F. 1818. *Descrizione dell'Etna con la Storia delle eruzione e il Catalogo dei Prodotti.* Palermo.

Gemmellaro, G. 1828. *Quadro istorico topografico delle eruzioni dell' Etna.* Vol. 1. Catania.

Gruppo Nazionale per il Volcanologia (GNV). 1990. *Mount Etna: The 1989 Eruption.* Pisa.

Hyde, W.W. 1916. "The Volcanic History of Etna." *Geographical Review* 1:401–18.

James, P., D. Chester, and A. Duncan. 2000. "Volcanic soils: their Nature and Significance for Archaeology." In *The Archaeology of Geological Catastrophes,* edited by W.J. McGuire, D.R. Griffiths, P.L. Hancock, and I.S. Stewart, 317–38. Geological Society Special Publication 171. London.

King, R. 1973. *Sicily.* Newton Abbot.

King, R., and A. Strachan. 1978. "Sicilian Agro-towns." *Erdkunde* 32:110–23.

Mack-Smith, D. 1968. *A History of Sicily.* Vol. 1, *Medieval Sicily 800–1713.* Vol. 2, *Modern Sicily after 1713.* London.

Middleton, W.E.K. 1982. "The 1669 Eruption of Mount Etna: Francesco d'Arezzo on the Vitreous Nature of Lava." *Archives of Natural History* 11(1):99–102.

Milone, F. 1960. *Sicilia La Natura e l'uomo.* Torino.

Quarantelli, E.L., and R.R. Dynes. 1972. "When Disaster Strikes It Isn't Much Like You've Heard (And Read About)." *Psychology Today* 5:67–70.

Rochefort, R. 1961. *Le trevail en Sicile Etude de Geographie Sociale.* Paris.

Rodwell, G.F. 1878. *Etna: A History of the Mountain and Its Eruptions.* London.

Romano, R., and C. Sturiale. 1982. "The Historical Eruptions of Mt. Etna (Volcanological Data)." In *Mount Etna Volcano, a Review of the Recent Earth Science Studies,* edited by R. Romano, 205. Memorie Della Società Geologica Italiana 23. Rome.

The Times (London). 20 December 1843, page 5, column c.

The Times (London). 2 October 1852, page 8, column f.

The Times (London). 1 August 1863, page 10, column c.

The Times (London). 7 September 1874, page 3, column a.

The Times (London). 6 June 1879, page 5, column b.

The Times (London). 23 March 1883, page 2, column c.

The Times (London). 27 March 1883, page 3, column b.

The Times (London). 2 April 1883, page 8, column c.

The Times (London). 18 April 1883, page 5, column a.

The Times (London). 28 May 1886, page 5, column e.

The Times (London). 29 May 1886, page 14, column f.

The Times (London). 21 July 1892, page 5, column d.

The Times (London). 26 July 1892, page 10, column e.

The Times (London). 13 July 1892, page 5, column a.

The Times (London). 18 July 1892, page 5, column b.

vön Waltershausen, W.S. 1880. *Der Ätna.* 2 vols. Leipzig.

Wadge, G. 1977. "The Storage and Release of Magma on Mount Etna." *Journal of Volcanology and Geothermal Research* 2:361–84.

Warrick, R.A. 1979. "Volcanoes as Hazard: An Overview." In *Volcanic Activity and Human Ecology,* edited by P.D. Sheets and D.K. Grayson, 161–89. New York.

White, G.F. 1973. "Natural Hazards Research." In *Directions in Geography,* edited by R.J. Chorley,, 193–212. London.

Whittow, J. 1987. "Hazards-adjustment and Mitigation." In *Horizons in Physical Geography,* edited by M.J. Clark, K.J. Gregory, and A.M. Gurnell, 307–19. London.

6

Cultural Responses to Risk and Disaster: An Example from the Slopes of the Popocatépetl Volcano in Central Mexico

◆

Patricia Plunket and Gabriela Uruñuela[*]

Prehispanic cults are closely linked to observations of nature, and one of the underlying principles of ritual is to seek control of the contradictory manifestations of these observed natural phenomena. The key for history and science is to understand how observation evolves or is transformed into myth and religion (Broda 1991, 462–3). This is a difficult problem during any time period, but for Mesoamerica, and particularly for the central highlands, where we lack written records for much of the Prehispanic period, our explanations regarding the link between observation and ritual are often naive and usually speculative. Frequently we are forced by a lack of alternatives to extend the information of the 16th century back in order to propose any kind of interpretation at all, and yet we know that our reading of those sources has influenced and defined our view of the past. This is not to say that we should avoid the chronicles and codices of the 16th century, but rather we should try to see in them the outcome of an extended interaction of mutually dependent ideas and experiences.

We rarely have a chance to see the link between an observed natural phenomenon and the development of a specific ritual in the archaeological record of Prehispanic Mexico. In this chapter we will discuss a rare instance that was preserved by a volcanic eruption during the first century A.D., and explore some of the possible continuities with later periods.

It has been assumed that mountains are symbolic elements in the mythology and religion of Prehispanic Mesoamerica. This results in part from their documented importance in the 16th-century sources, but also from their prevalence in indigenous beliefs. The Great Temple of the Aztecs was built and dedicated to two deities associated with mountains, Tlaloc, a god of mountains as well as a patron of rain, storms, and sustenance (Broda 1991), and the tutelary god Huitzilopochtli whose pyramid within the precinct was a symbolic replica of Coatepec, the "Hill of Serpents," where he had been born, miraculously attired as a fully-grown warrior (Matos 1982). In the Maya area, pyramidal platforms crowned with temples were iconographically defined as sacred mountains with caves leading to the underworld (Schele and Freidel 1990, 71–2). This relation between mountains, caves, and the supernatural world in central Mexico has been proposed as the motivating ideology for the construction of the massive Pyramid of the Sun early in the history of Teotihuacan (e.g., Heyden 1975 and 1981; Manzanilla 1994; Millon 1981). The very word for town or community in the Nahuatl language is *altepetl*, "mountain filled with water," and is represented graphically by the stylized image of a mountain with a cave at its base (Broda 1991, 480).

Volcanoes: Archaeology, Myth, and Religion

Volcanoes were held to be sacred since they were also mountains, but references to them as specific representations of particular deities or as objects of worship outside the more generalized mountain cults described by the chroniclers of the 16th century are uncommon. Although archaeologists have sometimes speculated that the first pyramidal structures of Mesoamerica were made in the image of volcanoes (e.g., Heizer 1968, 20), there exists little definitive corroboration of this replication. There is, however, fascinating circumstantial evidence that the Aztec Old Fire God known as Huehueteotl, originated during a period of significant volcanic activity in the Sierra de Chichinautzin and the Sierra Nevada, including the Popocatépetl and Iztaccihuatl volcanoes, that separate the Basin of Mexico from Morelos to the south and the Valley of Puebla-Tlaxcula to the east (fig. 6.1).

Miguel Covarrubias (1961, 44–5) was the first to suggest that the cult to the Old Fire God arose during the Terminal Preclassic as a direct response to the cataclysmic eruptions of the Xitle volcano that covered important

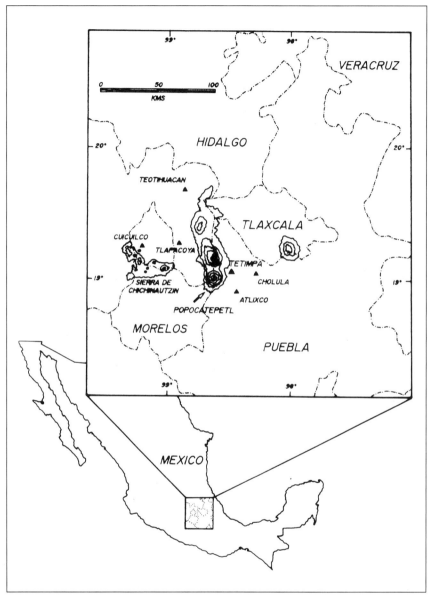

Fig. 6.1. Map of central Mexico showing sites indicated in the text.

human settlements in the Basin of Mexico, including Cuicuilco, with a thick layer of lava. The first known representations of the Old Fire God are found at Cuicuilco and at sites in the Valley of Puebla-Tlaxcala (Covarrubias 1961,

45, fig. 16; García Cook 1981, 250; Nicholson 1971, 96, figs. 5–6). He is depicted as a human figure, usually seated and bearing a large circular brazier, often decorated with fire symbols, on his head.

Cumulative evidence provided by archaeologists and geologists in recent years (Barba 1995, 66–7; Córdova et al. 1994; Panfil 1996; Plunket and Uruñuela 1998b, 2000) has shown that during the Late Preclassic and Early Classic, from perhaps 400 B.C. to about A.D. 400, there were numerous volcanic eruptions, some with dire consequences, in the Sierra de Chichinautzin and the Sierra Nevada mountain ranges. There is ample evidence that many of the civic-ceremonial centers and towns in the surrounding countryside of the Basin of Mexico and the Valley of Puebla-Tlaxcala were heavily affected by this sequence of volcanic events, and sites like Cuicuilco (Córdova et al. 1994, 592–5) and Tlapacoya (Barba de Piña Chan 1980, 174–5) show clear signs of abandonment during the first century A.D. It is surely more than mere coincidence that the anthropomorphic Old Fire God originates within this set of circumstances.

Luis Barba (1995) has taken the interpretation of this evidence a step farther by proposing a direct causal link between Prehispanic observations of the volcanic experience in this region and the emergence of a new cult at Teotihuacan at the opposite end of the valley. He suggests (Barba 1995, 70) that the construction of the Pyramid of the Sun at Teotihuacan, one of the largest structures ever built in the New World, was undertaken as a massive work of solidarity designed to placate the angry volcanoes by creating a monumental mountain shrine on top of a cave that provided a sacred connection to the underworld. The pyramid was raised in the first century A.D., very early in the city's history, a time that coincides with the period of intense volcanism described above.

Volcanic eruptions figure importantly in the creation myths recorded for central Mexico. The most significant of these is the account of the suns in the *Codex Chimalpopoca*, which relates the story of the five mythical epochs of creation and destruction. The first creation, or sun, was destroyed by water and its people were transformed into fish. The second sun was inhabited by giants who were eaten by jaguars when the heavens collapsed. The third sun, ruled over by the rain god, was destroyed by a rain of fire. The author's description makes it clear that the reference is to a volcanic eruption that must have been witnessed in antiquity:

The third Sun was established.
4-Rain was its sign; it was called the Sun of Rain.
In this sun it occurred that it rained fire
and the people were consumed by fire....
It rained stones.
They now say that this was when the stones we now see fell,
and the lava rock boiled up.
And also, it was when the great rocks formed into masses,
and became red (Sullivan and Knab 1994, 66).

The *Codex Vindobonensis*, a Mixtec document of the late Prehispanic period, graphically records volcanic activity. It depicts the snowcapped Popocatépetl volcano with smoke and fire emerging from the top and sides of the mountain and flames spewing from the crater in the form of a butterfly, a symbol for fire and for the souls of dead warriors (fig. 6.2) (Caso 1977, Vol. 1, Lámina XIXh; von Winning 1987, Vol. 1, 15). The volcano's impressive activity continued into the 16th century and was commented upon by Fray Diego Durán (1971, 253):

> The Mountain of Popocatzin*, which in our tongue means Smoking Mountain, is known to us all as the volcano which gives forth smoke two and three times a day (and often flames at the same time), especially at an early hour of the morning, as many have observed. Both the Spaniards and Indians affirm that this flaming is very common, as do the villages contiguous to this mountain, which is visible from many leagues away because of its height.

Two of the important feasts celebrated by the Aztecs involved mountains. The first, Tepeilhuitl (Sahagún 1981, 131–4), the Feast of Mountains, took place during the fall and was dedicated to the high mountains, and to the Popocatépetl volcano in particular (Durán 1971, 256). Models of the mountains were made of amaranth seed dough and these were used in ceremonies for those who could not be cremated, but, because of the circumstances of their deaths, had been buried. Four women (three of whom represented mountains while the fourth symbolized the maguey plant), and one man (the personification of a serpent), were sacrificed during this festival, and their

Fig. 6.2. Graphic representation of the snowcapped Popocatépetl volcano during an eruptive phase from the *Codex Vindobonensis*. (Redrawn from Caso 1977 Vol I:Lámina XIXh)

flesh was eaten. The second feast was Atemoztli (Sahagún 1981, 151–4), held at the beginning of winter and dedicated to the rain god Tlaloc, who was also a mountain deity. Models of mountains, including images of Popocatépetl, Iztaccihuatl, and Mount Tlaloc, and representations of the gods of fire, water, and wind were again produced from amaranth dough. During Atemoztli only the mountain effigies themselves were sacrificed by priests wielding a weaving baton in place of a stone knife.

As we have seen there is reason to believe that mountains, and volcanoes in particular, held an important place in Prehispanic Mesoamerican myth and religion since they figure in the rituals recorded by the Spanish, in the native creation myths, and in the graphic depictions of the codices. The evidence for the origin of cults and rituals related specifically to volcanoes, however, has always been suggestive rather than factual, and although some have proposed it as a rationale for the massive building projects of early urban society in the central highlands (e.g., Barba 1995; Sanders et al. 1979), there has, until now, been no incontestable evidence that the volcanic activity of the Terminal Preclassic resulted in any corresponding ritual activity. Some eruptions resulted in the abandonment of settlements, because of either the inhabitants' fear or actual destruction, but apart from the appearance of Old Fire God braziers in the Basin of Mexico and the Puebla-Tlaxcala Valley, there had been little solid evidence of a direct link between experience and ritual practices related to volcanic activity. This situation has changed, however, with our recent discoveries in the Tetimpa region on the lower slopes of the Popocatépetl volcano in the State of Puebla.

Tetimpa and the Volcano

On the northeastern flank of Popocatépetl volcano, between the towns of San Nicolás de los Ranchos and San Buenaventura Nealtican, is a large village that was buried by a huge plinian eruption during the first century A.D. The fragmented pumice that encased the site preserved many primary contexts that provide important information on a poorly understood time period in the central highlands of Mexico.

The initial occupation of Tetimpa took place at about 700 B.C. when houses were built in the fertile piedmont of the Popocatépetl. This early occupation was abandoned around 100 B.C.; the houses deteriorated, and the volcanic soil accumulated over their foundations. Tetimpa was resettled a few generations later, and the buildings of this second occupation were constructed directly on top of the scattered ruins of the first settlement. The houses consisted of two or three rooms placed around a central courtyard and were surrounded by furrowed agricultural fields. This cultural landscape was abruptly buried by a deposit of yellow pumice that protected and preserved the buildings and activity areas and made the region uninhabitable. Later a huge lava flow added to the destruction, covering part of both the

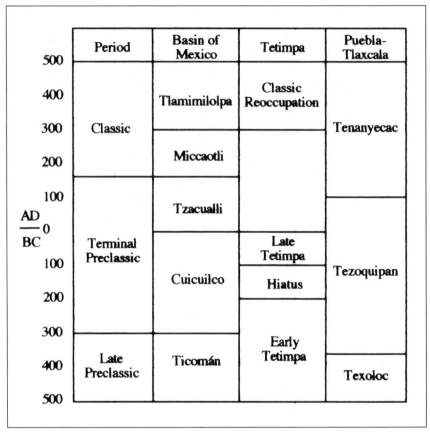

Fig. 6.3. Comparative chronology for the Tetimpa region in western Puebla.**

villages and the yellow pumice with more than 40 m of solid rock. A suite of calibrated radiocarbon dates, taken from sealed cultural contexts, indicate that this violent eruptive sequence took place during the Terminal Preclassic, probably about the middle of the first century A.D. (fig. 6.3).

Geological studies estimate that the plinian column of this eruption rose to about 25 km² (Panfil 1996), visible to all of the surrounding valleys. We have suggested elsewhere (Plunket and Uruñuela 1996, 1998a) that this impressive natural phenomenon must have had a significant impact on the development of ritual and ideology in most of central Mexico. Our rescue excavations at Tetimpa have revealed, however, that Prehispanic observations of volcanic activity were being translated into ritual even before this massive eruption of the first century A.D. (fig. 6.4).

Fig. 6.4. The Popocatépetl volcano seen from Tetimpa during the summer of 1996.

Fig. 6.5. A household compound from the Late Tetimpa phase.

The 25 residential areas we have explored at Tetimpa reveal a high degree of patterning (fig. 6.5). Each house compound consists of two or three low stone platforms placed at right angles around a central courtyard. The platforms each have a central staircase and their facades use the *talud-tablero* architectural system, a sloping wall crowned with a horizontal panel that is characteristic of constructions at Teotihuacan. The facades of some of the buildings were embellished with high-relief figures modeled in hardened mud and painted. The rooms constructed on top of the platforms are simple wattle-and-daub structures that quickly collapsed under the weight of the accumulating pumice, smashing the objects left.

Work areas were located at the edges of the central courtyard or in the corner spaces between platforms. In most cases the corners were left open and we found groups of large storage vessels that were broken during the eruption. In other cases we have recorded subterranean pits or wattle-and-daub rooms that appear to have been used for storage, and in several instances, kitchens with distinctive built-in stoves and low benches. Around the perimeter of the central courtyard are small mud-and-thatch grain silos, known as *cuexcomates,* that are still used in the environs of the Popocatépetl. These are raised off the ground on four or five large stones and the rounded bodies are made of wicker and mud, much like a swallow's nest.

At the center of each courtyard is a small household shrine. We have recovered shrines from 17 courtyards and have yet to find any exact duplications, although there are repetitive elements; a good deal of individual freedom of expression is evident. Most of the shrines consist of one or two carved stones (although uncarved stones are also used), including felines, snakes, and anthropomorphic heads. In some cases the images sit directly on the hardened dirt floor of the courtyard, and although it is possible that they once rested on wooded structures or mats, there is no evidence for this. In another case, the shrine consists of a small, plain stele, made from a slab of local andesite that perforates one end of a low, mud-plastered altar.

Most relevant, however, are the volcano shrines. In each case it is clear that the artist sought to depict a smoking volcano, but there are significant differences in their appearance and the nature of the carved stones associated with each of them. The volcano shrine found at Operation 2 during the 1994 field season (fig. 6.6) consisted of two miniature modeled platforms or hills, the smaller one abutting directly against the larger. On top of each platform was a carved stone head, and under each head was a chimney, made from the inverted mouth-and-neck fragment of an olla, that led to a charcoal-filled chamber that had been excavated into the courtyard floor (fig. 6.7). The larger head is carved from a porous light gray stone and represents an individual with furrowed hair, round protruding eyes, and cheeks puffed in the act of blowing. The smaller figure is poorly sculpted from dark gray to black lava and the back of the head has been excavated to form a small cavity. The face has goggle eyes and a simple headdress, but the features are not clearly defined; it bears the remains of red and yellow paint. The carved effigies face south, towards the entrance to the house compound, while the volcano itself rises in the background to the southwest. The entire composition measured only 80 cm long × 50 cm wide; the height of the large hill was 31 cm while the lower one was a mere 15 cm. Around the basal perimeter of the larger hill were five holes that seem to have been formed by poles stuck into the ground. We do not know how these might have been used, but paper streamers may have been tied to them as decorations, as was common in the rituals of 16th-century Mesoamerica.

Another volcano shrine was discovered at Operation 12 in 1996. This was a more elaborate version of a model volcano and it consisted of a rectangular stone and earthen basal platform, 1.50 m × 80 cm × 20 cm with burnished mud plaster. Set into the western end of the basal platform was a well-carved

Fig. 6.6. The volcano shrine from Operation 2 at Tetimpa.

Fig. 6.7. The chimneys underneath the effigies of the volcano shrine at Operation 2.

stone head, which, like the smaller figure at Operation 2, had a cavity carved into its posterior surface. On top of the platform was a smooth circular stone, crudely pecked to represent a human face, which rested on a small orifice. There was no charcoal inside, but remnants of ash were imbedded in the polished surface of the altar. At the eastern end of the platform, rising another 20 cm from its surface, was a conical "volcano" surmounted by a crudely carved stone serpent-effigy. Underneath this figure was a chimney formed from an olla neck that led to a specially made ceramic chamber.

Both of these volcano shrines are constructed so that smoke would have puffed out from under each carved stone in imitation of the plumes that are expelled from the volcano's crater. The image created clearly establishes that the people of Tetimpa witnessed many such pulses of vapor and ash before their settlements were buried by the collapsing plinian column of pumice.

From Observation to Ritual

We cannot be sure that these shrines are the first manifestations of a volcano cult, but we think it is significant that at the 11 houses we have excavated for the Early Tetimpa phase, we have found little evidence of such shrines. We suspect that the abandonment of the Early Tetimpa village was related to a period of increasing volcanism that eventually led to the development of cultic activity centered on the volcano shrines and their associated rituals. This new cult manifests itself clearly with the re-establishment of the community at Tetimpa in the first century B.C. The growing body of evidence from the southern perimeter of the Basin of Mexico indicates that this was a time of frequent volcanic activity in central Mexico (Barba 1995, 66–7; Córdova et al. 1994), further supporting the link between direct observation of natural phenomena and the development of specific cults and rituals.

There is enough variation between the two volcano shrines discussed here to suggest that some thematic liberty was accepted within the developing rituals. In each case, however, there are two openings into the modeled landscape surmounted by effigies: the shrine at Operation 2 has two anthropomorphic heads, while the one at Operation 12 has one human image and a serpent figure. Judging from the carved stones associated with the other shrines excavated at Tetimpa and from carved effigies found by local farmers in their fields, it seems that the three most common representations are the crudely carved goggle-eyed figure, the anthropomorphic head with the furrowed hair, and the serpent. The furrowed hair figure and the serpent both appear crowning a model of the Popocatépetl volcano, suggesting that they may be two sides of a compound deity associated with the personification of the mountain itself and the smoke plumes that emanate from its crater.

But why are there two openings? Might this indicate that there was a lower vent on the slope of the volcano, an entrance to the underworld associated with its own, somewhat less important, patron? Although we have no way of knowing this at present, we might suggest that the second opening, associated with the lower hill in the two volcano shrines, may represent the vent from which lava flowed to form the Pedregal de Nealtican just south of Tetimpa during the eruptive sequence that destroyed the communities on the northeast flank of the volcano.

Views from the 16th Century

Although it is a long way from the Terminal Preclassic to the 16th century, it is interesting to compare some of the details provided by the informants of Fray Bernardino de Sahagún (1981, 131–2) regarding the feast of Tepeilhuitl and the shrines from Tetimpa:

. . . they also at this time made representations of mountains.
They made them all of amaranth seed dough.

they went blowing wind instruments for them; they went
blowing pottery whistles and little seashells...it was as if they
came shouting. Thereupon they were given human form; they
were adorned. They gave them their foundation.

Thus did they give them human form: they applied liquid rubber
to the faces (of the figures) and they placed (a spot of) fish
amaranth (*chicalote*) upon (each) of their cheeks; they dressed
them in paper banners and they fitted them with their paper
headdresses, their forked heron feather ornaments.

And when it dawned, then they were set up in each one's house
upon reed foundations made perhaps of thin, fine reeds; perhaps of wide reeds; of large white reeds; perhaps of hollow
reeds. On these they placed them.

And when this was done, when they had arranged them, thereupon they laid offerings before them. They offered them fruit
tamales, and stews, or dog meat, or turkey hen. And they
offered them incense.

And at this time it was stated: "They are laid in the houses." And
where there was riches, there was singing, and there was
drinking of *pulque* for them. But elsewhere all they did was
make offerings to them.

Several elements of this description call our attention. First, this appears to
be a household-oriented ritual since the models are "laid in the houses" and
the offerings are supplied according to the economic possibilities of each
household. This seems to coincide with the nature of the rituals at Tetimpa
where the shrines are always found at the center of the residential courtyards.
A major difference is that by the 16th century, cult and ritual have become so
complex and diversified that the mountain shrines are only temporary structures, meant to be destroyed and consumed within a few days. The most fascinating part of Sahagún's description, however, is that the mountain models
are given human faces. Dibble and Anderson, the translators of Sahagún's
informants from Nahuatl into English, note that in the original Spanish version of the document, the text reads: "La cabeça de cada un monte tenja dos
caras, una de persona, y otra de culebra" (Sahagún 1981, 132, n. 9), that is to

say, the head of each mountain had two faces, one of a person and the other of a snake. The dual nature of these mountains is paralleled by the human and snake representations found on top of the models at Tetimpa and suggest an incredible conceptual continuity over 1,500 years.

Volcanic Eruptions and the Return of Cultic Activity

The villagers of San Nicolás de los Ranchos and San Buenaventura Nealtican still think of the Popocatépetl volcano in anthropomorphic terms. To them, he is Gregorio, a masculine being with long curly hair (thought by some to represent smoke tendrils that unfurl from the crater), who must be venerated with offerings left in special caves high on the slopes of the mountain. Ten years ago there were still specialists who were well versed in the rites of pro-pitiation of the volcano, but when the last of these died, the rituals were not performed correctly and the offerings were, for the most part, discontinued.

In December 1994 the Popocatépetl volcano erupted once again and has remained in a period of intermittent activity, occasionally spewing forth huge plumes of ash and vapor, and producing great rumblings from its crater. In response, the towns on the eastern slopes of the volcano have returned to the prescribed rituals to the best of their ability and have renewed the offerings in the caves in an attempt to appease Gregorio. The modeled images of the volcanoes, once made every year by the Prehispanic communities of the central highlands for the feasts of Tepeilhuitl and Atemoztli, have reappeared in the festivities of the Atlixcayotl, a regional dance festival held in late September in Atlixco, Puebla. The prototype for the modern mountain models was the volcano shrine found at Operation 2 in Tetimpa, and so the transformation of an observed phenomenon into cult and ritual draws upon the past and continues into the future.

REFERENCES

Barba, L. 1995. "El Impacto Humano en la Paleogeografía de Teotihuacan." Ph.D. diss., Universidad Nacional Autónoma de México.
Barba de Piña Chan, B. 1980. *Tlapacoya: Los principios de la teocracia en la Cuenca de Mexico.* Mexico City.
Broda, J. 1991. "Cosmovisión y Observación de la Naturaleza: el ejemplo del culto de los cerros en Mesoamérica." In *Arqueoastronomía y Etnoastronomia en Mesoamérica,* edited by

J. Broda, S. Iwaniszewski, and L. Maupomé, 461–500. Mexico City.

Caso, A. 1977. *Reyes y Reinos de la Mixteca.* 2 vols. Mexico City.

Córdova, C., A.L. Martín del Pozzo, and J. López. 1994. "Paleolandforms and Volcanic Impact on the Environment of Prehistoric Cuicuilco, Southern Mexico City." *Journal of Archaeological Science* 21:585–96.

Covarrubias, M. 1961. *Arte Indígena de México y Centro América.* Mexico City.

Durán, Fray Diego. 1971. *Book of the Gods and Rites and The Ancient Calendar.* Translated and edited by F. Horcasitas and D. Heyden. Norman, Okla.

García Cook, A. 1981. "The Historical Importance of Tlaxcala in the Cultural Development of the Central Highlands." In *Handbook of Middle American Indians.* Suppl. 1, *Archaeology,* edited by J. Sabloff and V. Bricker, 244–76. Austin.

Heizer, R. 1968. "New Observations on La Venta." In *Dumbarton Oaks Conference on the Olmec,* edited by E. Benson, 9–36. Washington, D.C.

Heyden, D. 1975. "An Interpretation of the Cave Underneath the Pyramid of the Sun in Teotihuacan, Mexico." *American Antiquity* 40 (2):131–47.

———. 1981. "Caves, Gods, and Myths: World Views and Planning in Teotihuacan." In *Mesoamerican Sites and World Views,* edited by E. Benson, 1–39. Washington, D.C.

Manzanilla, L. 1994. "Geografía sagrada e inframundo en Teotihuacan." *Antropológicas* 11:53–65.

Matos, E. 1982. "El Templo Mayor: economía e ideología." In *El Templo Mayor: Excavaciones y Estudios,* edited by E. Matos, 109–18. Mexico City.

Millon, R. 1981. "Teotihuacan: City, State and Civilization." In *Handbook of Middle American Indians.* Suppl. 1, *Archaeology,* edited by J. Sabloff and V. Bricker, 198–243. Austin.

Nicholson, H. 1971. "Major Sculpture in Pre-Hispanic Central Mexico." In *Handbook of Middle American Indians.* Vol. 10, pt. 1, Ar*chaeology of Northern Mesoamerica,* edited by G. Ekholm and I. Bernal, 92–134. Austin.

Panfil, M. 1996. "The Late Holocene Volcanic Stratigraphy of the Tetimpa Area, Northeast Flank of Popocatépetl Volcano, Central Mexico." Master's Thesis, Pennsylvania State University.

Plunket, P., and G. Uruñuela. 1996. "The Children of the Third Sun: Village Life and Volcanism in the Puebla Preclassic." Paper read at the Sixty-First Annual Meeting of the Society for American Archaeology, 13 April 1996, New Orleans.

———. 1998a. "Appeasing the Volcano Gods." *Archaeology* 51(4):36–42.

———. 1998b. "Preclassic Household Patterns Preserved beneath Volcanic Ash at Tetimpa, Puebla, Mexico." *Latin American Antiquity* 9(4):287–309.

———. 2000. "The Archaeology of a Plinian Eruption of the Popocatépetl Volcano in Central Mexico." In *The Archaeology of Geological Catastrophes,* edited by W.J. McGuire, D.R. Griffiths, P.L. Hancock, and I.S. Stewart, 195–203. Geological Society Special Publication 171. Bath.

Sahagún, Fray Bernardino de. 1981. *Florentine Codex: General History of the Things of New Spain. Book* 2, *The Ceremonies.* Translated from the Aztec with notes and illustrations by A. Anderson and C. Dibble. Santa Fe.

Schele, L., and D. Freidel. 1990. *A Forest of Kings: The Untold Story of the Ancient Maya.* New York.

Sullivan, T., and T. Knab. 1994. *A Scattering of Jades.* New York.

von Winning, H. 1987. *La Iconografía de Teotihuacan: los dioses y los signos.* 2 vols. Mexico City.

NOTES

* We would like to thank the Mesoamerican Research Foundation, the Sistema de Investigación Regional Ignacio Zaragoza, the Consejo Nacional de Ciencia y Tecnología, and the Instituto de Investigación y Posgrado of the Universidad de las Américas-Puebla for their generous support of the Tetimpa Project.

** Since this paper was originally written in 1996, the authors have completed nine more field seasons at Tetimpa and secured a large suite of radiocarbon dates. Although efforts have been made to update the text, the chronology presented in fig. 6.3 now has been modified so that the original occupation of Tetimpa is now considered to take place around 700 B.C.; a short hiatus of some but perhaps not all of the site is apparent around 100 B.C.; and the Late Tetimpa phase is placed between 50 B.C. and A.D. 50/100.

7

The Prehistoric Settlement Near the Salinelle di San Marco (Paternò, Catania Province, Sicily)

◈

Laura Maniscalco

Since Neolithic times the southwestern slopes of Mount Etna have hosted numerous settlements, probably because of the fertility of the volcanic soil and the abundance of fresh water in the Simeto River and at several springs (Cafici 1914, 1920; Cafici 1938; Bernabò Brea 1958; Maniscalco 2000). To date only one of these settlements, San Marco at Paternò, has been systematically excavated.

The low hill of San Marco is located midway between the acropolis of Paternò, which dominates it on the southeast and the bank of the Simeto River (fig. 7.1) and lies precisely in the center of an area marked by alternating volcanic and sedimentary formations. The hill is covered with almond and olive trees, cactus, and brush on its southwestern slope. The northern slope, where the *salinelle* (mud volcanoes) discharge gases, mud, clay, and hot salty water, is completely arid (figs. 7.2–7.3). The name "salinelle" describes the thick salt crust that forms on the ground surface as a result of summer evaporation. The Salinelle of Paternò is one of three such areas which exist in the area of Paternò and Belpasso. The other two are the Salinelle del Fiume by the Simeto River and the Salinelle di San Biagio near the Vallone Salato, and all three are part of a hydrothermal system associated with Etna's southern sector (D'Alessandro et al. 1993; Chiodini et al. 1996; AA.VV. 1992). This interesting example of sub-volcanism is also known in other parts of Sicily, as will be discussed below.

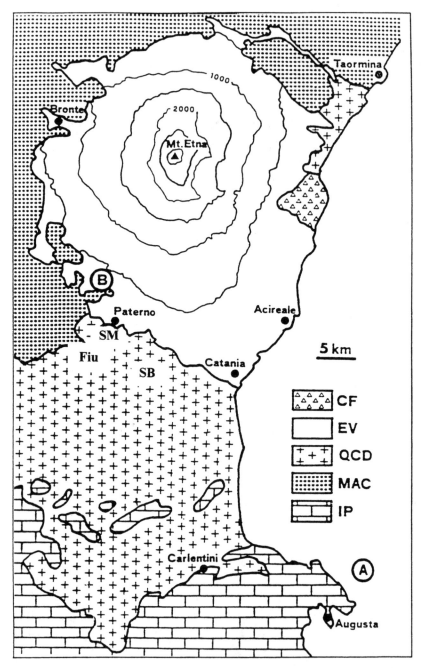

Fig. 7.1. Geological sketch of the area: *CF*, Chiancone fanglomerate; *EV*, Etnean volcanites; *QCD*, quaternary clastic deposit; *MAC*, Maghrebian-Appenninic chain; *IP*, Iblean plateau; *SM*, San Marco; *Fiu*, Salinelle di Fiume; *SB*, San Biagio. (Adapted from D'Alessandro et al. 1993, 172, fig. 7.2)

Fig. 7.2. Mud volcanoes at San Marco.

Fig. 7.3. A photograph of Paternò, Salinelle di San Marco from the early 20th century.

Fig. 7.4. A watercolor of Paternò, Salinelle di San Marco by Jean Houel. (The Hermitage, Saint Petersburg)

The geology of San Marco has been noted and studied since the 18th century by geologists, such as Chisari, and illustrated and described by travelers, including Jean Houel (fig. 7.4) and the Prince of Biscari. While salinelle mark volcanic activity, there are also significant sedimentary deposits such as

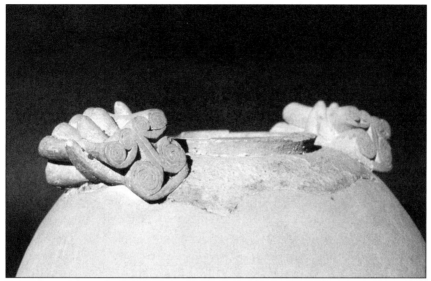

Fig. 7.5. A vessel in the Serra d'Alto style from San Marco. (Museo Paolo Orsi, Syracuse)

the well-known travertine of Paternò. This travertine crosses the site from northeast to southwest and was probably produced by the overflow of water from an ancient lake. The abundance of water in this area, so evident in antiquity, is also present today as numerous springs, some of which (such as Acqua Rossa and Acqua Grassa) are noted for their mineralogical content (Dall'Aglio and Tedesco 1968, 175). San Marco is the only site in the entire Etna region with three fundamentally different kinds of springs: freshwater, carbonized water, and carbonized water and mud.

The hill of San Marco has only recently been the subject of scientific archaeological exploration, despite the fact that it has been known since 1909 as the source for a series of splendid Neolithic vases in the Serra d'Alto and Diana ceramic styles (fig. 7.5; Orsi 1921).[1] In the neighboring Contrada Marmo, about 15 cist burials were discovered by chance in the 1930s. These contained single inhumations, which were datable to the Late Neolithic period (Cafici 1938). In 1994 the Superintendency for Cultural and Environmental Resources of Catania excavated two trenches at San Marco and despite the extremely dry and powdery soil deposits, which were difficult to interpret, it has been possible to identify the remains of settlements dating to the Late Neolithic period and the Early Bronze Age, a tomb and other structures of the Late Bronze Age, and structures of Roman date.

Neolithic Remains

The remains of the Neolithic settlement are located on the southern slope of the hill of San Marco. They consist of a segment of a large terrace wall and related floor levels. Based on associated ceramics, they may be attributed to the Diana phase of the Late Neolithic. This is the first time that the remains of structures, not just tombs or soil deposits, attributable to this phase of the Sicilian Neolithic have been found.

The wall segment, disturbed by modern agricultural terracing at its eastern end, has a length of 5 m and two courses are preserved to a height of 70 cm (fig. 7.6). It was made from large lava blocks carefully fitted together to form a solid wall facing on a core of smaller stones and earth with a total width of 1.8 m and was set on a deposit of travertine stone and earthen fill. Several floor levels were found on both sides of the wall recognizable because of the number of finds on their surfaces and the presence of foundation pebbles and small stones. Ceramics recovered from the floor surfaces included domestic vessels such as bowls, cups, and jars, many of which had the bobbin and trumpet handles typical of the Late Neolithic Diana style. This style is noted for its brightly colored slip, but several examples from San Marco also have a band in an ivory color (figs. 7.7 and 7.8). In order to determine the compo-

Fig. 7.6. Paternò, San Marco, trench 5, terrace wall.

sition of these slips, a number of samples were submitted for proton-induced x-ray emission analysis (PIXE). The results of this study have shown that while the red slip contains a significant quantity of iron, the ivory band consists of calcium.[2] Thin sections of some pottery fragments indicate that the ceramics were made from local clay with volcanic inclusions and were fired at very high temperatures (Lombardo et al. 2000).

Cores and tools of flint and obsidian and numerous bones of cattle, goats, and pigs were recovered from both trenches (see the appendices to this report). Functional analyses of lithic implements have shown traces of grain harvesting and cutting of lacustrine plants (Iovino 2000). Several radiocarbon samples of charcoal and bones associated with the floor levels date to between the mid-fifth to mid-fourth millennium B.C. (see app. 1). These dates are comparable to that obtained from the eponymous Contrada Diana on the island of Lipari in the first half of fourth millennium B.C. (Alessio et al. 1980).

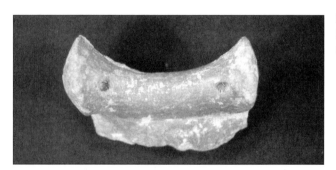

Fig. 7.7. Paternò, San Marco, pottery fragment from trench 5.

Fig. 7.8. Paternò, San Marco, pottery fragment from trench 5.

Early Neolithic and Early Bronze Age Remains

Just a short distance from this Neolithic structure there is another wall, created from heavy, squared blocks of lava, which is part of a large circular structure. The wall rests on three different deposits, a bed of lava rock, amorphous white calcite, and travertine (figs. 7.9–7.10). The wall is preserved to a height of three courses for a distance of about 10 m. Several sections of a terracotta pavement are preserved on the interior, and at one point this terracotta continues up the interior wall face as a surface finish. At regular 1.4- m intervals along the wall are holes that were probably for posts to support a superstructure. Ceramics in a black fabric with a burnished surface and painted wares with decoration typical of the later phase of the Castelluccian Culture (1600–1400 B.C.) were recovered from the terracotta pavement. Flint and quartzite implements and terracotta objects also come from this area.

Circular buildings are known from sites such as La Muculufa, where a canonical building type has been identified in the earlier part of the Sicilian Early Bronze Age (McConnell 1992). The find at San Marco, however,

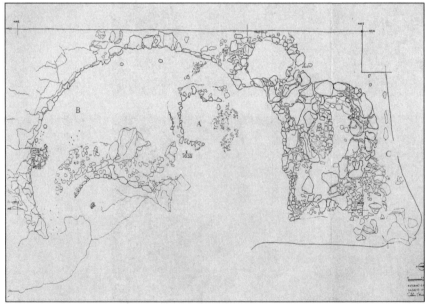

Fig. 7.9. General plan of Paternò, San Marco, trench 2. A, Early Neolithic; B, Early Bronze Age; C, Late Bronze Age.

seems to be one of the largest single buildings of the Castelluccian Culture yet identified. It must have been an impressive structure, and its carefully fitted stones reflect a relatively sophisticated masonry tradition.

Under the floor of the Early Bronze Age structure is a travertine formation. A structure of smaller lava stones, each 1.5 m long and placed at right angles, was set into a niche cut into the travertine. This construction must have been a wall socle in a building with walls of wattle and daub on a wooden frame. Similar overall dimensions have been noted for a Middle Neolithic structure at Serra del Palco at Milena, in the province of Caltanissetta (La Rosa 1985, 804). Many fragments of daub and a large jar attributable to the Early Neolithic period were found in the area enclosed by the wall socle. Charcoal recovered from a soil layer associated with the daub fragments and the jar yielded a calibrated radiocarbon date of the second half of the sixth millennium B.C. This date corresponds to dates obtained for levels with Neolithic impressed ware at the site of Piano Vento along Sicily's southern coast (Castellana 1995, 18).

Fig. 7.10. A view of the Early Bronze Age wall in trench 2, Paternò, San Marco.

Late Bronze Age Remains

Ceramics of the Middle Bronze Age Thapsos style that have been recovered occasionally from the surface in various places around the site demonstrate continuity of occupation after the Early Bronze Age. During the Late Bronze Age (1200–1100? B.C.) the large Castelluccian wall was cut and perhaps several of its blocks were reused to construct a tomb (tomb 2, fig. 7.11). The tomb has an ovoid plan, and is built of large irregular blocks of lava, and entered by way of a dromos on the southwest. The remains of at least six disarticulated individuals were found within the chamber; several of the crania had been placed on a rectangular funeral bed constructed along the northwestern wall (see appendix 2).

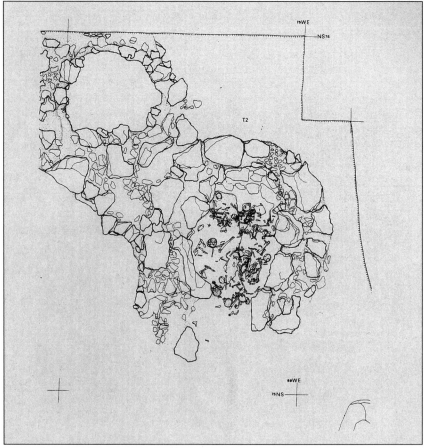

Fig. 7.11. The Late Bronze Age tomb in trench 2, Paternò, San Marco.

In many areas of Sicily it was a tradition from as early as the Copper Age to cut tomb chambers into the soft, calcareous rock. The Etna region is noteworthy for its lack of such tombs, perhaps because the extremely hard lava rock did not permit easy excavation. In fact, from the Copper to the Bronze Age volcanic caves were used as substitutions for rock-cut tombs (Privitera 1998). The Late Bronze Age tomb found at San Marco was built using what we might call megalithic construction. The need to bury in this area, combined with the tradition of the rock-cut tomb, seems to have forced the people of Paternò to invent a built rock tomb, which is very rare even in the Etna region.

There was a funerary assemblage in the tomb comprising four vessels in the Late Bronze Age Pantalica North style (fig. 7.12). This assemblage is an abbreviated version of the funerary banquet service and includes two amphorae and a spouted jar but lacks the traditional pedestal bowl that is found in Late Bronze Age burials elsewhere in Sicily (Maniscalco 1999). Twenty meters south of this tomb two groups of Pantalica North vessels were found around an ovoid construction similar to, but smaller than, tomb 2. These vessels suggest that the site was not itself a settlement, but rather a

Fig. 7.12. The Late Bronze Age tomb assemblage from trench 2, Paternò, San Marco.

necropolis probably related to a contemporary village identified on the acropolis of Paternò (Bernabò Brea 1958, 170).

Roman Remains at the Salinelle di San Marco

A few meters from the mud cones on the northern side of the hill of San Marco, Roman period structures were found enveloped in a thick deposit of clay beneath a very thin layer of soil. Two rooms have been uncovered and there may be other rooms that have not yet been found. The recovery of several *suspensurae* suggests that these rooms were once part of a small bath complex. We know of two other bath complexes in the vicinity of Paternò, one in Contrada Bella Cortina near the Salinelle, and the other at Orto del Conte in the center of the city of Paternò (Palermo 1994), both of which were served by a branch of an aqueduct running from Santa Maria di Licodia to Catania, although neither bath structure still exists.

People and Environment at San Marco

The influence of the geological setting at San Marco on the lives of the people living there is evident at different levels. At a basic level it supplied the materials they used in building. All of the structures found, from the earliest to the latest periods, were made of hard lava even when other kinds of stone were available. In trench 2, for example, the travertine bed was carefully cut away and a wall in lava rock was erected in the sixth millennium B.C. Although rounded cobbles of every size were available from the nearby Simeto River and were frequently used in walls of the Archaic period at neighboring archaeological sites (e.g., Monte Castellaccio), they appear never to have been used at San Marco. This would suggest that people, even in the Early Neolithic, were aware of the different characteristics of stone and consciously selected the lava, probably for its strength and durability.

Similarly, the presence of the salinelle, whose extent in antiquity was probably greater than it is today, offered useful material for other purposes. With its hot, salty water and abundance of clay, the salinelle may have supplied people since the Neolithic period with material for creating vessels and other goods. Jean Houel (Houel 1977, tav. CXXV, 85) notes that in his time (the late 18th century), the inhabitants of Paternò used the salinelle's salts for culinary purposes and the tepid waters for washing clothes and coloring cloth. He marveled at the variety of minerals that could be found in the soil around the salinelle, including chalk, alabaster, bitumen, iron, clay, and sulphur. The salty mud was used by the local inhabitants for therapeutic purposes, particularly to cure arthritis, into the 1930s (AA. VV. 1992, 21), and the newly discovered bath at San Marco may attest to the use of the mud and hot water for therapeutic purposes as early as Roman times.

While direct proof of Neolithic use of these resources is lacking, their presence seems to have encouraged people to settle and therefore was a determining factor in the settlement pattern. This pattern can be seen in the proximity of prehistoric sites to sub-volcanic phenomena at other locations in the immediate vicinity and farther away. In the territory of Paternò and Belpasso, prehistoric pottery fragments have been found in surface contexts at Coscia del Ponte near the Salinelle del Fiume (Simeto) and at Poggio Scala near the Salinelle di San Biagio, although neither site has been excavated. On the southern side of the plain of Catania, in the wide Margi River valley, a site dating from the Paleolithic to the historical period has been found in proximity to Napthia Lake (Bernabò Brea 1965; Maniscalco and McConnell 1997–1998) which, until its modern commercial utilization, emitted volcanic gasses which made it boil. North of Sicily, on the Aeolian island of Panarea, is the so-called Calcara, a small hollow with mud volcanoes that make the area around it sterile like the area immediately around San Marco (Bernabò Brea and Cavalier 1968, 8). Although this would seem to be a deterrent to settlement, Roman and Hellenistic occupation strata overlying prehistoric remains were found on the southeast side of the hollow. The prehistoric features include a terrace wall and a series of Early Bronze Age *bothroi* (offering pits) between 60 and 70 cm in diameter built from large cobbles. Beneath these remains, strata containing Late Neolithic Diana pottery were identified, indicating some degree of continuity. While simple proximity does not prove a direct response to the volcanic phenomenon, it does not seem to be a casual association since volcanic phenomena also have negative aspects, such as infertility of the soil, noxious vapors, and an unstable, active ground surface.

Determining a spiritual response to Mount Etna at San Marco is a more difficult matter given the nature and scarcity of the evidence. As in all the locations discussed, one is left with only the testimony of cults in historical times and analogies that can be drawn from them. Perhaps the sub-volcanic activity at these sites was seen as more than simply an economic resource.

These places may have been thought to have curative, perhaps even magical, powers, which generated cult beliefs among those who settled nearby. Ruth Whitehouse, who has studied prehistoric religion in connection with grottoes and other underground locations, has stressed the importance of water in prehistoric ritual. She states that water in an "abnormal" condition, such as gaseous or bubbling, can "make a place holy" (Whitehouse 1992, 138), and this contention is supported by the evidence from around Mt. Etna. The most famous of Sicily's indigenous cults, associated with the boiling Napthia Lake, was held to be sacred to the Sikel divinities called the Palikoi. Historical sources tell of a monumental cult center there as early as the seventh century B.C., and recent excavations have confirmed the monumental character of this cult site and also demonstrated a continuity of occupation from the Upper Paleolithic through the Roman Empire. On Panarea a cult similar to that of Hephaistos has been suggested in connection with the settlements on the Calcara. Returning to San Marco, a local tradition associates a cult of the Sikel goddess Hybla with the site in Roman times (La Rosa 1989, 5 and 57). Although the Roman-era divinity is separated from the Neolithic settlement by several millennia, the juxtaposition of Roman and prehistoric remains and the fact that the goddess was a Sikel divinity clearly with pre-Roman and non-Hellenic roots, suggests that the cult had its origin far earlier than the historical era—that it was rooted in the geological memory of the land itself.

REFERENCES

AA.VV. 1992. *Le Salinelle di Paternò e Belpasso. XXIII Distretto Scolastico, Assessorato Regionale BB.CC.AA. e PP.II.* Paternò.

Agozzino, P. 2000. "Analisi chimiche su ceramiche neolitiche da San Marco." In *La Neolitizzazione tra Oriente ed Occidente*, edited by A. Pessina and G. Muscio, 511. Udine.

Alessio, M., F. Bella, C. Cortesi, and B. Turi. 1980. "Datazione con il carbonio 14 di alcuni orizzonti degli insediamenti preistorici dell'Acropoli di Lipari e di Contrada Diana, isola di Lipari." In *Meligunis-Lipara IV. L'Acropoli di Lipari nella preistoria*, edited by Brea, Bernabo and Madelaine Cavalier. Palermo.

Bernabò Brea, L. 1958. *La Sicilia prima dei Greci.* Milano.

———. 1965. "Palikè, Giacimento paleolitico ed abitato neolitico ed eneo." *Bullettino di Paletnologia Italiana* 75:23–46.

Bernabò Brea, L., and M. Cavalier. 1968. *Meligunis-Lipara III. Stazioni preistoriche delle Isole Panarea, Salina e Stromboli.* Palermo.

———. 1980. *Meligunis-Lipara IV. L'Acropoli di Lipari nella preistoria.* Palermo.

Cafici, C. 1914. "Stazioni preistoriche di Trefontane e Poggio Rosso in territorio di Paternò (provincia di Catania)." *Monumenti Antichi dei Lincei* 23:485–358.

―――. 1920. *La stazione neolitica di Fontana di Pepe (Belpasso) e la civiltà di Stentinello in Sicilia.* Palermo.

Cafici, I. 1938. "Apporti delle ricerche alla conoscenza delle culture presicule." *Bullettino di Paletnologia Italiana,* N.S. 17:3–28.

Castellana, G. 1995. *La necropoli protoeneolitica di Piano Vento nel territorio di Palma di Montechiaro.* Agrigento.

Chiodini, G., W. D'Alessandro, and F. Parello. 1996. "Geochemistry of Gases and Waters Discharged by the Mud Volcanoes at Paternò, Mt. Etna (Italy)." *Bullettino di Volcanologia* 58:51–8.

D'Alessandro W., R. De Domenico, F. Parello, and M. Valenza. 1993. "Geochemical Anomalies in the Gaseous Phase of the Mud Volcanoes of Paternò-Sicily." *Proceedings of Scientific Meeting on Seismic Protection; Venezia, 12–13 July,* 171–5.

Dall'Aglio, M., and C. Tedesco. 1968. "Studio geochimico ed idrogeologico di sorgenti della Sicilia." *Rivista Mineraria Siciliana,* n.112–4. *Luglio Dicembre,* 171–210.

Di Rosa, M. 2000. "La fauna neolitica dell'insediamento di San Marco presso Paternò. Nuovi dati." In *La Neolitizzazione tra Oriente ed Occidente,* edited by A. Pessina e G. Muscio, 508–10. Udine.

Iovino, M.R. 2000. "Attività agricole nei siti neolitici della Sicilia orientale: rinvenimenti archeologici e analisi funzionale." In *La Neolitizzazione tra Oriente ed Occidente,* edited by A. Pessina and G. Muscio, 513–22. Udine.

Houel, J. 1977. "Storia di Napoli e della Sicilia." In *Viaggio in Sicilia e a Malta,* edited by G. Macchia, L. Sciascia, and G. Vallet. Palermo and Napoli.

La Rosa, V. 1985 (1987). "Un nuovo insediamento neolitico a Serra del Palco di Milena." *Atti della XXVI Riunione Scientifica dell'Istituto Italiano Preistoria e Protostoria,* 801–8. Firenze.

―――. 1989. "Le popolazioni della Sicilia Sicani, Siculi, Elimi." In *Italia, Omnium Terrarum Parens Antica,* edited by G. Pugliese Carratelli, 3–110. Milano.

Lombardo, T., L. Maniscalco, P. Mazzoleni, and A. Pezzino. 2000. "La produzione delle ceramiche in epoca preistorica dei siti di Marco e Poggio Monaco (Paternò-Catania): Caratterizzazione mineralogica e petrografica." *Bollettino Accademia Gioenia di Scienze Naturali* 33:347–62.

Maniscalco, L. 1985–1986. "Tipologie funerarie nella Sicilia del tardo bronzo: Pantalica, Dessueri, Caltagirone." In *Archivio Storico per la Sicilia Orientale* 81–2, 241–65.

―――. 1996. "The Prehistoric Settlement at San Marco (Paternò, Sicily)." *Abstracts, Annual Meeting of the Archaeological Institute of America,* San Diego. 100: 356.

―――. 1999. "The Sicilian Bronze Age Pottery Service." In *Social Dynamic of the Prehistoric Central Mediterranean,* edited by J. Morter, J. Robb and R. Tykot, 185–94. London.

―――. 2000. "Il neolitico attorno alla piana di Catania: l'insediamento preistorico presso le Salinelle di San Marco (Paternò)." In *La Neolitizzazione tra Oriente ed Occidente,* edited by A. Pessina and G. Muscio, 489–507. Udine.

Maniscalco, L., and B.E. McConnell. 1997–1998. "Ricerche e scavi attorno Palikè." *Kokalos* XLIII–XLIV, II, I: 173–88.

McConnell, B.E. 1992. "The Early Bronze Age Village of La Muculufa and Prehistoric Hut Architecture in Sicily." *AJA* 96:23–44.

Orsi, P. 1921. "Megara Hyblaea Villaggio neolitico e tempio arcaico e di taluni singolarissimi vasi di Paternò." *Monumenti Antichi dei Lincei* 17:109–50.

Palermo, D. 1994. "Paternò." *Bibliografia topografica della colonizzazione greca in Italia e nelle isole tirreniche* XIII:383.

Pappalardo, G., and L. Pappalardo. 1997. "Analisi non distruttive delle ceramiche reistoriche del sitole Salinelle di San Marco (Paternò)." In *Prima Sicilia. Alle origini della società siciliana,* edited by S. Tusa, 199–200. Palermo.

Privitera, F. 1998. "Recent Finds in the Prehistory of Mount Etna, in Volcanoes and History." In *Proceedings of the 20th INHIGEO Symposium, Napoli, Eolie, Catania, Italy, Sept. 1–25, 1995,* 545–53.

Stuiver, M., and P.J. Reimer. 1993. "University of Washington Quaternary Isotope Lab Radiocarbon Calibration Program Rev. 4.0." *Radiocarbon* 35:215–30.

Whitehouse, R. 1992. *Underground Religion.* London.

NOTES

[1] These vessels are on display at the Museo Archeologico Regionale Paolo Orsi.

[2] PIXE Analyses were performed by Prof. G. Pappalardo of LANDIS (Laboratorio di Analisi non Distruttive dell'Istituto di Fisica nucleare dell'Universita' di Catania) and Dr. L. Pappalardo, who also analyzed by x-ray fluorescence clay from these Diana vessels and other vessels from San Marco now located in the Syracuse Museum. This compositional analysis shows little variation among the vessels and suggests that only one or two clay sources may have been utilized (Pappalardo and Pappalardo 1997).

APPENDIX I:

Preliminary Report on the Chipped Stone Tools from Salinelle di San Marco

Fabrizio Nicoletti

This work provides a first look at the chipped stone tools found in the archaeological excavations of 1994–1996 at the site of Salinelle di San Marco near Paternò, Sicily. Apart from erratic finds, our collection includes a Late–Final Neolithic assemblage and an Early Bronze Age assemblage, each of them with their own peculiarities, reflecting coeval prehistoric Sicilian lithic industries and at the same time offering new information.

The lithics appear fresh with only occasional patinas that are often related to more or less intense thermoclastic alteration of small finds from all stratigraphic levels. Flint or chert and quartzite, in about the same percentages, are the most frequent raw materials. The flint, from ancient Miocene geological structures, is always fine-grained and of intermingled shades of yellow, red, gray and black. The chert is much more coarse-grained (resembling a kind of quartzite), gray or brown in color, and is typical of the Upper Cretaceous Sicilian period. Both the flint and chert are in pebble form on the Simeto River alluvial soils, and this is probably the source of the San Marco artifacts. The quartzite, more frequent in the Bronze Age levels, is gray, brown, or green in color and judging from the cortical convexity seems to have the same origin as the flint and chert. Obsidian artifacts are also attested which are black in reflected light (gray in transmitted light), and sometimes containing small pumice spheroids. X-ray fluorescence (XRF) analysis has confirmed that all the obsidian comes from Lipari. Based on the evidence from other Sicilian sites, obsidian is much more frequent in Neolithic levels, where it often forms more than a quarter of the raw materials. Apart from a single core, obsidian has until now been found in the form of simple blanks, evidence of an intrinsic value deriving from the distance of origin. At every level, other kinds of raw materials are found only occasionally. These materials include jasper, siliceous limestone, and basalt, a local volcanic stone especially suitable for polished tool production also used at San Marco in a small number of flaked tools.

Similar flaked cores were found in every level. Discoidal biface cores are the most common for flakes or short blades, especially when the raw material is quartzite; more rarely the same implements were detached from polyhedric cores. Long blades of flint or chert, were detached from prismatic (pyramid-shaped) cores. Core preparation is in every case badly executed, as frequent cortex residuals often on the implement's dorsal surface attest. A better degree of technical elaboration was usually reserved only for blade production, although the small number of faceted platforms and the rare cases of crested blades are exceptions. The clear prevalence of punctiform platforms, and later of plain platforms, suggests an insufficient preparation of fracture planes and a choice of a simple indirect blow alternating with the so-called block against block blow.

The majority of flakes and blades were intentionally broken. More than half of the blanks were broken by bending, but more elaborate techniques were used, though rarely, in the different periods. In the Neolithic, for example, use of the microburin technique is attested by finds of a microburin, bladelets *piquant trièdre,* and geometric microliths. Notches near fractures are used more frequently in the Early Bronze Age.

Many blanks were used with further retouch, most frequently simple and marginal retouch on the blades, and simple and intrusive on the flakes. Specific retouch, like raised, scaled and backed retouch, is limited to some tools, and there are occasional burin spall removals (attested by the presence of a burin spall) and flat retouch. Thus the most frequent tools are those retouched in a simple way, either rectilinearly, like retouched blades and scrapers, or denticulately, like notches, denticulate scrapers, and *epines.* In the latter case the retouch delineation may have been deeply influenced by the tool wear, since the spalls can be alternated on both implement surfaces. Backed retouch, generally deep and unifacial, is generally limited to banal typologies, such as drills and especially truncated blades. Scaled retouch is located mainly on the transverse ends.

These implements, all considered typical, are only indistinctly attested throughout the life of the Salinelle site, but two categories of implements seem to characterize the two different periods of the collection. The so-called sickle elements are more common in the Neolithic than in the Early Bronze Age. From a technical and typological point of view, they are regular blades, broken by bending with simple and marginal retouch, on both sides and on both edges. In some cases the retouch is limited to barely visible abrasion marks; more often the retouch is marked and continuous and takes on a frankly denticulate trend. The association of this denticulate trend with different kinds of retouch is only occasional. The main attribute of sickles from this site is the presence of silver gloss on the functional edges that, unlike that on similar implements known from other parts of Sicily, is discontinuous and hardly visible. It is possible that many of the similarly retouched blades that lack this gloss also had the same function. Use-wear analysis of the implements will test the traditional assumption connecting this special form of wear to grain farming.

Some sickle elements are also attested in Early Bronze Age levels, perhaps as a residual element, but the more characteristic implement in this period, at Salinelle as well as at other coeval Sicilian sites, is the end scraper. This tool type, which can be very large, has convex or ogival raised retouch on the transversal end since the original flake or blade is always particularly thick. A pair of Campignan bifaces (an ax and a pick) found in layers whose dates are not well attested probably also date to this period.

APPENDIX 2:

Anthropological and Paleopathological Analysis of Human Skeletal Remains from San Marco (Paternò-Sicily)

Maurizio Di Rosa

During excavation at Contrada San Marco several tombs with skeletal materials of anthropological interest were discovered. The remains come from a burial dated to the Late Bronze Age (12th–11th centuries B.C.) and could be part of a necropolis. The grave is oval, built of large lava blocks, with an entrance from the south. It contained a funerary bed and cranial and post-cranial fragments which were not anatomically connected and clearly belonged to several individuals, but because of the taphonomic processes and the preservation of the remains, we could not recognize individual skeletons. Considering the scarcity of human skeletal materials dated to the Northern Pantalica Culture, this discovery is of great importance for our knowledge of ancient Sicilian populations.

The presence of multiple but disarticulated remains forced us to calculate the minimum number of individuals buried in the tomb, and after considering size, sex, and age, we concluded that there were at least six. The group includes an infant, an adolescent, and four adults, but remains of infants and juveniles may have been lost because of their fragility and the poor state of preservation. Of the five adult and juvenile skeletons, three have been identified as male, one as female, and one is of uncertain gender.

Cranial Skeleton

Analysis has been possible only for sample b, which is better preserved than the others. It is the calva of an adult identified as male from his overall morphology. The shape of the cranial vault is ovoid and phenozigy is present. In the norma lateralis the vault is uniformly curved with slight clinocephaly, and the glabellar region is bulging. The frontal area is curved backward and there is a faint trace of supraglabellar fossa, the occipital contour being rounded with a fairly good development of the inion. In the norma frontalis we can observe evident superciliary arches and underdeveloped frontal eminencies.

The metrical values (table 7.1) show a short skull (1 MS), broad (8 MS), with a high minimum frontal breadth (9 MS) and medium height at porion (20 MS). The analysis of these values shows that the horizontal cranial index falls into the range of brachycrany, the longitudinal-auricular index is at the upper limit of ipsycrany, the transversal-auricular index indicates metriocrany, and the transversal fronto-parietal index has a value of eurymetopy. The cranial capacity, calculated through the Lee and Pearson formulae, gives a value of 1375 cc, falling into the euencephalic range.

Table 7.1. MS (Martin-Saller, 1957–1959) indices and measurements of skull b.

Indices	Measurement (mm)
1	167
2	155
3	169
8	140
9	102
20	114.8
26	142
27	145
28	114
29	113
30	118
31	89
8/1	83.8
20/1	68.7
20/8	82
9/8	72.8
29/26	79.5
30/27	81.3
31/28	78

Postcranial Remains

In examining the postcranial remains, morphological and morphometrical characters were taken into consideration, with particular attention paid to the analysis of markers of skeletal stress and pathologies. A brief summary of our observations is presented here.

The humeri show eurybrachy, which in some cases is quite evident. Two have values of platibrachy and are quite robust in the male subjects. On the whole, we recorded short humeri with well-marked muscular impressions, especially of the muscles of the scapula-humerus joint such as the deltoid.

The radii have a medium robusticity index while, in relation to the diaphy-seal index, the shaft of this bone at mid-length is flattened. Radial tuberosity and muscular insertion of pronation-supination muscles are sometimes well marked; this could be related to working activities that implied repeated pronation movements of the forearm.

The ulnae are of medium length and are generally robust; their mor-phology shows marked muscular attachments, especially in male subjects. In two cases the triceps brachii and anconaeus muscular impressions devoted to the extension of the forearm can be connected to stress due to the repeated carrying of heavy objects with both arms.

The femora have quite low robusticity indexes and underdeveloped pilasters; most of the specimens are platimeric and one is hyperplatimeric, showing an engagement of the bone of the thigh. The tibiae have mesoc-nemic values and two platicnemic samples. Stature estimation gave an average value of 167 cm.

Paleopathological Observations

The pathological lesions most frequently observed are dental, traumatic, degenerative, and metabolic ones. Some caries were observed, especially on the occlusal surfaces of teeth, indicating a high degree of wear and several cases of periodontal disease, which can be related to the consumption of tough food and/or stone-ground grains with continuous attrition and subse-quent formation of caries and abscesses. Among nutritional and pathological skeletal markers, we record only one case of enamel hypoplasia on an incisor tooth. Healed traumas were recorded, on upper limb bones.

8

The Island of Vivara: An International Port of Trade of the Middle of the Second Millennium B.C. in a Volcanic Landscape

◈

Claudio Giardino and Carla Pepe

Geology of Vivara

Vivara is one of the three islands of the Phlegraean Archipelago. It is linked to the larger island, Procida, by a bridge (figs. 8.1 and 8.2). Originally— and probably up to Roman times—it was connected by a now-submerged isthmus to the Santa Margherita promontory of Procida. This small volcanic island, whose half-moon shape recalls the ancient crater, was probably a promontory of Procida with a strategic position during prehistory. With a height of 120 m, it dominated and controlled both the inlet of the Ischia Channel (the stretch of sea between its western side and the little peninsula on Ischia), and the Procida Channel. From here, any vessel entering the Gulf of Naples from the Punta Campanella could be sighted.

Vivara is the western section of a volcanic tuff caldera; the other surviving section is the promontory of Santa Margherita on the southwestern side of the island of Procida. The islands of Vivara and Procida are both parts of the volcanic district that extends from Ischia to the Phlegraean Fields (fig. 8.1), an area where volcanic phenomena occurred extensively in the late Pleistocene and Holocene, continuing up to the modern period.

The Vivara-Procida area is formed by several eruptions, and has the remains of craters which form semicircular inlets often surrounded by steep cliffs. The oldest of these craters is Vivara itself, while the youngest is the

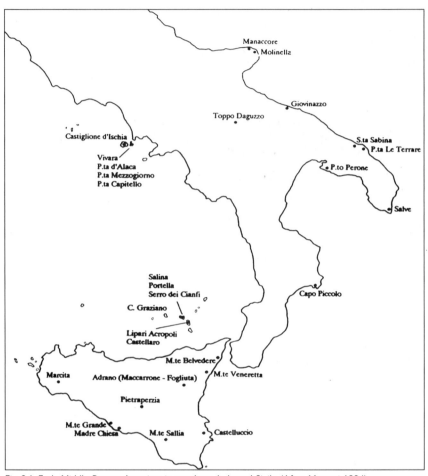

Fig. 8.1. Early Middle Bronze Age sites in southern Italy and Sicily. (After Marazzi 1994)

Solchiaro crater on the east-central side of Procida, produced by an eruption that occurred around 19,000 years ago.

The island emerged from an explosive eruption produced by the interaction of seawater and magma. This led to the formation of the Vivara Tuff, reddish tuff (lapilli-tuff) passing to gray-blackish tuff in the upper strata that forms most of Vivara and Santa Margherita. This initial stage was followed by the partial erosion of the pyroclastic ring. A second explosive eruption, probably from the crater called Formiche di Vivara I, located in the Ischia Channel, created the breccia and tuff, so-called lower pyroclastites of the Ischia Channel, on Vivara. This was followed between 74,000 and 55,000

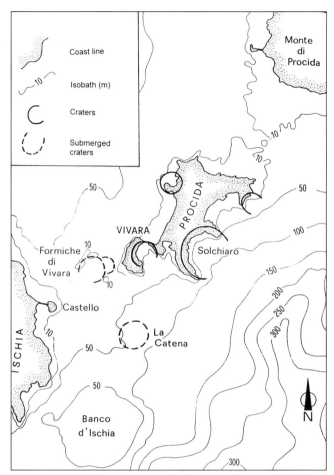

Fig. 8.2. Volcanic craters of the Vivara-Procida area. (After Rosi et al. 1991)

years ago by a sequence of plinian eruptions from Ischia that deposited white trachytic pumice. Another eruption in the Ischia Channel (Formiche di Vivara II) caused a rain of lapilli, bombs, ash, and breccia on the island (the upper pyroclastites). There were long intervals between the eruptions, allowing paleosols to form.

Above the upper pyroclastites of the Ischia Channel we find further levels connected with eruptions on Ischia and the Phlegraean Fields. The pumice and breccia deposit covered by a whitish ash layer of unknown origin probably came from one of the plinian eruptions of Monte Sant'Angelo on Ischia. The so-called Breccia Museo, a characteristic deposit consisting of obsidian,

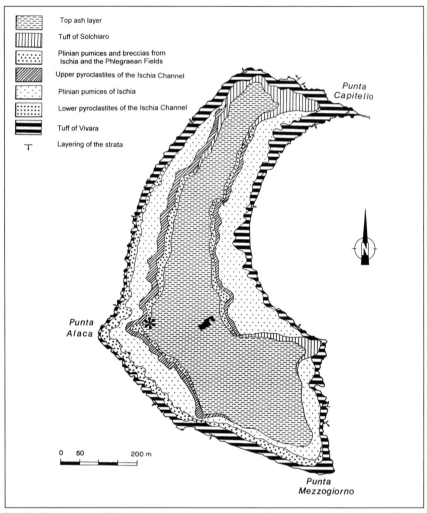

Fig. 8.3. Geologic map of Vivara; the asterisk shows the area of the prehistoric settlement of Punta d'Alaca. (After Rosi et al. 1991)

pumice, debris, and blocks of various types, is linked with the deposition of Campanian Ignimbrite approximately 35,000 years ago and both are related to volcanic activity in the Phlegraean Fields. Partially lithified gray tuff deposits on Vivara date from 19,000 years ago, and are related to the activity of the Solchiaro crater on the island of Procida. The deposition of the light gray top ash layer, produced by a series of separate eruptions on Ischia and in the Phlegraean Fields, began around 14,000 years ago.

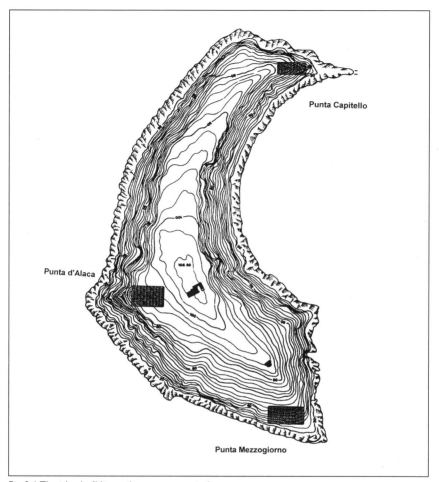

Fig. 8.4. The island of Vivara: the areas excavated.

The Middle Bronze Age site of Punta d'Alaca is located in this top ash layer (fig. 8.3). It is covered by two thin volcanic strata, one consisting of pumice lapilli and the other of white ash. These layers were probably produced by an eruption from Ischia, since they seem to correspond to the ash deposit covering Bronze Age layers at the Colle di Castiglione.

This complex geological background of the island of Vivara has formed the setting where the Bronze Age settlements originated and developed (fig. 8.4). The volcanic and accompanying seismic activity of the entire Phlegraean area must have had significant impact on the life of the inhabitants of these protohistoric settlements.

Historic Framework

After the Middle Bronze Age, there is no further evidence of occupation up to the Archaic period (sixth century B.C.) when pottery typical of the Punta Capitello area and Campanian and early Imperial age ceramics are found.

In 13th- and 14th-century texts and maps we find the name Vivara, evidently associated with the island's function as a vivarium (fish pond). Until the 17th century, Vivara was a sort of hunting reserve and in 1681, a hunting lodge was built on the island's plateau by Don Giovanni di Guevara, Duke of Bovino. Agriculture was initiated and farmers' houses spread around the manor house and over the island.

Around the beginning of the 19th century, two English architects built a round building, originally designed as a house and belvedere, on the south side of the plateau, facing towards Capri. After the island passed from the Bourbons to the Procida municipality in 1818 (fig. 8.5), it was transferred first to the Scotti family by emphyteusis. They later (1868) redeemed it, and Vivara became the site of a French garrison with military structures at both

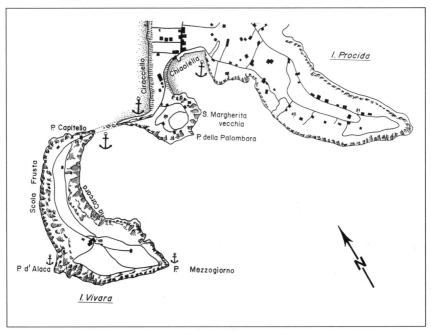

Fig. 8.5. Vivara with the southwestern side of Procida: the anchors show the natural harbors. (After Tusa 1991)

the Punta Mezzogiorno and Punta Capitello. In 1870, the Scotto la Chianca family became the owners of the island. When the family died out in 1940, the island was left to the Albano Francescano Hospital of Procida. Today the island is still owned by the Ente Albano Francescano and has been leased to the Campania Region, which has the task of ensuring that the island is protected as a reserve for Mediterranean fauna and flora.

The Archaeological Research

Because of its peculiar shape, the island could offer any vessel the possibility of docking and haulage at three points, to the north and south of the isthmus joining it with the Santa Margherita promontory and to the south of Santa Margherita in the little gulf of Chiaiolella. All three landing points were clearly visible and could be controlled from the north of the island. Underwater. surveys are currently underway between Vivara and Santa Margherita to reconstruct the original morphology of the area, and the ports and landing sites related to the Bronze Age settlement.

In the mid 1930s, G. Buchner started the first archaeological surveys and exploratory excavations on the island in order to collect data on life in the Phlegraean Archipelago from prehistory to Roman times. His research (Buchner 1936–1937, 1937) showed that the earliest remains of human activity on Vivara date from the early part of the Middle Bronze Age and that the island underwent a period of intensive growth during the Middle Bronze Age. The island became a key trading center for Mediterranean routes thanks to the shape of the old crater, which offered an excellent natural port for ships. After the end of the Bronze Age the island had been uninhabited, except for a few traces of Archaic (sixth century B.C.) and Roman occupation on the northern part of the island (Punta Capitello), until the construction of the manor house on its plateau in 1680. In his exploratory excavation on one of the natural terraces overlooking Punta Capitello, Buchner found a considerable variety of ceramics, which can be attributed to the classical Apennine Culture (corresponding to the Italian late Middle Bronze Age in relative chronology) and to the Proto-Apennine facies (Italian early Middle Bronze Age). Other important finds included two fragments identified as coming from Mycenaean Greece (figs. 8.6–8.8). Their assignment to Late Helladic II/III made them the earliest evidence of Mycenaean navigation in the west. Buchner discovered three more Mycenaean ceramic fragments dating from

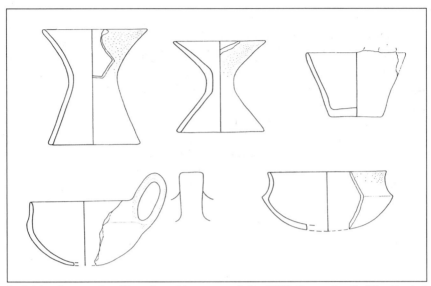

Fig. 8.6. Local pottery from Vivara-Punta Mezzogiorno (Italian Middle Bronze Age 1). (After Damiani et al. 1984)

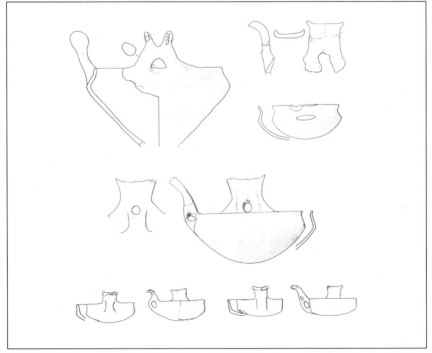

Fig. 8.7. Local pottery from Vivara-Punta d'Alaca (Italian Middle Bronze Age 2). (After Damiani et al.1984)

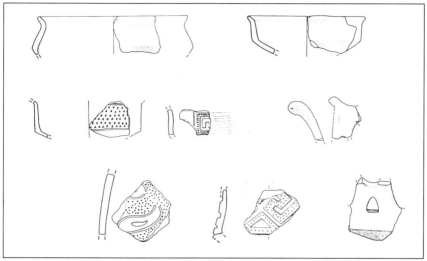

Fig. 8.8. Local pottery from Vivara-Punta Capitello (Italian Middle Bronze Age 3). (After Damiani et al. 1984)

between Late Helladic II/III and IIIA among the Middle Bronze Age local pottery from a settlement on the Castiglione d'Ischia hill (along the coast between Porto and Casamicciola).

These narrow exploratory digs, however fruitful and important, were not followed up in subsequent years. The importance of the Phlegraean area was due to the remains of the oldest Greek emporium, dating to before the early colony of Cuma, discovered between Lacco Ameno and San Montano.

It was not until 1975 that A. Cazzella, M. Marazzi, M. Moscoloni, and S. Tusa resumed research on Vivara under the patronage of the Archaeological Superintendenze for Naples, starting excavations on the two most important settlements on the terraces above Punta Mezzogiorno in the south and Punta d'Alaca in the west. This research, conducted annually until 1982, confirmed and expanded the information from Buchner's excavations (Cazella 1983; Cazella et al. 1975–1980, 1981, 1982, 1986; Cazella and Moscoloni 1991).

Research resumed in 1994 at the Punta d'Alaca site and is currently being conducted by the Vivara Archaeological Mission of the Istituto Universitario Orientale of Naples in collaboration with the Archaeological Superintendence for the provinces of Naples and Caserta, under the guidance of Professor M. Marazzi. The research involves interactive cooperation of experts in various disciplines, including archaeologists, geologists, archaeometallurgists, and archaeometrists.

Excavation Results

Punta Mezzogiorno

The excavations have shown that the most ancient settlement on Vivara dates to the Early to Middle Bronze Age transition in Italy, and is concentrated mainly on Punta di Mezzogiorno.

The earliest layers show traces of frequent contacts with the seafaring culture in the lower Tyrrhenian Sea, exemplified by the Capo Graziano Culture centered in the Aeolian Islands. The earliest traces of contacts with the Aegean appear in the more recent strata, and include significant amounts of fine and cooking pottery (fig. 8.9). They come mainly from the Peloponnesian area, but also from the Kythera workshops and the Cyclades. These ceramics are typical of the transition period from Middle to Late Helladic, the age when the first elite groups appeared.

Punta Mezzogiorno is also the site of the first clear traces of bronze foundries, including a structure probably used for annealing metal and the remains of two crucibles. Investigation on the slaggy patinas on the crucibles using x-ray fluorescence has shown that binary alloys containing copper and tin were processed, evidently to produce bronze objects (fig. 8.10). This metallurgical activity shows that during this period, Vivara (and the Phlegraean Archipelago as a whole) were a part of the seagoing trade linking settlements

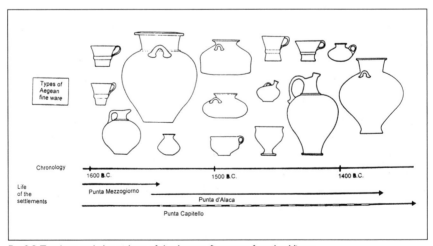

Fig. 8.9. Typology and chronology of the Aegean fine ware found at Vivara

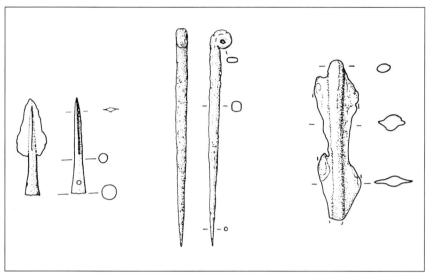

Fig. 8.10. Bronzes from Vivara: arrowhead from Punta Mezzogiorno; pin and blade from Punta d'Alaca

from the north-central Tyrrhenian to Sicily, the Ionian coast, and the Gulf of Taranto, which were in turn linked to the coast of Epirus in the north and Messene in the south.

Punta d'Alaca

Early in the Middle Bronze Age, in a later phase of the Proto-Apennine culture, a new settlement developed at Punta d'Alaca, a terrace dominating the western side of the island and controlling access to the Ischia Channel and to the coast from Aragon Castle to the Monte Vico promontory.

The main settlement on Vivara, occupying the entire top plateau, flourished at the time of the Punta d'Alaca settlement, but it is now lost because of late 17th-century buildings and farming, and only indirect evidence survives in the waste deposits on the western side of the island.

The Punta d'Alaca excavations have brought to light what can be called the peak development of prehistoric culture on Vivara. Relatively limited areas have been excavated because of the fill (both ancient and modern), which in some places is 3 m deep, but the remains and artifacts discovered are of fundamental importance. Remains of rather large rectangular dwellings have been found associated with a small round type possibly used for storage, and have led researchers to regard the site as a rapidly changing community. The roof for one of the huts consisted of tiles made of thin slates from the tuff deposits on Vivara and Procida. The tuff tiles and pumice for sharpening blades are not the only example of the inhabitants' use of local volcanic materials. Numerous obsidian fragments, some of which probably originate locally, have been found at the Punta d'Alaca site. There was a considerable amount of Aegean ware fragments, mainly in the storage areas, along with large jars (fig. 8.9). The chronology ranges from Late Helladic IIA to IIIA1, the period of the formation of Greek-Mycenaean culture from the mid-16th to the mid-15th century B.C. Archaeometric examination shows that some of the Aegean-type fragments were produced locally.

That the Punta d'Alaca settlement must have been directly involved in metal processing is seen from the numerous whole and fragmentary metal works, casting drops, slag, and pumice whetstones for sharpening blades. The metallographic analysis of some of the drops has revealed sulfur compound inclusions in the copper matrix. These traces, discovered by means of scanning electron microscopy, suggest that the copper may have been derived from mixed sulfide ore, totally absent in Campania but common in Tuscany and Sardinia. The search for new metal supplies must have induced the Aegean seafarers to sail west. During this period Vivara was an advanced Mycenaean outpost for collecting metal from the Italian region and among the metal finds there are also Aegean-type weapons such as socketed arrowheads.

The identification of a complex system of calculation and record-keeping by means of pottery tokens—similar to the ones used in the Near East—has shown that in this historical context forms of record-keeping existed despite the lack of writing. Taken as a whole, the data show a community in which there was constant cultural interaction between the Mycenaeans and the local inhabitants.

Conclusions

The fact that Vivara can be considered to be a link in the metal supply route between Europe and western Mediterranean centers and the central and eastern Mediterranean—as well as the destination of the earliest Helladic navigation to the west—has induced researchers to reconsider the theory that western "purchasing markets" for late Middle Helladic and Early Mycenaean centers, together with the gradual entry of the Helladic component into the Levantine and Aegean trade routes, were possible causes of social stratification underway in Greece. The Vivara discoveries have thus provided a highly significant stimulus to research on the earliest Helladic seafaring in the west. Vivara has also provided a unique opportunity to study the duration and extent of late Middle Helladic and Early Mycenaean ceramics manufacturing outside of Greece, since the island, being a destination for Aegean vessels, has an exceptionally extensive, high quality range of ceramics.

REFERENCES

Adinolfi, R. 1982. *I Campi Flegrei nella preistoria (Dal Neolitico medio-superiore al Bronzo finale).* Napoli.

Béguinot, A. 1901. "Contributo alla flora di Procida e di Vivara." *Bullettino della Società Botanica Italiana* 1901:386–99.

Bietti Sestieri, A.M. 1988. "The 'Mycenaean connection' and Its Impact on the Central Mediterranean Societies." *Dialoghi di Archeologia* 6(1):23–51.

Buchner, G. 1936–1937. "Nota preliminare sulle ricerche preistoriche nell'Isola d'Ischia." *BPI* n.s. 1:65–93.

———. 1937. *Vita e dimora umana nelle Isole Flegree, dall'epoca preistorica ai tempi romani (Ischia, Procida, Vivara).* Roma.

Buchner, G., A. Cazzella, F. di Gennaro, M. Marazzi, S. Tusa, and A. Zarattini. 1978. "L'isola di Vivara. Nuove ricerche." *ParPass* 33:197–237.

Capaldi, G., L. Civetta, and P. Gasparini. 1977. "Volcanic History of the Island of Ischia (South Italy)." *Bulletin Volcanologique* 40:1–12.

Cazzella, A. 1983. "Vivara-Punta di Mezzogiorno." *Magna Grecia e mondo miceneo, Atti del XXII Convegno di studi sulla Magna Grecia*, 147–50. Taranto.

Cazzella, A., I. Damiani, F. di Gennaro, M. Marazzi, M. Pacciarelli, P. Petitti, A. Saltini, and S. Tusa. 1975–1980. "Vivara. Terza campagna di ricerca sull'isola." *BPI* 82:167–216.

Cazzella, A., I. Damiani, F. di Gennaro, M. Marazzi, M. Moscoloni, M. Pacciarelli, L. Re, A. Saltini, S. Tusa, and I. Valente. 1982. "Isola di Vivara (Procida, Napoli)." In *Magna Grecia e mondo miceneo. Nuovi documenti*, edited by L. Vagnetti, 141–54. Taranto.

———. 1986. "L'isola di Vivara." In *Traffici micenei nel Mediterraneo. Problemi storici e di documentazione archeologica*, edited by M. Marazzi, S. Tusa, L. Vagnetti, 147–54. Taranto.

Cazzella, A., M. Marazzi, M. Moscoloni, and S. Tusa. 1981. "La preistoria dell'isola." In *Vivara. Oasi di Protezione Naturale*, "Reg. Compania" 105–52. Napoli.

Cazzella, A., and M. Moscoloni. 1991. "Gli scavi alla Punta di Mezzogiorno." In *Vivara. Centro commerciale mediterraneo dell'età del bronzo.* Vol. I, *Gli scavi dal 1976 al 1982*, 48–74. Roma.

D'Erasmo, G., and M.L. Benassai Sgadari. 1958. *Campania. Bibliografia Geologica d'Italia.* Vol. III. Napoli.

Damiani, I., M. Marazzi, M. Pacciarelli, L. Re, and A.C. Saltini. 1985. "L'insediamento preistorico di Vivara." In *Napoli Antica,* 35–50. Napoli.

Damiani, I., M. Pacciarelli, and A.C. Saltini. 1984. "Le facies archeologiche dell'isola di Vivara e alcuni problemi relativi al Protoappenninico B." *AION* 6:1–38.

De Lorenzo, G. 1904. "L'attività vulcanica nei Campi Flegrei." *Rendiconti dell'Accademia della Scienze Fisiche e Matematiche (Napoli)* 10:203–21.

De Lorenzo, G., and C. Riva. 1900. "Il cratere di Vivara nelle isole flegree." *Atti Acc. Sc. Fis. e Mat.* 10:1–60.

Di Girolamo, P. 1981. Lineamenti geologici, vulcanologici e petrografici dell'isola di Vivara." In *Vivara. Oasi di Protezione Naturale,* 19–34. Napoli.

Di Girolamo, P., M.R. Ghiara, L Lirer, R. Munno, G. Rolandi, and D. Stanzione. 1984. "Vulcanologia e petrologia dei Campi Flegrei." *Bullettino della Società Botanica Italiana* 103:349–413.

Di Girolamo, P., and G. Rolandi. 1975. "Vulcanismo sottomarino latitebasaltico-latitico (serie protassica) nel canale d'Ischia (Campania)." *Rendiconti dell'Accademia della Scienze Fisiche e Matematiche (Napoli)* 42:561–96.

Di Girolamo, P., and D. Stanzione. 1973. "Lineamenti geologici e petrologici dell'isola di Procida." *Rendiconti della Società Italiana di Mineralogia e Petrologia* 29:81–125.

Fuchs, C.W.C. 1873. *L'isola d'Ischia, monografia geologica* Mem. per serv. alla descr. carta geol. d'It. 2:1–59. Firenze.

Giardino, C. 1994. "Strategie insediamentali e sviluppi economici nell'area campana del Bronzo medio in relazione ai traffici transmarini." In *Vivara. Centro commerciale mediterraneo dell'età del bronzo.* Vol. II. *Le tracce dei contatti con il mondo egeo (scavi 1976–1982),* 66–98. Roma.

Gregori, B., M. Marazzi, and M. Pacci. 1983. "Le importazioni ceramiche egeo-micenee dall'Isola di Vivara." *Magna Grecia e mondo miceneo. Atti del XXII Convegno di studi sulla Magna Grecia,* 158–82. Taranto.

Jones, R.E. 1994. "Chemical Analysis of the Aegean Painted and Unpainted Wares from Vivara." In *Vivara. Centro commerciale mediterraneo dell'età del bronzo.* Vol. II. *Le tracce dei contatti con il mondo egeo (scavi 1976–1982),* 303–16. Roma.

Mammina, G., M. Marazzi, and S. Tusa. 1990. "Espedienti di computo: il caso di Vivara." *DdA* 8(2):5–48.

Marazzi, M. 1988. "La più antica marineria micenea in occidente." *DdA* 6 (1):5–22.

———. 1994. "Vivara e le prime navigazioni egeo-micenee in occidente." In *Vivara. Centro commerciale mediterraneo dell'età del bronzo.* Vol. II. *Le tracce dei contatti con il mondo egeo (scavi 1976–1982),* 17–39. Roma.

Marazzi, M., and L. Re. 1986. "Importazioni egeo-micenee dall'isola di Vivara (Procida)." In *Traffici micenei nel Mediterraneo. Problemi storici e di documentazione archeologica,* edited by M. Marazzi, S. Tusa, L. Vagnetti, 155–74. Taranto.

Marazzi, M., and Tusa S. 1976. "Nuove testimonianze micenee dall'isola di Vivara." *La Parola del Passato* CLXXI:473–85.

———. 1991. "Relazione preliminare sui lavori nell'isola di Vivara negli anni 1986–1987." *DdA* 9(1–2):111–40.

Pacciarelli, M. 1991. "Le ricerche di superficie." In *Vivara. Centro commerciale mediterraneo dell'età del bronzo*. Vol. I. *Gli scavi dal 1976 al 1982*, 43–7. Roma.

Parascandola, A. 1924. "I crateri dell'isola di Procida." *Boll. Soc. Naturalisti in Napoli* 36:57–60.

———. 1953. "Sui lavori compiuti nell'isola di Procida, nel comprensorio di Monte di Procida, Monte di Cuma, Miseno e Vesuvio, per il foglio 184 della Carta Geologica d'Italia." *Bollettino del Servizio Geologico de Italia* LXXXV(I):766–78.

Pichler, H. 1970. *Italienische Vulkangebiete II. Phlegräische Felder, Ischia, Ponza-Inseln, Roccamonfina (Sammlung geologischer Führer, 52)*. Berlin-Stuttgart.

Rittmann, A. 1950a. "Sintesi geologica dei Campi Flegrei." *Bollettino della Società Geologica Italiana* 69:117–28.

———. 1950b. "Cenni sulla geologia di Procida." *Rivista Geolica Italiana* fasc. III.

———. 1951. "Cenni sulla geologia di Procida." *Bollettino della Società Geologica Italiana* 70:533–44.

———. 1971a. "Introduzione alla Geologia delle Isole Flegree e Ponziane." In *Ricerche contributi e memorie del Centro di Studi su l'Isola d'Ischia, Atti relativi al periodo 1944–1970*, 183–97. Napoli.

———. 1971b. Origine ed evoluzione geo-vulcanologica dell'Isola d'Ischia. In *Ricerche contributi e memorie del Centro di Studi su l'Isola d'Ischia, Atti relativi al periodo 1944–1970*, 695–703. Napoli.

Rittmann, A., and V. Gottini. 1980. "L'isola d'Ischia–Geologia." *Bollettino del Servizio Geologico de Italia* 101:131–274.

Rittmann, A., L. Vighi, F. Falini, U. Ventriglia, and P. Nicotera. 1950. "Rilievo geologico dei Campi Flegrei." *Bollettino della Società Geologica Italiana* 69:117–362.

Rosi, M., and A. Sbrana, eds. 1987. *Phlegraean Fields. Progetto Finalizzato 'Geodinamica', Monografie finali*. Vol. 9, CNR, Quaderni de la Ricerca Scientifica 114. Roma.

Rosi, M., A. Sbrana, and L. Vezzoli. 1991. "Geologia dell'isola di Vivara." In *Vivara. Centro commerciale mediterraneo dell'età del bronzo*. Vol. I *Gli scavi dal 1976 al 1982*, 14–22. Roma.

Tusa, S. 1991. "Geografia e storia." In *Vivara. Centro commerciale mediterraneo dell'età del bronzo*. Vol. I *Gli scavi dal 1976 al 1982*, 7–13. Roma.

Vezzoni, L., ed. 1988. *Island of Ischia. Progetto Finalizzato 'Geodinamica', Monografie finali*. Vol. 10, CNR, Quaderni de la Ricerca Scientifica 114. Roma.

9

Local Volcanic Building Stones
Used in the Construction of Ancient Rome

◆

Donatella De Rita and Ciriaco Giampaolo[*]

Recent Geological Evolution of the Roman Area

The geology around Rome is largely a result of recent geodynamic processes affecting the western Mediterranean area. The geomorphology is mainly due to the Quaternary explosive activity of two volcanic districts, the Sabatini to the northeast and the Colli Albani to the southeast. Both deposited sequences of pyroclastic flows creating a flat and regular morphology that was subsequently deeply excavated by postglacial erosional processes (fig. 9.1).

About one million years ago, the Roman region was still submerged under the Pliocene sea. Outcrops of Pliocene clay and sandy-clay sediments were deposited between 3.40 and 1.79 million years ago (Ma), and compose topographically the highest parts of Rome: the Vatican, the Gianicolo, and Monte Mario. These sediments were deposited in basins developed as a consequence of the Apennine orogeny and the subsequent opening of the Tyrrhenian Sea (Funiciello 1995) and were uplifted to their present position by tectonic processes active during volcanism. The Pliocene clay sediments have a thickness of more than 800 m, and constitute the bedrock of the Roman area; their tectonic and stratigraphical relationships with the younger volcanic sediments strongly influenced the development of Rome, and are responsible for some of the problems affecting the land stability of various sectors in the city (Funiciello 1995).

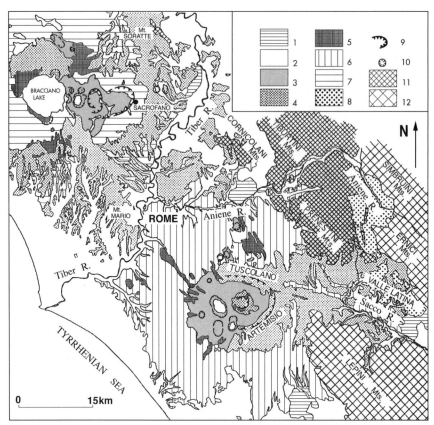

Fig. 9.1. Sketch map of the Roman area. *1*, travertine; *2*, Plio-Pleistocene sedimentary units; *3*, hydromagmatic deposits; *4*, air-fall deposits; *5*, lava flows; *6*, pyroclastic flow deposits from the Colli Albani volcanic district; *7*, pyroclastic flow deposits from the Sabatini volcanic district; *8*, flysch units of Tortonian age; *9*, caldera rim; *10*, crater rim; *11*, Meso-Cenozoic calcareous units of the Cornicolani-Prenestini; *12*, Meso-Cenozoic calcareous units of the Simbruini-Ernici-Lepini. (After De Rita et al. 1992)

The Roman area remained submerged until 0.88 Ma, but during this period several variations in sea level and tectonic processes affected the environment and it was eventually characterized by shallow water sedimentation. Three main marine cycles occurred during this interval. The first, from 3.4 to 1.79 Ma, was characterized by the deposition of clay sediments (Marra et al. 1994); the second by the deposition of sand and sandy clay (Marra 1994), and the third by the deposition of infralitoral clays (Marra 1994). The second and third cycles occurred between 1.79 and 0.88 Ma and were separated by epicontinental sediments, indicating a brief period of subaerial deposition (Funiciello 1995).

At the end of the third cycle the Roman region emerged from a marine environment and continental sedimentary conditions developed (fig. 9.2a; Funiciello 1995). This was an important step in the recent evolution of Rome because the geomorphology of the area began to be transformed by erosional and depositional processes in a manner similar to the present day. At about 0.5 Ma, for example, the paleo-Tevere (Tiber) River shifted from a more eastern course to its present position, mostly because of topographic changes resulting from extensional tectonics affecting the coastal area of Latium, from glacio-eustatic variations of the sea level, and from the emplacement of the oldest pyroclastic flows from the Sabatini and the Colli Albani. The volcanic activity of these two districts started at about 0.6 Ma, and emplaced several intermediate-volume pyroclastic flows most of which reached Rome, creating a wide, flat plateau (fig. 9.2b). Finally, fluvial erosive processes related to the Würm glacial period caused the excavation of deep valleys in the volcanic plateau. These processes formed the famous seven hills upon which Rome began to grow (fig. 9.2c and 9.2d).

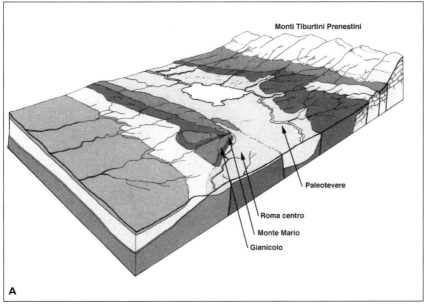

Fig. 9.2. Block diagrams illustrating the geological evolution of the Roman area. A, at about 0.88 Ma, the Roman area emerged from a marine environment and continental conditions began to develop. The paleo-Tiber River was in an easternmost position. B, the volcanic products from the Sabatini volcanic district to the north and from the Colli Albani volcanic district to the south reached the Roman area, strongly modifying the preexisting topography. C, erosional processes related to the Würm glacial period caused the excavation of deep valleys in the volcanic products. D, the erosional processes caused the formation of the seven hills upon which Rome grew. (From Funiciello 1995)

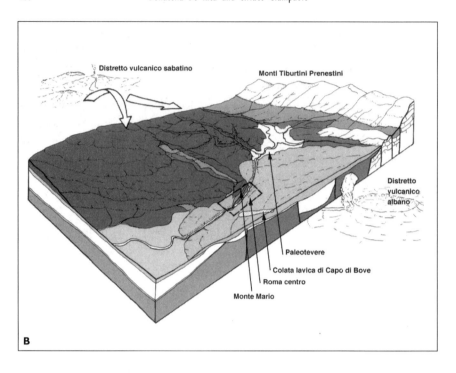

B

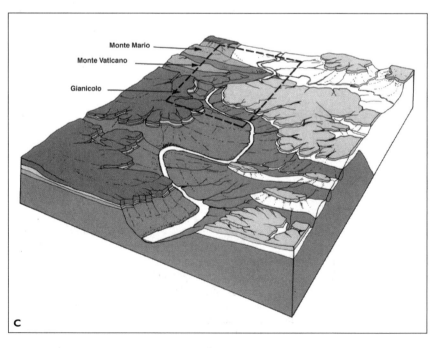

C

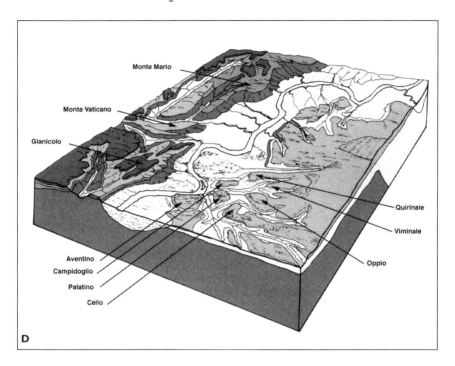

Volcanic Units from the Sabatini and Colli Albani Districts

Most of the volcanic bedrock on which Rome was constructed is from the Colli Albani volcanic district, although some pyroclastic flows from the Sabatini volcanic district reached the northwestern-most part of the present city. Partially reworked airfall deposits from the Sacrofano volcano were the first volcanics emplaced in the Roman area and crop out mainly in the northwestern sector of Rome. The first lithotype used in Rome is the *tufo pisolitico*, which is the oldest pyroclastic flow from the central Tuscolano-Artemisio volcano of the Colli Albani district (De Rita et al. 1988). The tufo pisolitico is not a single unit, but is the result of subsequent pyroclastic flows erupted less than 0.6 Ma during the first and second cycles of the Tuscolano-Artemisio eruptive epoch (De Rita et al. 1988, 1995; Rosa 1995). These two cycles were separated by a long period of quiescence, evidenced by the presence of a paleosol. During both the eruptions, magma-water interactions

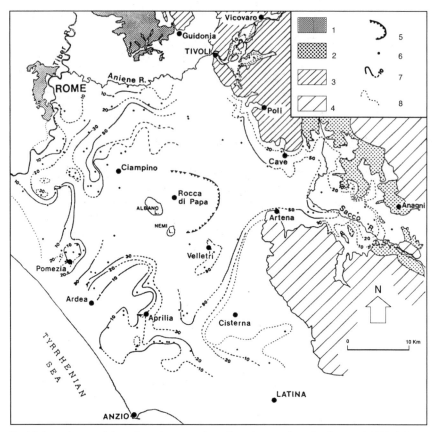

Fig. 9.3. Isopach map of the *tufo pisolitico* pyroclastic flow deposits from De Rita et al. 1992. *1*, Plio-Pleistocene sedimentary units; *2*, flysch of Tortonian age; *3*, Meso-Cenozoic pelagic units; *4*, Meso-Cenozoic calcareous units; *5*, caldera rim; *6*, location of wells; *7*, isopachs in meters; *8*, limit of the tufo pisolitico tuff.

occurred as evidenced, inter alia, by the fine grain size of the units, the presence of "accretionary lapilli" (from which the name pisolitico is derived), cross-bedded stratification of the pumice layers, and zeolite alteration of the glassy matrix containing chabasite and phillipsite (Fornaseri et al. 1963).

The eruptions emplaced intermediate volume pyroclastic flows with a thickness of about 5–10 m as far as the Tiber River, (fig. 9.3; De Rita et al. 1995). The thickness of the tufo pisolitico units is greatest within paleovalleys, which were in some cases completely filled by the pyroclastic flows. This is visible within the Capitoline area in the historical center of Rome where outcrops suggest that the tufo pisolitico filled a paleovalley, located approximately in the position of the Roman Forum. The valley was completely filled by this volcanic deposit and the river course was shifted toward the present street of the Imperial Fora.

Almost contemporaneously other similar pyroclastic flows from the eastern sector of the Sabatini volcanic district reached the northwestern part of the present area of Rome. This yellow *tufo della Via Tiberina,* which is a pyroclastic flow deposit originating from the Sacrofano volcano, located about 30 km to the north of Rome (fig. 9.4; De Rita et al. 1993). The eruption, dated at 500,000 B.P., most likely involved the partial interaction of water and rising magma and caused the deposition of more than one flow unit—Cioni (1993) recognized at least seven units—that covered a surface of more than 400 km^2 and attained a total volume equal to approximately 8 km^3 (De Rita et al. 1993; Rosa 1995). The considerable quantity of erupted material had a significant impact on the geomorphology, including the obstruction of the Tiber River near Monte Soratte and the shifting of its valley toward the east, approximately coincident with its present course (Alvarez 1972, 1973; Rosa 1995). After the emplacement of these units there was a period of volcanic quiescence, when the Roman area experienced local tectonism and intense fluid circulation that deposited travertine and altered sands. The circulation of the altering fluids probably was facilitated by the presence of north–south faults partially responsible for the deviation of the course of the Tiber (Funiciello 1995).

With a cyclicity of almost 100,000 years (De Rita et al. 1994), a sequence of pyroclastic flows from the Colli Albani volcanic district next reached the Rome area. The oldest of these units is called *pozzolane rosse* or *il colata piroclastica del Tuscolano-Artemisio volcano.* It represents the most important explosive event in the life of the volcano, having a volume of more than 34 km^3 (De Rita et al. 1988). The deposit is composed of red-pink scoria in a loose scoriaceous matrix with free crystals of leucite, pyroxene, and biotite and containing characteristic thermo-metamorphosed sedimentary lithics. Gas escape structures such as those inside the present city area are typical, even at great distances (more than 20 km) from the vent localities. The *pozzolane rosse* and the subsequent *pozzolane nere,* which is lithologically very similar, are separated by reworked volcanics and alluvial sediments, indicating a quiescent period between the two eruptions, and both have been quarried since Roman times and used to make cements. A complex eruption deposited two important flow units, the *tufo lionato* and the *tufo di Villa*

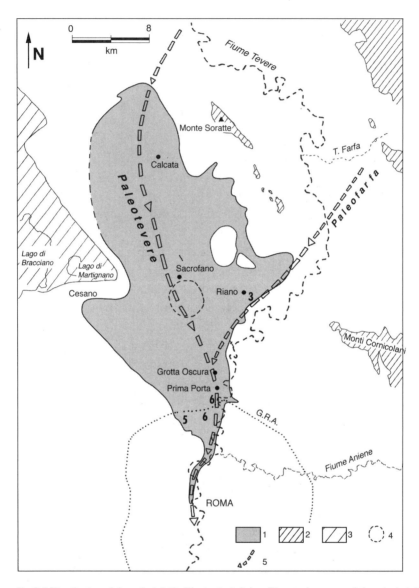

Fig. 9.4. Distribution of the *tufo della Via Tiberina* ignimbrites. The emplacement of these ignimbrites caused the movement of the Tiber valley toward the east (from Rosa 1995). Before the emplacement of the tufo della Via Tiberina, the Tiber course was in the position indicated by number 5. The infilling of the valley by the tuff deposits shifted the course at the present position indicated by the dashed line. *1*, extension of the tuff; *2*, calcareous sedimentary units of pelagic sequences; *3*; flysch units buried below volcanics, delimiting topographic high areas not reached by the flow units; *4*, location of the vent of the tufo della Via Tiberina; *5*, ancient courses of the paleo-Tiber and paleo-Farfa rivers. Numbers refer to the maximum size in cm of the three lithics.

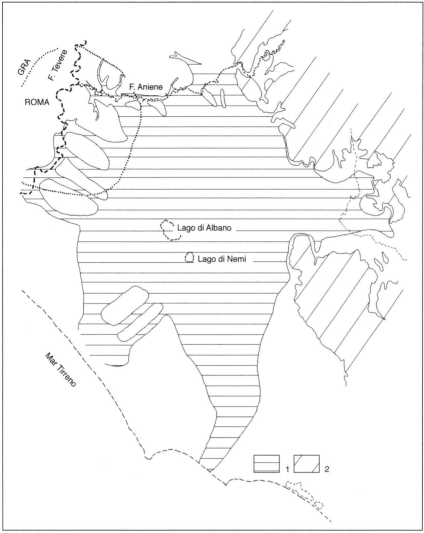

Fig. 9.5. Distribution of the *tufo lionato*. The figure shows the extension of the unit around the volcano. *1*, extension of the tufo lionato pyroclastic flow units; 2, sedimentary units.

Senni, which both reached Rome at 336,000 B.P. (fig. 9.5). This eruption concluded the activity of the Tuscolano-Artemisio volcano and caused the collapse of the central part of the edifice (De Rita et al. 1988; Funiciello 1995). The lithological and depositional characteristics of the tufo lionato indicate that it sustained limited water-magma interaction during eruption,

whereas its high degree of lithification is due to zeolitic alteration, to her-
scelite, chabasite and phillipsite (Fornaseri et al. 1963) of the glassy matrix.
The litoide flow was deposited in the valley previously filled by the tufo
pisolitico. When this area was eventually excavated to form the present
Velabro Valley, the pisolitico and the upper litoide ignimbrite plateau were
isolated, constituting the famous *Rupe Tarpea.*

After these eruptions, activity of the Colli Albani and of the Sabatini volcanic districts decreased and explosive activity was localized close to the central area of the volcanoes. Only the southeastern periphery of the Roman
area, close to the Cecilia Metella Tomb, was overrun around 280,000 years
B.P. by a huge lava flow named *Colata di capo di Bove* (Bernardi et al. 1982),
which forms one of the most impressive extrusions of the Faete edifice in the
central area of the Colli Albani (fig. 9.6, De Rita et al. 1988). The lava was
channeled in a valley that was almost radial to the central volcanic structure
and extended 20 km to the area on which Rome was eventually built. The
flow was named after the ox head perched on the Tomb of Cecilia Metella,
built at the distal end of the flow. *Cecilite* was the earlier scientific name of
this aphyric variety of melilite leucitite. The highly undersaturated chemistry
of the lava permitted it to flow great distances from its eruptive vent and
allowed it to form a very smooth and flat upper surface, a feature which the
Romans used for the famous Appia Antica road surface.

During the first part of the Imperial period, Romans frequently used volcanic building blocks, called *peperino,* which were quarried further from the
city. The name peperino refers to two different lithotypes: *lapis Gabinus* and
lapis Albanus. Both these deposits are the result of violent hydromagmatic
eruptions, the former related to the Gabii or Castiglione crater and the later
related to the Albano crater. The eccentric Castiglione and Albano craters were
formed as a result of the final hydromagmatic activity of the Colli Albani volcanic district (De Rita et al. 1988, 1995) active between approximately
200,000 B.P. and the late Pleistocene. Lapis Albanus developed from a detrital
flow deposit erupted from the Albano crater during its final phase, at least
20,000 years ago (Mercier 1993). The two lithotypes have very similar litholo-
gies and have, as their principal characteristic, a high level of lithification due
to the presence of zeolites of chabasite, phillipsite, and harmotome derived
from the alteration of volcanic glass in the rock matrix.

Finally, in the Imperial period another kind of stone, named *sperone* was
used in the construction of the Colosseum. Sperone is a welded scoria

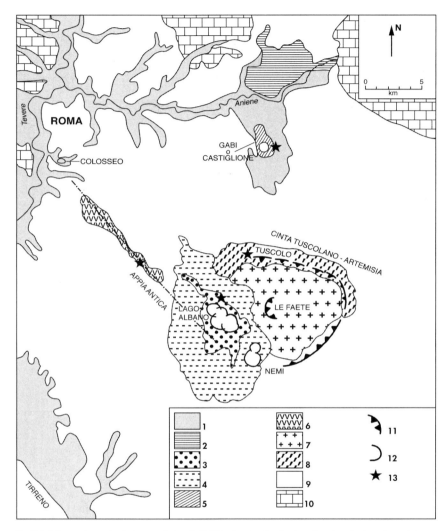

Fig. 9.6. Schematic geological map of the Colli Albani volcanic district, showing the location of the Capo di Bove lava flow, coinciding with the route on which the ancient via Appia was built. The Gabii and Albano craters with the distribution of their products and the location of identified roman quarries, and the Tuscolo locality are shown. *1*, alluvia; *2*, travertine; *3*, distribution of the volcanic units from which *lapis Albanus* is quarried; *6*, Capo di Bove lava flow; *7*, deposits of the Le Faete edifice; *8*, spatter scoria deposits (*sperone*); *9*, deposits of the Tuscolano-Artemisio edifice; *10*, sedimentary units; *11*, caldera rim; *12*, craters; *13*, location of the ancient Roman quarries.

deposit resulting from fountains of lava, erupted from the fractures which controlled the collapse of the central part of the Colli Albani volcano (fig. 9.6), less than 336,000 years ago (De Rita et al. 1988, 1995). These rocks compose the entire northern border of the Tuscolano-Artemisio belt and are located at an elevation of between 200 and 600 m.

Development of Rome and Use of Building Stones

An ancient morphological map (fig. 9.7) clearly shows that Rome developed mainly on the southeastern margin of the present city and that the seven hills are located on the east side of the Tiber River valley. At present, most of the hills are not recognizable because of urbanization. The most ancient part of the city grew at the foot of the Capitoline and Palatine hills, next to the Isola Tiberina, in a place where crossing the river Tiber was easiest. Shortly thereafter, the Romans moved to the top of the hills because of their defensible position and because of better climatic conditions. This geographical situa-

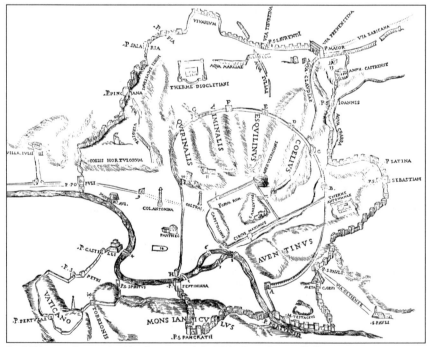

Fig. 9.7. Ancient Roma edited by Gamucci in A.D. 1565. (From Fruitaz 1962)

tion helped to encourage the rapid development of Rome. During the Archaic period (third to fourth century B.C.), large erosional blocks on the sides of the valleys were used as building stones, defensive walls, and shelters. It is not surprising that the oldest structures used tuff blocks excavated from within the growing city. Because of the limited excavation and transport capabilities of more ancient Romans, the areas of rock supply and habitation overlap.

Tufo Pisolitico or Cappellaccio

During the Archaic period the most commonly used stone was *cappellaccio* or tufo pisolitico. The name cappellaccio has been improperly used to indicate several different volcanic tuffs. Quarrymen used cappellaccio for any friable and/or weathered volcanic rock, without any specific reference to a particular lithology or stratigraphic unit. This is probably the origin of the confusion within the archaeological literature regarding cappellaccio as a rock type. In some cases, for example, cappellaccio indicates building stones of the litoide or lionato pyroclastic flow unit. For these reasons we prefer tufo pisolitico, and we propose to drop the term cappellaccio. Although the physical-mechanical characteristics of tufo pisolitico are inferior to those building stones used subsequently (see table 9.1), the ease of excavation and limited amount of transport made this material an efficient choice in the Archaic period.

Many examples of the use of the pisolitico blocks as building stones are still visible in Rome, but probably the most significant example is illustrated by the Mura Serviane (Servian Wall), the first defensive wall constructed around Rome (fig. 9.8). Some of the quarries that supplied building stone for the wall

Table 9.1. Main Physical-Mechanical Characteristics of Volcanic Rock Types Used as Building Stones

	Weight per Unit of Volume Kg/m³	Compression Breaking Load Kg/cm²	Compression Breaking Load after Imbibition Kg/cm²	Imbibition Coefficient Weight %
Tufo Pisolitico	1300 ÷ 1500	90 ÷ 100	–	–
Tufo Lionato	1460 ÷ 1850	52 ÷ 115	59 ÷	6 ÷ 14
Tufo della Via Tiberina	1340 ÷ 1710	70 ÷ 127	55 ÷ 171	5
Sperone	2037 ÷ 2131	106 ÷ 158	133	7.7
Lapis Gabinus	1950 ÷ 2440	154 ÷ 193	149 ÷ 167	17.6
Lapis Albanus	1540 ÷ 2180	55 ÷ 130	58 ÷ 145	6.3 ÷ 4.0
Travertine	2424	572	657	1.4
Leucitite	2810	2856	–	0.73

Fig. 9.8. Mura Serviane along via Salandra.

Fig. 9.9. An Archaic cistern excavated in the tufo pisolitico and covered by blocks of the same material.

are still recognizable in archaeological excavations below Termini railway station. Many other constructions of the Archaic period preserved near the Roman Forum were built of tufo pisolitico (Lugli, 1957, 452). For example, an archaic cistern was excavated in the tuff and its walls were covered over by small blocks of the same material (fig. 9.9). The earliest hut village at the top of the Palatine hill was set into tufo pisolitico.

The Yellow Tufo Della Via Tiberina

With technological advance and the expansion of their territory, Romans began using small blocks of tuff from outside the city in their buildings. One of the first lithotypes substituted for the tufo pisolitico was the yellow tufo della Via Tiberina, which crops out to the north of Rome at Grotta Oscura (Coarelli 1974 and references) along the Via Tiberina.

Because the physical and mechanical characteristics of the tufo della Via Tiberina are significantly better than those of the tufo pisolitico (table 9.1; Nappi et al. 1979) the tufo della Via Tiberina was commonly used as an

Fig. 9.10. Serviane restored with blocks of tufo della Via Tiberina, Aventino.

ornamental or building stone for houses. It is important to note that the use of this tuff became common only after the Roman conquest of Veii, the city that dominated the region rich in this resource (Coarelli 1974 and references).

The use of this tuff in Roman buildings during the entire Roman period is well documented. The basal plate of the Lapis Niger in the Roman Forum, for example, is made of yellow tufo della Via Tiberina (Lugli 1957, 106), but the first use of this tuff was the restoration of the Servian Wall after 390 B.C., following the damage caused to the original wall by the Gallic invasion. Where presently visible (fig. 9.10) the wall is constructed of rows of blocks 59 cm high alternately placed horizontally and vertically, creating a structure that is up to 10 m high and sometimes greater than 4 m thick (Coarelli 1974 and references). The reconstructed rock junctions do not always fit together perfectly, indicating that the restoration took place simultaneously in various locations. The total length of the wall has been calculated at around 11 km, encompassing a surface of 426 ha and enclosing Rome as it became the largest city on the Italian peninsula during the Republican epoch.

The Capo Di Bove Lava Flow (Melilite Leucitite)
The Romans continued to obtain building stones of optimal physical and mechanical characteristics during the Republican Period at the end of the fourth century, as demonstrated by the extensive use of lava blocks for paving stone. The via Appia, the consular road between Rome and the Colli Albani area, was built in this period directly on the upper surface of the Capo di Bove lava flow (fig. 9.11) and many other examples of lava roads are visible inside and outside the city. The Capo di Bove lava continues to be

used for small truncate square pyra-
mids, called *sampietrini* and for *opus
incertum* and *opus reticulatum.*

Peperino and the Tufo Lionato

During the Imperial period, which
began a long period of prosperity,
Rome greatly extended its dominion
across the entire Mediterranean area,
and the Romans imported many
exotic stones for ornamentation and
construction of both their public
and private buildings. Many of these
buildings, however, still used local
building stones for their foundations
and internal structures. The monuments of this epoch used four principal types of volcanic building stone
from the Roman area: tufo lionato
(or litoide), peperino (lapis Gabinus
and lapis Albanus) and the sperone
tuffs.

Fig. 9.11. Lava blocks of the Capo di Bove lava
flow deposit used for paving the ancient via
Appia.

The most significant examples are visible in the Roman Forum, where the
temple of Antoninus and Faustina was constructed in part with lapis
Albanus (fig. 9.12). The Forum of Augustus was largely created using lapis
Gabinus and the tufo lionato (or litoide), with the latter unit also being used
for the Forum and as a base for the Temple of Mars Ultor (fig. 9.13). Lapis
Gabinus also forms the foundation and walls of the Tabularium. The contemporaneous use of lapis Gabinus and tufo lionato suggests that the two
lithotypes were quarried in adjacent areas of the Colli Albani volcanic district. In fact, the lapis Gabinus quarries occur along the border of the
Castiglione crater (in the northern sector of the district near the Aniene
River), not far from the tufo lionato quarries located along Via Tiburtina. It
is highly probable that the Anio River was the most direct route for transporting these two lithotypes from the countryside to the city. The tufo
lionato stone used during the Imperial period was most likely excavated in
the Settecamini area *(tufo dell'Aniene)*; other quarries were located closer to

Fig. 9.12. Temple of Antoninus and Faustina inside the Roman Forum. The structure of the temple is made by blocks of lapis Albanus.

Fig. 9.13. Forum of Augustus. The wall and the base of the Temple of Mars Ultor were created using blocks of *lapis Gabinus* and of tufo lionato.

the city at the foot of the Monteverde hill (*tufo di Monteverde*). The tufo lionato at Monteverde was not quarried extensively because it was not of high quality and also because the deposit on Monteverde hill is in direct contact with clay and alluvial sediments and is therefore at risk for major landslides. The Roman quarries of lapis Albanus were located along the northern borders of the Albano crater, near the city of the same name, or in the valley below the town of Marino. Lapis Albanus differs from lapis Gabinus because it was excavated until the end of the most recent epoch and is still mined to a limited extent today.

Sperone

The structural base of the Colosseum, the monument that represents the most important symbol of imperial Rome, was constructed with travertine and sperone. Although no definitive Roman quarries have been found, it is highly probable that the original source of sperone was located near the

Fig. 9.14. Tuscolo locality.

towns of Grottaferrata and Frascati, close to the principal transportation routes to Rome, but now obliterated as a result of the growth of these two cities. Sperone has optimum physical and mechanical properties because of the welding of the scoria during its formation. It is likely that its use was limited because of the difficult access and transportation from the quarries to Rome. All the depositional and lithological characteristics of sperone can be clearly observed in the Tuscolo area, one of more impressive localities related to the history of Rome in the Colli Albani volcanic region (fig. 9.14). The perfectly preserved remains of a Roman village and a small theater built entirely with sperone are still visible at this location.

After the Imperial period, the study of volcanic rocks used as building stones in Rome becomes nearly impossible for several reasons. As the Romans began to use manufactured bricks as their most important construction materials they also commonly reused the stones of more ancient monuments that were either deteriorated with age or demolished by subsequent emperors. The borders and power of the Roman Empire were by this point so vast that the import and use of stone from around the Roman world was very extensive. This extensive interaction between humans and their environment reflected the power of Rome.

Conclusion

In terms of the petrography, the lithotypes used for construction in Rome show comparable physical and mechanical characteristics (Penta 1956), and all have an elevated level of lithification owing to zeolites, the minerals that formed as a result of alteration of the glassy matrix. Furthermore, all units were produced by eruptions that involved, to different extents, the interaction of rising magma and ground water. These observations are important in the research and characterization of the building stones and underscore the necessity for humankind to clearly understand its environment in order to obtain the best resources from it.

The use of volcanic stone as a construction material responded through time to the needs of the evolving Roman civilization, giving further confirmation to the inseparable bond between humanity and nature. In this chapter, we identified seven important volcanic building stones that were used in the construction of many of the important monuments of ancient Rome. The types of stones used by the Romans to build, protect, and beautify the city closely followed their territorial expansion and technological development. With time, rocks with increasingly better physical and mechanical characteristics were chosen and excavated at increasingly greater distances from their building sites in ancient Rome. Each monument represents the history of a period or of a fundamental phase in the evolution of Roman civilization.

REFERENCES

Alvarez, W. 1972. "The Treia Valley North of Rome: Volcanic Stratigraphy, Topographic Evolution and Geological Influences on Human Settlement." *Geologica Romana* 11:153–76.

———. 1973. "Ancient Course of the Tiber River Near Rome: An Introduction to the Middle Pleistocene Volcanic Stratigraphy of Central Italy." *Geological Society of America Bulletin* 84:749–58.

Bernardi, A., D. De Rita, R. Funiciello, F. Innocenti, and I.M. Villa. 1982. "Geology and Structural Evolution of Alban Hills Volcanic Complex, Latium, Italy." *Workshop on Explosive Volcanism* (abstract). Italy.

Cioni, R. 1993. "Il Complesso Di Bolsena E Il Vulcanismo Alcalino-Potassico Del Lazio Settentrionale." Tesi Di Dottorato V Ciclo. Università di Pisa.

Coarelli, F. 1974. *Guida Archeologica Di Roma*. Roma.

De Rita, D., R. Funiciello, and M. Parotto. 1988. *Carta Geologica Del Complesso Vulcanico Dei Colli Albani*. Roma.

De Rita, D., R. Funiciello, and C. Rosa. 1992. "Volcanic Activity and Drainage Network Evolution of the Colli Albani Area (Rome, Italy)." *Acta Vulcanologica* 2:185–98.

De Rita D., R. Funiciello, L. Corda, A. Sposato, and U. Rossi. 1993. "Volcanic Units." In *Sabatini Volcanic Complex*, edited by Michele Di Filippo, 33–78. CNR Quaderni de la Ricerca Scientifica 11. Roma.

De Rita D., S. Milli, C. Rosa, F. Zarlenga, and G.P. Cavinato. 1994. "Catastrophic Eruptions and Eustatic Cycles: Examples of Latium Volcanoes." *Atti del Convegno dei Lincei* 112, *Int. Symp.* 136:142.

De Rita, D., C. Faccenna, R. Funiciello, and C. Rosa. 1995. "Stratigraphy and Volcano-Tectonics." In *The Volcano of the Alban Hills,* edited by Raffaello Trigila. Roma.

Fornaseri M., A. Scherillo, and U. Ventriglia. 1963. *La Regione Vulcanica Dei Colli Albani*. Roma.

Fruitaz, A.P. 1962. *Le piante di roma*. Roma.

Funiciello, R. 1995. *La Geologia Di Roma*. Roma.

Lugli, G. 1957. *La Tecnica Edilizia Romana Con Particolare Riguardo A Roma E Lazio*. Roma.

Marra, F. 1994. "Stratigrafia Ed Assetto Geologico-Strutturale Dell'area Romana Compresa Tra Il Tevere Ed Il Rio Galeria." *Geol. Rom.* 29:515–35.

Marra, F., C. Rosa, D. De Rita, and R. Funiciello. 1994. "Stratigraphic and Tectonic Features of the Middle Pleistocene Sedimentary and Volcanic Deposits in the Area of Roma Italy." *Quaternary International* 47/48:51–63.

Mercier, N. 1993. "The Thermoluminescence Dating Technique: Applications and Possibilities." *Quaternary Stratigraphy in Volcanic Areas, Rome: September 20–22* (abstract).

Nappi G., G. De Casa, and E. Volponi. 1979. "Geologia e Caratteristiche Tecniche Del 'Tufo Giallo Della Via Tiberina'." *Bollettino della Società Geologica Italiana* 98:431–45.

Penta, F. 1956. "Materiali Da Costruzione Del Lazio." *La Ricerca Scientifica* 26:11–201.

Rosa, C. 1995. "Evoluzione Geologica Quaternaria Delle Aree Vulcaniche Laziali: Confronto Tra Il Settore Dei Monti Sabatini E Quello Dei Colli Albani." Tesi di Dottorato di ricerca in Scienze della Terra dell'Università degli Studi di Roma La Sapienza, VII ciclo.

NOTES

* The authors wish to thank Marie Jackson for many important discussions and suggestions, which strongly improved the manuscript. The figures have been drawn by Decographic of Rome.

10

Pozzolana: The Contribution of the Volcanic Landscape to the Creation of a New Architectural Aesthetic

◈

Miriam S. Balmuth

Three centuries of growing comprehension of the properties of the volcanic landscape resulted in a new use of construction materials. The subsequent exploitation of these properties is visible in experimentation and improvement in building techniques begun by the second century B.C. and continued to the first century A.D. The evolution of Roman wall construction from *opus incertum* and *opus reticulatum* involves the use of a rubble core (*caementum*) faced with a veneer of pyramidal pieces of tuff (*tufa*) with pointed ends fixed in the core. Baked brick (*opus testaceum*) followed tuff in the development of facings (figs. 10.1–10.3).

The mortar of the core had initially been composed of an aggregate (*materia*) of broken stone and ceramic, mixed with lime (*calx*) and mud. It should come as no surprise that these architectural advances spread primarily in Italy. A plastic, moldable material for shaping space was at hand precisely because of the volcanic landscape: *pozzolana* (*pulvis Puteolanus*), the dust from lava flows, was first isolated and exploited in the countryside of Campania, the home of Vesuvius and other volcanoes. It was praised in the first century B.C. by Vitruvius (*De Arch.* 2.4.2) in his discussion of the composition of the rubble core, in which he claims that pit-sand (*harena fossica*) and sea-sand (*harena marina*) both have advantages and disadvantages, but that volcanic dust has the overriding advantage, "quod efficit naturaliter res admirandas. . . ." It is likely

Fig. 10.1. Opus incertum.

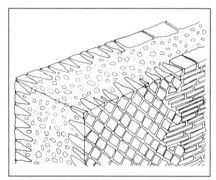

Fig. 10.2. Opus reticulatum.

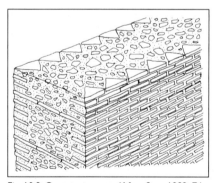

Fig. 10.3. Opus testaceum. (After Sear 1982, 74, fig. 40)

that when seaside buildings were being constructed at Puteoli early in the second century B.C. (Blake 1947, 346), the hydraulic quality of *pulvis Puteolanus* was first appreciated as the most useful for mixing with lime mortar to produce a concrete that hardened even under water *etiam... sub aqua solidescunt* (Vitr., *De Arch.* 2.6.1), making it an ideal material for the construction of harbors and bridges. The widespread recognition of this quality was responsible for its importation for use in construction as distant as Herod's Harbor at Caesarea in Palestine and as early as the first century B.C.

Pozzolana was available in the province of Latium as well as in Campania. Although it had initially been imported to Rome from Campania, the local pozzolana was regularly used in the capital by the time of Augustus in the first century B.C., (Ward-Perkins 1981, 98, quoting Pliny, *N.H.* 16.202). Vitruvius (*De Arch.* 2.6.2) also mentions pumice (*pumex*) or spongestone (*spongia*), a lighter product of volcanism that he knew primarily from the area around Vesuvius (*pumex Pompeianus*), Etna, and on the hills of Mysia.

At first pozzolana was mixed with random rubble and used as the filling of the tuff-crusted sandwich that characterized the walls of Roman Republican buildings from the second century B.C. onward. Gradually it supplemented and then almost entirely replaced the debris of the aggregate filling, so that by the early first century B.C., its strength enabled the shaping of curvilinear elements and vaults that enhanced elaborate villas and added dimensions to the grand sanctuaries at the time of the dictator Sulla, around 80 B.C. The evolution of the *opera* facings has been accurately traced and dates the accessibility to Rome of areas that produced the types of tuff used (Frank 1924; DeRita, this volume). Combined with baked brick, the successor of the tuff facings (fig. 10.3), the pozzolana-assisted mortar allowed for the subsequent development of curving walls, vaulted ceilings, and ultimately of domes.

At one time, it was customary to present Roman features in art and architecture as imitations of the Greek. The Roman temple, however, is more derivative of the Etruscan in orientation and in aspects of the religion that shaped it. The Greek temple can best be understood as sculptural because of its emphasis on external design, including texture and color; the space in the interior is almost negligible. In Roman buildings, both public and private, the emphasis is on space, both interior and exterior.

The Greek temple is columned on four sides and gives an impression of visual symmetry; the Roman temple stands higher on a podium, thereby emphasizing frontality. It has a wider porch and faces a space on the ground, allowing the performance of such rites as reading the sky and its reflection on land for divine omens. It often has free-standing columns only in front, with any that might be on the side and back engaged. The inner chamber, the *cella*, is generally single in Greek temples, accommodating a cult image, but is single or triple in Etruscan and Roman temples. In the architecture of temples, however, the resemblance between Greek and Roman is superficial except for Roman imitations of the externals of Greek temples and Greek decorative motifs, which eventually became more historical or respectful than merely imitative (MacDonald 1982, 180).

In treating Greek and Roman architecture, sanctuaries rather than temples allow a better comparison and contrast. The earliest Greek sanctuaries to which religious pilgrimages were made from the eighth century B.C. onward, had begun, like temples, with an open-air altar and a stoa, used for shelter from the elements. By the later centuries B.C., however, rather than being fossilized like temples, the external space configuration of the Greek *stoai* as well as the areas that they enclosed had been altered in the course of development. The presence of Roman businessmen at the Agora of the Italians on the Greek island of Delos, and of Greek artists and philosophers

Fig. 10.4. Lindos. (After MacKendrick 1981, 420, fig. 7.15)

in Campanian villas, illustrate the cultural interaction of the time, further showing ways in which the two civilizations were approaching each other towards the end of the millennium.

Hellenistic sanctuaries of the third and second centuries B.C., such as the Sanctuary of Athena Lindia at Lindos on the island of Rhodes and the Sanctuary of Asklepios on the island of Kos, provide comparisons to their Roman counterparts in their use of ascending levels, staircases, terraces, and small shrines above. The dramatic effect of changing views and the play of light and shadow on the ascending levels afforded the pilgrims a sequence of experiences. A Roman sanctuary in the early first century B.C., the Sanctuary of Fortune at Praeneste in Latium, was close in architectural spirit to the contemporary Greek sanctuaries. The scenographic qualities of rising height against the sea were enhanced by the ability to shape space, both laterally and vertically. The comparison of the complex at Lindos with that at Praeneste shows similarities such as Roman-style arches at ground level (figs. 10.4–10.5). What does not show, however, is the critical difference: brick vaults at Lindos, concrete at Praeneste.

The change of the Roman government from republic to empire promoted new concepts in architectural design. Architects, rarely identified by name, could be inspired by imperial patronage and available funds. Emperors of the

Fig. 10.5. Praeneste. (After Sear 1982, 25, fig. 12)

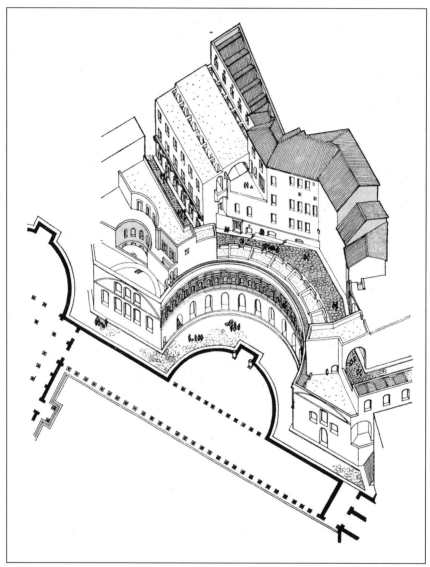

Fig. 10.6. The Market of Trajan in Rome. (After Sear 1982, 160, fig. 92)

first century A.D. required palaces as well as villas, and had increasingly elaborate ones built in Rome. They also gave such conspicuous gifts to the popu-
lace as amphitheatres, *fora*, and markets. The Market of Trajan, an outstanding
product of brick-faced concrete, was built around A.D. 100 and was the functional equivalent of today's mall (fig. 10.6). Placed alongside the Forum and

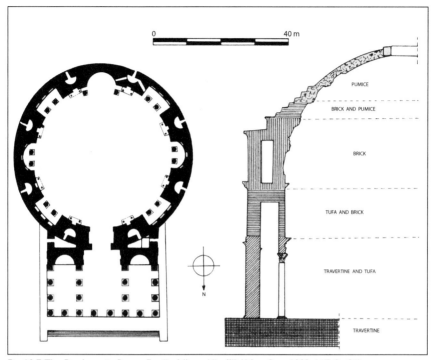

Fig. 10.7. The Pantheon in Rome. For "tufa" read "tuff." (After Sear 1982, 167, fig. 96)

Basilica of Trajan, the market furnished needed facilities on several levels and served to hold up the hillside behind as well. The curved sidewalk outlines the shape of the eastern hemicycle; vaulted ceilings repeat the curves.

In the second century A.D., the emperor Hadrian had built a temple to "all the gods," the Pantheon (fig. 10.7). Like many of the buildings attributed to his reign, it featured remarkable innovations. Now considered the culmination of the use of material and construction techniques developed over the past centuries, it utilized the round building form that earlier had been used for tombs and baths, but could now serve new functions. It was subsequently turned into a Christian church; the round shape better satisfied the need for space for congregation than the rectangular shape originally designed for a pagan temple that housed a cult-image (MacKendrick 1983, 358). With its soaring dome, a spiritual mood still permeates the building. Internal space is decorated with coffers and niches alternating rounded and rectilinear shapes, harmonious with the pavement of circles and squares. The gradation of material from travertine to pumice within the supporting piers is responsible for the successive lightening of the concrete within, and represents a sophisticated response to the requirements of dome construction and support.

In summary, pozzolana from the fields of Campania was the catalyst that generated significant change in the creation of a new architectural aesthetic. While that change is the product of the confluence of material refinement and technological innovation shown in the evolution in wall construction from *opus incertum* to concrete, it reflects as well a confluence of political, social, economic, and religious circumstances, which are themselves agents of change. These include:

1. The transition from republic to empire, leading to the presence of an absolute monarch who had the power and the money to dictate style and to patronize architects.

2. Architects who had the ability to innovate, and who might not have needed to be Roman citizens (cf. Trajan's architect, Apollodorus of Damascus), implying competition that no longer restricted the practice of architecture to Roman natives.

3. Evolving style in Greek architecture and the growing convergence in Greek and Roman cultural taste and architectural styles and decoration.

4. Religious transformation from pagan to Christian in the early centuries of the first millennium reflected in the growing need for a spiritual place of congregation.

5. The Roman predilection for and manipulation of space, perhaps a reminiscence of early cave dwelling (cf. DeRita, this volume) and subsequent architectural preference of high ceilings (cf. the artificial renovation of a natural cave at Sperlonga at the time of Tiberius).

With the passing of time, the one characteristic that remained specifically Roman is the manipulation of space. It is primarily the ability to shape space that concrete provided that characterizes the Roman architecture of the empire and its transition for use in Christian Europe.

REFERENCES

Blake, M.E. 1947. *Ancient Roman Construction in Italy*. Washington.

Brown, F. 1971. *Roman Architecture*. New York.

Frank, T. 1924. "Roman Buildings of the Republic: An Attempt to Date Them from Their Materials." *Papers and Monographs of the American Academy in Rome* III. Rome.

DeLaine, J. 1995. "The Supply of Building Materials to the City of Rome." In *Settlement and Economy in Italy 1500 B.C.–A.D. 1500: Papers of the Fifth Conference of Italian Archaeology*, edited by N. Christie, 555–62. Oxford.

DeRita, D. Forthcoming. In *A Tuff Handbook*, edited by G. Heiken.

Lechtman, H., and L. Hobbs. 1987. "Roman Concrete and the Roman Architectural Revolution." In *Ceramics and Civilization* III, *High Technology Ceramics - Past, Present and Future,* edited by W. D. Kingery. American Ceramic Society, Columbus, OH, 1987.

Lugli, G. 1957. *Forma Italiae* I.

MacDonald, W.L. 1976. *The Pantheon*. Cambridge.

———. 1982. *The Architecture of the Roman Empire*. Rev. ed. New Haven.

MacKendrick, P. 1983. *The Mute Stones Speak*. 2nd ed. New York.

Ruiz Priego, M. 1997. "The West of Iberia: Meeting Point between the Mediterranean and the Atlantic at the End of the Bronze Age." In *Encounters and Transformations. The Archaeology of Iberia in Transition*, edited by M. Balmuth, A. Gilman, and L. Prados-Torreira. Sheffield.

Sear, F. 1982. *Roman Architecture*. Ithaca, New York.

Ward-Perkins, J.B. 1981. *Roman Imperial Architecture*. Oxford.

APPENDIX

This treatment of the volcanic derivation of concrete and its subsequent place in the development of Roman architecture drew inspiration from several sources, each adding an original dimension. It is appropriate here to acknowledge the debt owed and to cite the words—some almost poetic—and concepts used in the discussion of Roman architecture, its materials, social implications, and, of course, concrete. The Latin terms cited are taken from Vitruvius, *De Architectura*, Book 2.

The expression adopted for the concept of catalyst and other considerations is inspired by Ruiz Priego's list of cumulative criteria to be considered in Columbus' discovery of America:

> Although what Columbus was looking for was the shortest route to Asia and not a new continent, the discovery was by no means a product of chance. It involved, rather, the confluence of a series of technical innovations and of political, ideological, and economic circumstances, some of which, such as the transmission of Greek and Arabic science to Europe, had been developing for several centuries. It is fairly probable that other navigators precede Columbus but the historically effective discovery of America took place only when it was materially and humanly possible, and not before (1997, 99-100).

"The architecture of the Romans was, from first to last, an art of shaping space around ritual" (Brown, 1971, 9).

DeLaine (1995, 555–62) points out the significant relationship between the location of Praeneste and the presence of lime.

Lechtman and Hobbs, in their groundbreaking article (1987), not only describe the action of the chemical components of concrete but also contribute the idea of competition among architects as a spur that promoted excellence:

> ... the dramatic and visible realization of a new concept of the city [was] rendered by an imperial vision but accomplished largely by an urban middle class. The revolution in architecture was an urban

revolution and a social revolution as well as a revolution in architectural form and in the building of buildings. These multiple changes were accompanied and facilitated by the use of Roman concrete . . . (1987, 81–128).

"The vaulted style, with its relatively seamless continuity of surface, its tendency of rhetorical persuasion, and its capacity to call up strong sensations of fixed and ordered places, reflected both the claims and the realities of imperial society" (MacDonald, 1982, 179). MacDonald (1982, 180) refers to a definition of the empire of another day in the language of architecture and sculpture, writing that "Roman and Greek forms were mingled in an expression of the nature of Rome's world at the moment of its widest imperial expansion."

"The interior [of the Pantheon] carries forward that liberation of religious architecture from the Greek tyranny of the rectangular box, which can only come about through the use of poured concrete . . ." (MacKendrick, 1983, 358).

"In the fully developed Roman concrete . . . these properties were the result of mixing lime with the local volcanic sand (*pozzolana*). This was not a sudden, dramatic discovery; still less was it the result of any theory of the chemical processes involved. It was the product of centuries of trial and error, each generation adding its quota of practical experience until, by the last century of the Republic, what had started as the inert fill suitable only for the interiors of platforms, city walls, etc., had become a building material in its own right, which could be used not only for the construction of walls, but also of arches and vaults" (Ward-Perkins 1981, 98).

The first century Latin poet Horace (*Odes* 3.1.34) illustrates the displacement by concrete of products of nature (land and sea):

> contracta pisces aequora sentiunt
> iactis in altum molibus; huc frequens
> caementa demittit redemptor
> cum famulis dominusque terrae
> fastidiosus.

> With each new jetty, fish sense shrunken seas.
> The contractor with his crowd of slaves,
> The master eager for land,
> Dumps his cement here.

Landscape Evolution and the First Human Settlements in Sardinia

Sergio Ginesu and Stefania Sias*

Volcanism on Sardinia

The island of Sardinia is located in the center of the western Mediterranean. Along with the island of Corsica, it constitutes a typical continental crustal structure. During the Tertiary, about 30 Ma (million years ago) an important volcanic episode began that lasted until 13 Ma. The volcanic activity was characterized by explosive eruptions that created a continuous vertical stratigraphy that can be seen in the current morphology of stepped slopes, structural surfaces sometimes referred to as small mesas. Different levels of this volcanic tuff are visible in many parts of the island but especially in the central section (fig. 11.1).

After a period of relative volcanic dormancy, the island was again affected by periodic volcanic activity that lasted from the early part of the Pliocene Epoch (5 Ma) until the Late Pleistocene, (0.14 Ma). Between the two volcanic cycles, the land went through a period of relative volcanic dormancy.

The later episode of volcanism was characterized by mostly extrusive volcanic activity with basaltic lava flows, while ash and other explosive deposits were less abundant and only a few tuffaceous deposits were formed. Basaltic lava flowed into the river valleys and preserved the existing fluvial network. During the Pleistocene, basalt flows preserved landscape morphologies from all the climatic stages of the Quaternary (Ginesu 1991; Marini 1983; Sias

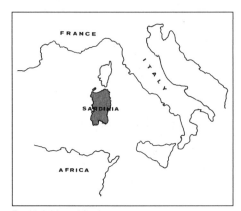

Fig. 11.1. Map of Sardinia.

Fig. 11.2: Key to Map of Sardinia

Key	Places	Age Approx. (M.Y.)
1	Monte Lisir	0.1
2	Monte Poddighe	0.2
3	Monte Austidu	0.3
4	Monte Cuccuruddu	0.1
5	Monte Sos Pianos	0.1
6	Monte Massa	0.3
7	Monte Oes	–
8	Monte S. Matteo	0.4
9	Monte Meddaris	0.5
10	Monte Mannu	0.6
11	Monte Ruju	0.6
12	Monte Cujaru	0.7
13	Monte Pelao	2.0
14	Pranu Mannu	3.0
15	Campeda Mesa	3.1
16	Gollei Mesa	2.1
17	Pedra Dorules	3.9
18	Zeppara Manna	2.7
19	Monte Guzzini	2.6
20	Taccu Majore	2.0
21	Sa Struvina	3.8
22	Capo Ferrato	5.0
23	San Pietro Island	14.6
24	Logudoro	16.3
25	Costa Paradiso	16.6
26	Fordongianus	17.2
27	S. Antioco Island	17.6
28	Montiferru	18.0
29	Marmilla	17.4
30	Ottana	19.5
31	Castelsardo	19.8
32	Monte Arcuentu	19.8
33	Sarroch	21.6
34	Capo Marrargiu	23.8
35	South. Campidano	24.9
36	Siliqua	27.6
37	Sulcis	28.5
a	Sos Furrighesos	–
b	S. Andrea Priu	–
c	Sant' Antine	–
d	Mont' Essu	–

1994, 1997). Subsequently, both the tuffaceous and ignimbritic rocks were eroded to produce a new landscape in the central part of the island (fig. 11.1).

Both tuff and basaltic lavas were utilized by early inhabitants of the island. Tuff cliffs were used for ancient burials during the Pre-Nuragic period (ca. 2400–1800 B.C.) and later, during the Nuragic Age (from 1800 B.C. on), loose tuff and other volcanic rocks were used to build *nuraghi,* the ancient Cyclopean monuments widespread on Sardinia (fig. 11.2). The greater resistance of many volcanic rocks to erosion and weathering must have persuaded the Nuragic people to utilize this material to build the nuraghi, even occasionally searching for it at a distance.

The Volcanic Landscape and Human Settlements

In sum, much of the volcanic landscape on Sardinia shows a typical morphology characterized by relatively narrow mesas, steep slopes, and rocky

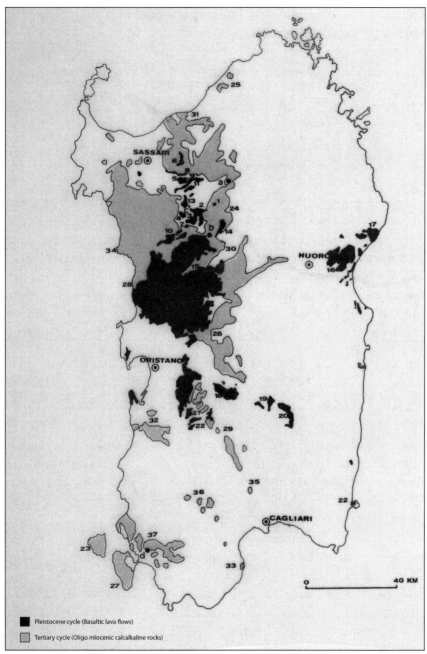

Fig. 11.2. Distribution of tertiary and pleistocene volcanic outcrops on the island. The dating of the volcanic rocks are from the analysis by C. Savelli, R. Campredon, and G. Feraud (1981–1987) and show the evolution of volcanic activity.

walls carved into small valleys. This topography and its landforms were significant for the following reasons:

1. The mesa (plateau) shape of the volcanic outcrops became strategic points, easily defensible areas;
2. the presence of clay minerals could be utilized as domestic material;
3. the presence of many springs, mainly around the mesas or stratified tuff levels, provided a water supply.

From a geomorphological point of view, areas with tuffaceous and ignimbritic rocks allow easy interpretations of the development of the landscape. The succession of volcanic layers promotes selective erosion, better preserving the natural events. To explain the possible results of geomorphological reconstruction with archaeological implications, we shall describe two examples in the volcanic regions of Sardinia. The first is in the north-central part of the island at the archeological site of Sos Furrighesos, and the second is near the volcano of S. Mateo, which, along with its lava flow, forms the Coloru Mesa.

The Sos Furrighesos Necropolis

Throughout Sardinia, there are typical Neolithic burials called *domus de janas*. They are generally dug in tuffaceous rocks, often with an articulated series of chambers (fig. 11.3). The name for these structures means "house of the fairies" or "witches" in the Sardinian language. About 1000 are known on the island. The most important burials are in tuff deposits such as the sites of Montessu near the village of Villaperucciu, Sos Furrighesos, and Sant' Andrea Priu in the central part of the island.

The prehistoric chambers buried in the Sos Furrighesos site are part of the northern piedmont belt of the little mesa of Pianu Oschiri (fig. 11.4), and have a differential erosion surface near the wide Pranu Mannu plateau that was formed by a basaltic lava flow during the Late Pliocene (2.9 Ma, Beccaluva et al. 1981), and that represents a change in the volcanic landscape of the Tertiary in the Sos Furrighesos area. The necropolis is located on the wall of an escarpment, which marks a structural surface of one level of Tertiary ash. The presence on the cliff of several underground burials gives the place its name, Sos Furrighesos, meaning "the little holes."

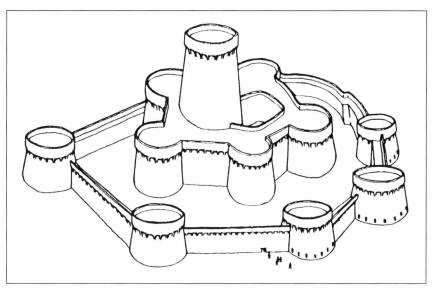

Fig. 11.3. Ideal reconstruction of a *nuraghe*. from a plan of Nuraghe Arrubiu by E. Contu [1966]

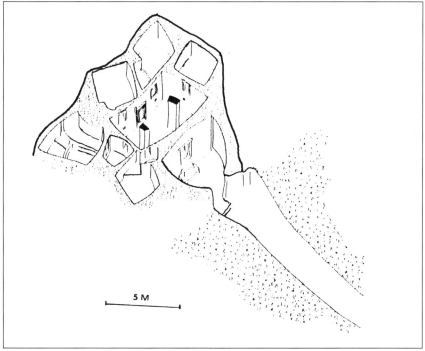

Fig. 11.4. Schematic map of a multicellular *domus de janas* (such as Sos Furrighesos). (From a representation of the *domus Santu Pedru* by E. Contu [1966])

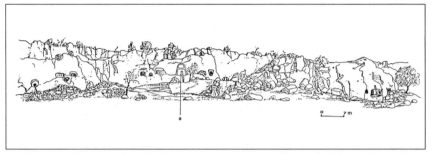

Fig. 11.5. A general sketch of the Sos Furrighesos burials in the tuffaceous wall (a re-elaborated tomb).

Morphologically the area is characterized by flat-topped mesas protected by basaltic caprocks and interrupted by small creeks cutting the tuff. The Sos Furrighesos valley is a ravine cut into the tuffaceous rocks. However compact, these levels show many fractures along the outer wall. One of these is located in the central part of the cliff where the *hypogea* (underground chambers) are situated. It is evident that in that part of the wall it was impossible to dig anything in prehistoric times because the condition of the site was already precarious.

The morphological evidence that we have seen at Sos Furrighesos demonstrates the presence of a slope movement connected with a generalized collapse of blocks from the cliff (Ginesu and Sias 1992). After examining the necropolis (Tanda 1984), it was observed that some of the burials are without walls. This indicates that there was a possible reworking of the burials at a later date, possibly about 100 years after the first settlement (fig. 11.5, tomb 9). The similarities between the landslide morphology and the burials, which appear cut outside of the walls, are most clear in burial IX, but are also evident in some of the other burials. At all burials where the landslide had intersected the wall the tombs are still complete and show the whole monument.

On the basis of archeological studies, we can document a wide landslide that involved the whole prehistoric site after the first settlement, dating from the first part of the third millennium B.C. The geomorphological evidence indicates the reuse of some tombs in a later period, and allows a new interpretation of the site. The burials reused after the collapse were decorated in a new style that postdated the time of the first settlement. Undamaged tombs were not changed in their original appearance, while those severely damaged by the landslide were completely abandoned.

The Coloru Lava Flow and the Process of Relief Inversion

Another example of archeological data obtained through geomorphological studies is offered by the reconstruction of landscape evolution and the survey of the paleosurfaces in the volcanic areas. In northern Sardinia, near the town of Sassari the San Matteo Volcano formed a lava flow nearly 9 km in length. The following is an evolutionary model for the stepped slopes produced by erosion of the lava flow.

The interpretation is based on the pre-existing forms protected by the basaltic flow of the San Matteo Volcano (5,000 B.P., Beccaluva et al. 1981). This flow, which is only a few hundred meters in width, so narrow that it is called *Altopiano del Coloru* or "Snake Plateau," provides evidence of a well-developed paleostream. The slope of the flow is 2–3% and the high elevation of the whole area is formed by large-scale topographic inversion (fig. 11.6). The configuration of the original paleovalley during the middle Pleistocene was asymmetrical, with Oligocene through Miocene ignimbritic rocks on the northern slope and Miocene arenaceous and tuffaceous sediments on the south.

This difference resulted in two kinds of evolution along the slopes of the valley during the process of topographic inversion. On the northern volcanic outcrops, the landscape developed with typical pediment forms and fan deposits in four distinct surfaces; the highest of these formed at the end of the latest Tertiary or the Early Pleistocene (Ginesu 1991). Along a lateral valley formed by erosion in the northern part of the lava flow, the slope in the volcanic rocks was stepped in a sequence of terraces that seem to reflect the oscillating climatic regimes of the Pleistocene. In fact, starting with the Mindel Glacial Stage, terraces from each successive cold stage can be identified. The hydrographic system initiated more erosion during cold stages, forming erosional shapes such as terraces or fans in the volcanic outcrop, and pediments (without sediments) in the stratified rocks. The Miocene Age sediments, composed of alternating calcareous and tuffaceous units, have favored the formation of erosion surfaces along the resistant planes.

Also in part of the area, the slope profile depicts a succession of levels correlated to various periglacial stages (fig. 11.7). The absence of a deposit on the surfaces of the Miocene outcrops suggests that their origin is associated with the movement of ice. In the same studied area, the stratified slope deposits were found at an elevation of 300 m in the Miocene limestone cliffs.

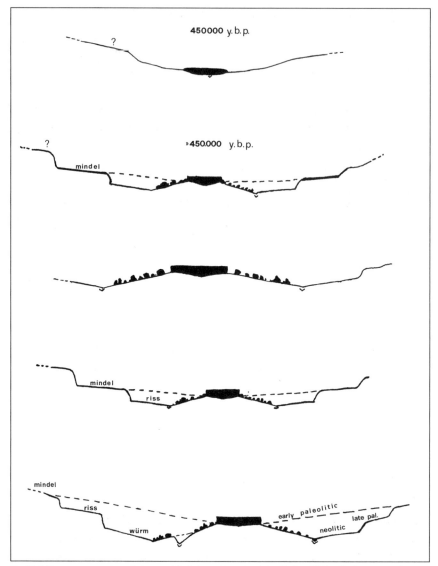

Fig. 11.6. Transverse section of the stratified slope deposit of the Coloru Valley. Each step can be referred to a paleoclimatic stage of the Pleistocene and to a corresponding archeological surface.

From an archeological point of view, each climatic stage can be correlated to a prehistoric surface; landscape reconstruction is an important element from which to start an archeological survey from the Paleolithic to the Neolithic Age.

Fig. 11.7. The stratified slope deposit near Orosei (eastern Sardinia). This deposit often reaches actual sea level.

Climatic Changes

The conditions described above are for level surfaces on terraces or pediments in which recent stream incisions have allowed the development of relatively short stepped slopes through easily eroded volcanic materials. These
typical landforms are the products of cold climate processes that, on
Sardinia, have produced a large quantity of fragmented rock carried by the
movement of glacial ice and deposited by its melting in the valley bottoms
or the lower parts of the slope.

On Sardinia, deposits from periglacial periods are known from many
localities on the island, but with different components (Pelletier 1960; Ozer
and Ulzega 1981; Ginesu 1990). One of the most common deposits is the
eboulis ordonnes (stratified slope deposits, known in English by the French
name *grezes litée*). These are formed from fractured rocks, usually limestone,
which form thick deposits, sometimes in the lower part of the island or in
the bottom of the small valleys in the inner regions (fig. 11.7). On Sardinia
there are beautiful examples along the east-central coast and near the cliffs in
the Miocene limestone of the northern part of the island.

In collaboration with the Soprintendenza Archeologica per le Provincie di
Sassari e Nuoro, an investigation has focused on the building of nuraghi in the
Sardinian Early Bronze Age (ca. 1800–1500 B.C.). The typical shape of a
nuraghi is that of an upturned, truncated cone surmounted by a terrace; the
monument is composed of Cyclopean blocks that form a massive structure
where each stone is fitted on the side and internally (fig. 11.3). During the excavation at the nuragic site of Santu Antine in the Logudoro region on Sardinia,
a 1.5 m-deep trench near the monument showed a deposit of fragmented stones
near the surface, under 0.5 m of soil (fig. 11.8). In the archeological and architectural reconstruction of the nuraghe, this level had been interpreted as a man-
made external floor pavement because it was still present in excavations around
the nuraghe's central tower, but it proved to be an eboulis ordonnes deposit
formed during a cold stage of the Pleistocene (fig. 11.9). The debris sequence is
composed of 5 cm-thick layers of highly angular 1–3 cm rock fragments, and
does not seem to vary in different layers. The quantity of this material is tied to
the environment and the presence of certain rock types. In the Logudoro region
and near the archeological site of Santu Antine, the situation was not favorable
to the formation of this deposit.

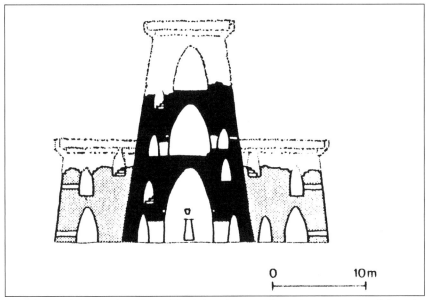

Fig. 11.8. Plan of Nuraghe Santu Antine. The darkened portion shows the inner section of the main tower.

Fig. 11.9. A trench near Nuraghe Santu Antine where an outcrop of a thin stratified slope deposit defines the flat morphology of the valley and a climatic change before the Nuragic and pre-Nuragic settlement. (Ginesu 1991)

Conclusions

The present investigations have demonstrated how profitable a cooperation between archeologists and geomorphologists may be. The geomorphological survey not only allowed many of the major volcanic activities to be identified, but also supplied important information on settlement and land use in both the prehistoric and protohistoric stages of human development. Figure 11.10 provides further details that have emerged from the application of techniques of geomorphological survey to archeological sites located in the volcanic areas of Sardinia.

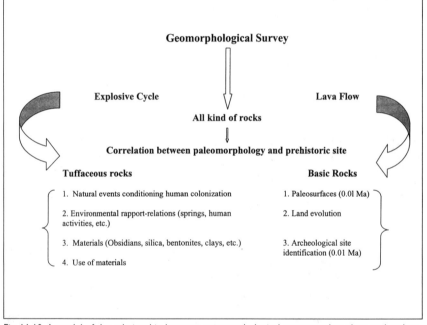

Fig. 11.10. A model of the relationship between geomorphological surveys, volcanology, and archaeology in Sardinia.

REFERENCES

Beccaluva, L., M. Deriu, G.P. Macciotta, and C. Savelli. 1981. *Carta Geopetrografica Del Vulcanismo Plio-Pleistocenico Della Sardegna Nord-Occidentale.* Scale 1:50,000. Firenze.

Ginesu, S. 1990. "Periglacial Deposits in Sardinia: The Blockstreams near Pranu Mannu." *Geografia Fisica e Dinamica Quaternaria* 13(2):179–83.

———. 1991. "The Coloru Lava Flow and Its Implications in the Landscape Evolution During The Cold Stages In The Pleistocene." *INQUA XIII Int.* Congr. Beijing.

Marini, A. 1983. "Correlazioni tra le Colate Basaltiche Pleistoceniche e Le Paleoidrografie Relitte nella Valle del Coloru (Logudoro, Sardegna)." *Bollettino Società Sardi di Scienze Naturale* 22:81–92.

Martini, F. 1990. "Laerru (Sassari). Località Sa Coa de Sa Multa: Giacimento del Paleolitica Inferiore." *BdArch* 4:105–6.

Martini, F., and G. Pitzalis. 1987–1988. "Notiziario: Sa Coa de Sa Multa (Laerru - SS)." *RSP* 46(1–2):387.

Ozer, A., and A. Ulzega. 1981. "Sur la Répartition Des Éboulis Ordonnés En Sardaigne." *Biuletyn Peryglacjalny* 28:259–65.

Pelletier, J. 1960. "Le Relief De La Sardaigne." *Mjm. Docum. Et. Rhodanien. Univ. Lyon.* 13:1–466.

Sias, S. 1994. "La Piana Di Paule Nel Quadro Evolutivo Delle Piane Del Logudoro." *Geografia Fisica e Dinamica Quaternaria* 17:73–8.

———. 1997. *Le Modificazioni Del Paesaggio Indotte Dal Vulcanismo Plio-Pleistocenico Del Logudoro - Mejlogu (Sardegna Centro Settentrionale).* Tesi di dott., Università di Ancona-Sassari.

Tanda, G. 1984. *Arte e Religione Della Sardegna Preistorica Nella Necropoli Di Sos Furrighesos,* edited by Chiarella. 2 vols. Sassari.

NOTES

* Professor Jack Ridge of Tufts University acted as geological consultant.

12

Ignimbrites, Rock-Hewn Churches and Underground Settlements in Cappadocia (Turkey)

❦

Ezio Burri, Raniero Massoli-Novelli, and Marco Petitta

Cappadocia constitutes a large part of the Anatolian tableland. It is characterized by a unique plateau geomorphology, having a mean height of around 1,000 m and being formed from several ignimbrites. The climate of the region combines continental and sub-desert elements; the rainfall, often intense, is concentrated in the spring and winter seasons, with some of the precipitation in the latter falling as snow. Summers are usually dry and temperatures are at their highest in July and their lowest in January.

Over time, various elements have acted together to form a distinctive landscape. Faults, systems of fractures and seismicity, combined with erosion by runoff, streams, aeolian processes, and ice aided by weathering caused by diurnal temperature fluctuations have gradually produced a distinctive geomorphology on the soft ignimbrites. This comprises branched and deeply incised valleys and low hills divided by a wide structural tableland and the well-known pinnacles known as "fairy chimneys."

Cappadocia was inhabited from roughly 3000 B.C.; about a millennium later it came under the influence of the Kingdom of the Hittites. Around A.D. 300, Christians, under Byzantine rule, began to take refuge in this semi-desert region, and their activities gradually marked the whole region as they produced their unique system of underground settlement. Over time, the extensive geomorphological and archaeological heritage of Cappadocia has suffered erosion. In order to reduce the effects of such processes,

UNESCO has designated the region a World Heritage area and has promoted some, albeit limited, palliative measures designed to reduce further
deterioration. In addition, several important churches, particularly in the
Göreme area, have been restored.

Geological Outline

The most notable feature of the geological history of the region is a pro-
tracted period of volcanic activity, which began in the Oligocene and only
ended some centuries ago. Today this area is termed the Cappadocia
Volcanic Province, or CVP (Toprak et al. 1994), and is placed within the
much more extensive Volcanic Province of Central Anatolia. Volcanic products occur along a northwest to southeast-tending direction of tectonism,
which extends from Karaman to Kayseri and comprise: lava flows, ign-

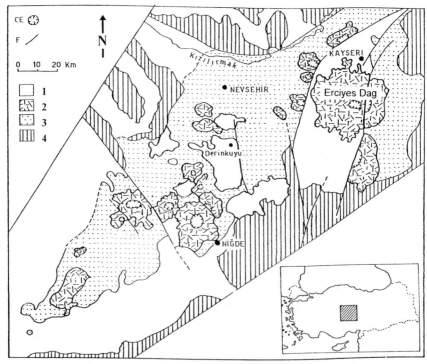

Fig. 12.1. Simplified geological map of the Cappadocian Volcanic Province. *CE,* main eruptive centers;
F, faults; *1,* continental deposits; *2,* lavas and other volcanic complexes; *3,* ignimbritic flow deposits;
4, basement rocks. (Redrawn by Toprak et al. 1994)

imbrites, surges, fallout deposits, domes, and composite volcanoes. As figure 12.1 shows, ignimbrites are concentrated in the Ürgüp, Göreme, Zelve and Nevşehir areas.

The evolution of the Cappadocia Volcanic Province may be divided into three main periods. The first (13.5–8.5 Ma [million years ago]) is strongly associated with andesitic lavas, the second (8.5–2.5 Ma) is represented by the eruption of at least 10 ignimbritic units and the third (2.5 Ma to the first century A.D.) is characterized by the further eruption of ignimbrites, together with a number of large andesitic/basaltic stratovolcanoes. Within the region, the most prominent landmark is Erciyes Dağ (3,916 m), one of the youngest and best-preserved of these stratovolcanoes.

Ignimbrites

The ignimbrites of Cappadocia are attributed to two phases of eruption; the more important occurs in the Neogene (8.6–2.5 Ma), and the less important—comprising just a few deposits—in the Quaternary (0.2–0.1 Ma, Innocenti et al. 1975). There are other volcanic rocks in the area, including middle basic to acidic lavas, pumice, and surges, but ignimbrite is the most abundant rock type and covers an area of 11,000 km², reaching a thickness of 450 m. Eight centers of Neogene eruptive activity, now virtually totally eroded, have been identified and the only preserved Quaternary center is located within a caldera at Acigöl (Ercan et al. 1994). Ignimbrites are generally white to rosy-colored on fresh faces typically with a gray patina composed of Fe-Mn over more exposed surfaces. Pasquarè et al. (1998) have identified 10 stratigraphic units that have a mostly rhyolitic composition and SiO_2 percentages of 68–76%.

Ignimbrites have a low coefficient of compressibility; our analysis shows average values of 30 MPa (megapascal) (about 300 kg/cm²), which decrease during the rainy season because of microporosity, implying a soft rock and suggesting the principal explanation for the origin of the pinnacle-like morphology of the region. A second reason for the presence of this morphology is a more compact level within the ignimbrites, which covers much softer materials. Erosion by water percolating along vertical fractures—caused by cooling and tectonic and seismic processes—divides and then isolates single pinnacles, which are then preserved because of the presence of a harder capping of ignimbrite, or hat-like feature. When the hat eventually collapses, the soft ignimbrite core is eroded in just a few years (figs. 12.2 and 12.3).

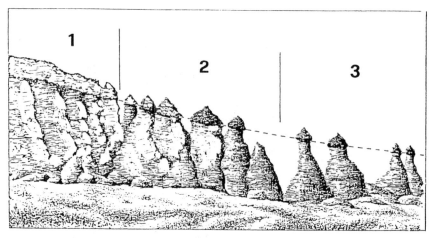

Fig. 12.2. Cappadocia ignimbrite pinnacle formation. *1*, pre-existent vertical fractures (cooling + tectonic + seismicity); *2*, erosion (mostly water) begins to separate vertical blocks, protected by a harder ignimbrite "hat"; *3*, pinnacles are rounded by water and wind; as soon as the hat falls down, the cone is quickly eroded.

Some researchers (e.g., Bowen 1987) have claimed that hats may be composed of basalt and other lavas, but our analysis shows the universal presence of a harder layer of ignimbrite, the dark color being imparted by the patina of Fe-Mn oxides, which originated through the thermal extraction and concentration of these metals from the outer few centimeters of rock by means of daytime evaporation and nocturnal humidity. Similar processes have been described in order to explain the dark patina of the pinnacles found in Hoggar National Park in the Algerian Sahara and for the sandstone "mushroom" landforms of the Utah Plateau (U.S.) in Canyonlands National Park.

Simple gauging stations which we have installed within the region show very high rates of erosion; initial results suggest a rate of 2.5 mm/year. This rate should, however, be considered as indicative only. Higher quality quantitative data will emerge in the near future once further gauging stations become operational.

Rock-Hewn Churches

Rock-hewn churches represent the most important and well-known features of the Cappadocian region (Jolivet-Levy 1991). There is no published catalogue of Cappadocian churches, but producing such a document would be

Fig. 12.3. Erosional evolution of ignimbrite pinnacles. (Photo by R. Massoli-Novelli)

extremely difficult because the Christian settlers excavated small chapels and room-sized churches virtually everywhere and many are either wholly or partially destroyed. The total number of churches could consist of many hundreds, with the most important concentration found in the Göreme Valley, today an open-air museum located 7 km northwest of the town of Ürgüp (fig. 12.4). The principal sites are the following:

1. Tokatlı Kilise (The Church of the Buckle). This is the largest and best decorated monument in Cappadocia, with splendid paintings on all its walls and on the narthex vault. The blue coloration of the mural decoration is unique to this particular church.

2. Karanlık Kilise (The Dark Church). Here light can only enter by means of a small window in the narthex. Outside the church, at its entrance, two arcades are all that remain of a former monastery. Bowen (1987) reports a field test of new grouting using a mixture of ignimbrite powder, lime and sand in the ratio of 2:1:1. Unfortunately, some fissures have again opened.

3. Elmalı Kilise (The Church of the Apples). This is a beautiful church with four columns and a central dome. As figure 12.5 shows, there is evidence of fissures and fractures on the floor of the church; the most prominent of these correspond to similar features on the ceiling. These fractures allow the ready ingress of water, which is associated with high humidity and damage to and deterioration of the decorative murals. New grouting was put in before 1982, but high humidity represents an ever-present danger and it is probable that this deleterious situation is being further exacerbated by the capillary rise of groundwater.

4. El Nazar Kilise (an isolated church). Christian settlers excavated this church during the 11th century. There is evidence of fractures both inside the church and near the door; the collapse of ignimbrite blocks, moreover, presents an ever-present danger. The church shows the rapid infiltration of water, both on one side of the structure and inside the crypt, and subsidence of the floor may also be observed.

Fig. 12.4. The exterior of the Karanlık ignimbrite church near Göreme. (Photo by R. Massoli-Novelli)

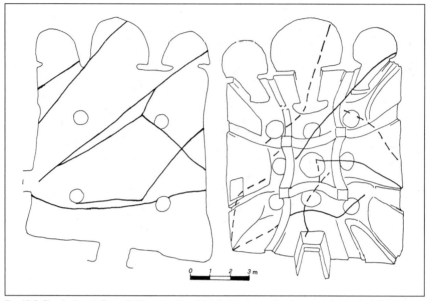

Fig. 12.5. Elmalı church floor (left) and ceiling (right) showing major fractures in the ignimbrite rock. (Redrawn from Restle 1967)

Settlements

Besides churches, settlements occur within the study area.

1. Wall villages. Houses in these villages are independent units in which adjoining rooms are placed one upon another and on different levels. Sometimes the units are connected by *cunicoli,* or tunnels, with steps.
2. Cone villages. These are complex structures constructed within pinnacles. Because the upper parts of pinnacles are more resistant to erosion, the lower rooms have a degree of natural protection from the elements. Exterior rooms are often closely integrated with those located underground.
3. Isolated cones. These have been dug into isolated pinnacles, but are generally less extensive and lack the complexity of other forms of settlement.
4. Castle villages. Using ignimbritic towers, these are considered to be a variant of the "wall village," having a similar settlement morphology (fig. 12.6).

Fig. 12.6. Üçhisar ignimbrite castle near Urgüp. (Photo by R. Mussoli-Novelli)

5. Underground towns. These were excavated at several levels under expanses of the ignimbritic plain. The plans of these towns are functional and it is thought that defense was an important consideration. Access points are few in number and well hidden; inside routes are not only branched, but are also further protected by "millstone doors" which are constructed of hard basalt. Underground towns are without doubt the most complex settlement structures in Cappadocia.

6. Underground villages. These are smaller structures, which have been excavated in the ignimbritic rocks of isolated hills. They are notable for the protection of one or two levels by millstone doors. Today, admission to these underground rooms is often possible by means of service places, such as cowsheds, which are connected to the outside.

Service Structures

In Cappadocia, ignimbrite has often been excavated to create numerous service structures, those relating to water supply and drainage being particularly important.

1. Drainage canals. These are deeply incised valleys cut in alluvium and ignimbrite, which were and still are used for cultivation of terraces (Burri 1995). High rates of slope erosion were controlled by the construction of underground canals, with the aim of draining surface runoff to avoid the erosion of the cultivation terraces.

2. Groundwater canals. Short cunicoli have been excavated. In summer, these were used to intercept rainfall.

3. Cisterns. These do not differ significantly from cisterns used throughout the circum-Mediterranean region. In many cases several unused rooms have been connected to construct a cistern.

4. Pigeon houses. The low level of soil fertility under natural conditions and the need for intensive crop production caused the settlers of the region to construct numerous and very distinctive pigeon houses. Indeed, unused churches, storerooms,

and other structures were sometimes used for this purpose.

5. Storerooms. These are characteristic of the area and numerous. In some cases underground living rooms were converted to this new use.

6. Tombs. These contain decoration, which makes them of great archaeological importance. Many tomb sites are pre-Byzantine in age and cannot be related to the more extensive and complex settlement phenomena in Cappadocia that are the subject of this chapter.

Causes of Degradation

The UNESCO World Heritage declaration was made to try to arrest the degradation of the area, which is both advanced and diffused over a wide area (Bowen 1987, 1990). With the large number of sites from this complex heritage, choices about what and what not to preserve are difficult to make. Indeed the conservationist's task is made more difficult because these precious sites are increasingly the focus of tourism, which is adding a new cause of degradation. The main factors causing degradation are listed below.

Erosion

This is the principal cause of the collapse of large parts of the more exposed sections of rock-hewn churches and of the frescoes that are found within them. Erosion also adversely affects some of the underground settlements, particularly the drainage canals. Rapid erosion changes both valley sides and valley bottoms, resulting in a morphology that is in a state of constant transformation, as valleys widen and a planar valley bottom morphology is produced. Where rivers do not flow in channels, valley bottoms are covered by eroded debris. Even valley bottoms developed for agriculture lack stability, because water is collected in seasonal and transitory watercourses leading to the removal of much sand and gravel-sized sediment.

Structural Causes

Tectonic fractures and faults affect the whole valley system. Fractures are in part contemporaneous with the deposition of the ignimbrites and partly related to later seismic events. Fractures have also been caused through the excavation of underground living spaces and from their partial demolition by explosions. These are fracture systems that characterize the vaults and passages of hypogeal places. There are levels within the stratigraphy showing poor cohesion and discontinuities. Differential erosion develops along these lines of weakness; this factor contributes to partial collapse. There is also a well marked infiltration of water along faults, fractures and fissures, and this factor, combined with the high porosity of the ignimbrite, may adversely affect the overall stability of many monuments.

Working together, the natural factors of erosion have led not only to the progressive collapse of many of Cappadocia's precious churches from their exteriors inward, but the inner areas of underground works have also suffered badly.

Anthropogenic Factors

Agricultural terraces are required for cultivation within valley bottoms and require rock fragments of the correct size and, if possible, already roughly hewn. For this reason, abandoned hypogeal sites have often been deliberately destroyed with explosives and, in an Islamic society, there has often been a preference for the reuse of the materials found in rock-hewn churches.

Tourist pressure in the valley is a relatively new problem. Tourism to these heritage sites is considered necessary for the economic development of the region, but there are two factors which have not fully been considered: the erodibility of many of the lithotypes and the lack of control and management of tourists over this wide area. It must be remembered that, in other parts of the world, when management of protected areas under tourist pressure is being planned, these two factors are often considered in advance. In the Cappadocian valleys, where the number of tourists engaged in walking, cycling, riding, driving, and exploring sites of artistic interest is increasing rapidly, the lack of control over tourists is exacerbating the natural and structural degradation of the landscape. The ignimbrites of the region, for instance, do not show a high degree of tolerance to the excessive foot traffic.

Tourist pressures in underground sites are problems that are well known from investigations of tourists in natural cave systems. Factors related to humidity, temperature, and the emission of CO_2 are particularly important. On some of the most precious sites there is little control of visitors, and some of the paintings are being damaged by graffiti, while corrosion has removed whole sections of the frescoes.

Conclusions

In order to reverse the observed trends toward irreversible degradation and destruction by erosion to these World Heritage monuments in Cappadocia, we argue that it is necessary to take the following policy initiatives.

1. There is a need for coordination. Too often in the past the numerous national and international studies have been uncoordinated. We suggest that funding be made available only for interdisciplinary studies.
2. A detailed survey needs to be undertaken, and the state of the churches, underground settlements, and the more important pinnacles should be monitored.
3. The monuments that are most at risk must be strengthened. This may be achieved by grouting the most dangerous rock fissures and fractures with resins to limit the ingress of water—one of the most active factors of degradation.
4. An attempt should be made to control the impact of tourists on those underground churches and settlements that are most in danger.

REFERENCES

Bowen, R. 1987. "Geology and Conservation of Antiques. Monuments in Turkey." *Environmental Geology* 9:71–84.

———. 1990. "The Future of the Past at Göreme in Turkey." *Environmental Geology* 16:35–61.

Burri, E. 1995. "Canalizzazioni Sotterranee Per il Drenaggio e L'emunzione Idrica nelle Antiche e Recenti Attività Agricole. Esempi Comparati nell' Etruria Meridionale (Italia) ed in Cappadocia (Turchia)." *Atti del Conv. Geogr. Intern.: I Valori dell'Agricoltura nel Tempo e nello Spazio.* Rome.

Burri, E., R. Massoli-Novelli, G. Pensabene, and M. Petitta. 1996. "Problems about the Preservation of Geomorphologic Environment and Underground Settlements in Cappadocia (Turkey)." *Atti II Symposium Intern. ProGEO. Memorie del Servizio Geologico d'Italia.* Rome.

Ercan, T., A. Turkecan, and M. Karaibyikoglu. 1994. "Neogene and Quaternary Volcanics of Cappadocia." *Excursion Guide of International Volcanological Congress.* IAVCEI Ankara 94. Ankara.

Giovannini, L. 1971. "Il Territorio e gli Ambienti Rupestri." *AAVV. Arte della Cappadocia,* 67–80. Geneva.

Innocenti, F., R. Mazzuoli, G. Pasquarè, F. Radicata di Brozolo, and L. Villari. 1975. "The Neogene Calc-Alkaline Volcanism of Central Anatolia. Geochronicological Data of Kaisery-Nidge Area." *Geological Magazine* 112:349–60.

Jolivet-Levy, C. 1991. *Les Églises Byzantines de Cappadoce.* Paris.

Le Pennec, J.L., A. Temel, T Druitt, J.L. Froger, E. Aydar, J.L. Bourdier, G. Cams, and M.N. Gundogdu. 1994. "The Neogene to Quaternary Ignimbritic Field of Cappadocia." *Excursion Guide of International Volcanological Congress.* IAVCEI Ankara 94. Ankara.

Massoli-Novelli, R. and F. Di Gregorio, 1990. "Geological impact of some tailings dams in Sardinia (Italy)." *Environmental Geology* 19 (3):147–153. Elsevier, Amsterdam.

Massoli-Novelli, R. and M. Petitta, 1997. "Hydrogeological impact of the Gran Sasso tunnels (Abruzzi, Italy)." *Proceedings of the International Symposium on Engineering Geology and the Environment. Athens, Greece, June 1997,* 3:2785-2790. Athens.

Pasquarè, G., S. Poli, L. Vezzoli, and A. Zanchi. 1988. "Continental Arc Volcanism and Tectonic Setting in Central Anatolia, Turkey." *The Origin and Evolution of Arcs, Tectonophysics* 146:217–30.

Schumacher, R., U. Mues, and U. Koberski. 1992. "Petrographical and Geochemical Aspects and K/Ar-Dating of Ignimbrites in Cappadocia, Turkey." *Abstracts of the Sixth Cong. of the Geol. Soc.* Athens.

Temel, A. 1992. "Kapadokia ekplosif volkanizmasinin. petrolijk ve jeokimyasal ozellikleri." Ph.D. diss. İstanbul Üniversitesi Fen Bilimleri Enstitüsü, Ankara.

Toprak, V., J. Keller, and R. Schumacher. 1994. "Volcano-Tectonic Features of the Cappadocian Volcanic Province." *Excursion Guide of International Volcanological Congress.* IAVCEI Ankara 94. Ankara.

13

Pyroclastic Temper in Apulian Bronze Age Pottery: The Far-reaching Impact of a Vesuvian Eruption

**Sara T. Levi, Alessandro Vanzetti, Raffaello Cioni,
Fabio Fratini, and Elena Pecchioni**[1]

A recent project of archaeometrical analyses of Bronze Age pottery from Apulian sites showed the existence of a massive use of pyroclastic material as temper (Amadori et al. 1995, Levi et al. 1995, 1999). The archaeological material comes from the province of Foggia: Coppa Nevigata – Manfredonia (Cazzella and Moscoloni 1987); Terra di Corte (ipogeo 3) – S.Ferdinando; Madonna di Loreto – Trinitapoli (Tunzi Sisto 1992a); Madonna di Ripalta – Cerignola (fig. 13.1; Tunzi Sisto 1992b). For comparison, some samples from La Starza – Ariano Irpino (Province of Avellino; Albore Livadie 1990–1991) were also analyzed.[2]

Identification of Pumice

Thin section analysis identified that some different kinds of temper had been added to the clay, mainly pumice, calcite, and grog, as shown by their dimensional and morphological characteristics (fig. 13.2). Pyroclastic material is allogenous in northern Apulia but is now absent from known geological outcrops, and the area is characterized by sedimentary formations of calcareous rocks.

At Coppa Nevigata, where pottery tempered with pumice was first discovered and where 200 samples have been analyzed, the maximum use of volcanic temper is attested in the lowest Bronze Age levels of the site. In the Protoapennine levels more than 50% of the pots contain pumice, either alone or combined with other tempering materials, but during the following periods (Apennine and Sub-Apennine) a sharp decrease is observed (Amadori et al. 1995).

The following are some other considerations for identification of pumice.

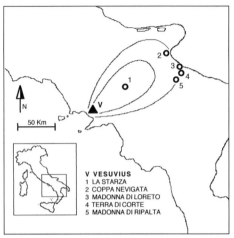

Fig. 13.1. Provenance of samples. The curve traces the dispersion of the fallout of the Avellino eruption.

1. Pumice in the pottery is often associated with other kinds of temper, particularly with the local calcareous minerals and rocks.
2. Volcanic material was used as temper also for daub, ovens, and other constructions.
3. A long distance exchange of large quantities of pottery during the Bronze Age is archaeologically untenable, because of technological and social considerations.[3]
4. X-ray fluorescence (XRF) analyses of the complete composition of the sherds, both temper and clay (table 13.1), performed at the Earth Science Department of the University of Florence show that all the Apulian samples have a similar composition, indicating that they were regionally produced. There are some minor compositional differences between pottery with different kinds of temper from the same site and between pottery from different sites. Samples from La Starza, the most distant site, are the most different (fig. 13.3).

The archaeological and archaeometrical data prove that Apulian pottery was locally produced. Where, then, does the pumice come from?

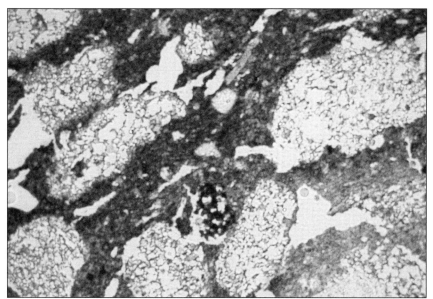

Fig. 13.2. Microphotograph of the thin-section of a sherd (sample 21) from Coppa Nevigata (Manfredonia) with pumice as temper. Plane polarized light; frame size 3.6 x 2.4 mm.

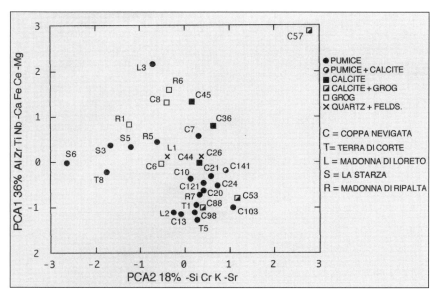

Fig. 13.3. Chemical classification (by principal components analysis, PCA) of the pottery consisting of a plot of principal components 1 and 2, using the statistical package Systat 5.1 for Macintosh.

Table 13.1. Results of X-Ray Fluorescence (XRF) Analysis of Samples

N.	Shape	CHRON.	L.O.I.	Na₂O	MgO	Al₂O₃	SiO₂	P₂O₅	K₂O	CaO
S3	Sherd	Protoap.	3.30	1.48	2.24	17.39	60.73	0.30	3.72	4.16
S5	Sherd	Protoap.	6.10	1.14	2.12	17.73	60.31	0.14	3.16	2.77
S6	Sherd	Protoap.	5.90	1.19	1.77	16.66	60.78	0.68	3.09	3.69
L1	Car. bowl	Apenn.	10.80	0.87	1.99	16.76	51.94	0.20	2.51	7.62
L2	Car. bowl	Apenn.	13.20	1.51	2.50	14.91	47.58	0.13	3.30	11.00
L3	Jar	Apenn.	5.90	0.97	2.80	18.51	54.67	0.45	2.73	5.08
T1	Handle	Protoap.	10.50	0.60	2.52	14.47	47.22	0.22	3.16	14.79
T5	Jar	Protoap.	9.60	1.48	2.49	14.21	45.40	0.39	3.18	17.27
T8	Car. bowl	Protoap.	4.70	0.83	1.92	16.05	64.65	0.37	3.32	2.33
R1	Daub	Bz. Age	3.80	0.84	1.53	18.04	63.42	0.16	3.95	2.43
R5	Sherd	Bz. Age	7.00	1.01	1.99	16.91	56.48	0.36	4.11	5.42
R6	Sherd	Bz. Age	7.20	0.69	1.64	19.44	56.97	0.17	4.57	1.17
R7	Sherd	Bz. Age	11.30	1.70	2.58	14.32	44.96	0.44	4.34	14.42
C6	Car. bowl	Subap.	5.70	0.74	2.56	15.42	58.46	0.25	3.97	5.93
C7	Car. bowl	Apenn.	4.30	1.73	2.60	16.99	57.86	0.19	4.89	4.11
C8	Car. bowl	Subap.	5.70	0.86	1.95	19.33	57.82	0.50	4.28	1.94
C10	Car. bowl	Subap.	10.20	2.04	2.47	14.94	49.07	0.21	4.33	10.52
C13	Jar	Apenn.	10.80	1.28	2.45	13.17	47.71	0.22	4.19	14.73
C20	Bowl	Protoap.	9.70	1.74	2.36	14.14	48.25	0.49	4.35	12.93
C21	Bowl	Protoap.	9.10	1.35	2.61	15.73	49.13	0.43	4.07	10.63
C24	Cooking pot	Protoap.	6.80	1.72	2.86	15.00	48.84	0.25	3.78	13.77
C26	Cleps. stand	Protoap.	6.80	0.93	2.42	15.54	56.47	0.22	4.84	5.40
C36	Cooking pot	Subap.	11.50	0.79	1.75	17.19	48.25	0.10	3.57	8.03
C44	Cooking pot	Apenn.	14.80	1.02	1.68	16.04	42.93	0.62	3.46	12.32
C45	Cooking pot	Apenn.	10.20	1.20	1.59	18.91	49.59	0.50	4.23	5.89
C53	Cooking pot	Protoap.	12.50	1.14	2.43	12.68	42.24	0.53	4.14	16.13
C57	Cooking pot	Subap.	6.20	1.39	1.73	21.27	46.14	0.39	6.53	5.17
C88	Car. bowl	Apenn.	13.70	1.01	2.61	12.98	43.91	0.26	4.29	14.79
C98	Jar	Protoap.	11.90	1.46	2.59	13.15	45.90	0.34	4.13	14.63
C103	Jar	Protoap.	13.70	1.11	2.13	11.22	42.02	0.25	6.75	16.50
C121	Bowl	Subap.	6.30	1.95	2.85	15.24	50.05	0.45	4.05	12.28
C141	Cooking pot	Protoap.	9.70	1.52	2.19	15.52	46.12	0.63	4.44	11.96

Note: S = La Starza; L = Madonna di Loreto; T = Terra di Corte; R = Madonna di Ripalta; C = Coppa Nevigata

Detailed Examination of Pumice

The petrographic features of the magmatic material in several samples were observed. We also analyzed pumice chips and minerals in the matrix of pottery from several of these samples. Analyses were performed with microanalytical facilities at the Earth Science Department of the University of Pisa. A Philips 515 SEM equipped with an EDS microanalytical system EDAX PV 9900 was used (operating conditions: 20 kV acceleration voltage, 100 s live time, 200–500 nm of beam diameter).

Pumice fragments and glass sherds in the analyzed samples are unaltered

TiO$_2$	MnO	Fe Tot	Zr	Y	Rb	Nb	Sr	Ce	La	Ba	Cr
0.64	0.12	5.91	233	22	198	36	2039	141	63	909	66
0.63	0.06	5.85	243	19	216	33	1042	127	56	84	71
0.54	0.08	5.63	210	22	159	26	2091	108	43	1330	51
0.69	0.15	6.46	230	16	140	25	383	193	72	561	73
0.59	0.09	5.19	143	2	130	15	367	109	46	671	66
1.12	0.10	7.67	404	38	131	63	995	441	192	1452	67
0.64	0.11	5.77	163	13	128	16	263	97	48	405	78
0.56	0.11	5.30	159	9	151	17	325	101	50	462	69
0.63	0.07	5.11	219	10	144	15	252	97	37	802	57
0.63	0.18	5.01	379	27	153	43	199	196	75	563	45
0.68	0.18	5.85	280	24	170	38	344	150	63	968	59
0.77	0.11	7.27	343	23	177	45	160	162	58	875	78
0.58	0.14	5.23	233	13	177	39	481	127	53	632	56
0.69	0.14	6.14	219	30	144	26	314	124	65	1007	74
0.72	0.26	6.34	258	30	208	33	372	155	72	970	83
0.84	0.10	6.68	332	44	190	39	349	192	96	758	84
0.60	0.10	5.54	257	28	183	39	426	118	59	614	60
0.55	0.13	4.77	176	18	143	26	456	112	58	764	57
0.63	0.14	5.28	242	35	152	34	455	110	54	585	66
0.68	0.14	6.12	219	26	151	36	415	91	47	491	80
0.69	0.15	6.15	241	61	160	32	405	117	57	461	73
0.74	0.16	6.48	215	26	137	25	207	125	56	545	82
0.78	0.08	7.36	316	61	163	32	135	145	67	396	101
0.68	0.12	6.32	267	42	138	36	215	139	59	696	74
0.79	0.13	6.97	356	102	189	47	244	203	90	754	76
0.66	0.13	7.42	162	39	143	18	483	92	45	559	84
1.36	0.14	9.68	423	51	170	68	434	211	110	429	122
0.60	0.11	5.73	186	27	137	25	407	113	57	662	64
0.52	0.15	5.24	216	22	161	30	415	99	52	511	50
0.62	0.16	5.55	203	21	146	27	442	101	53	759	56
0.67	0.12	6.04	213	24	170	30	566	126	62	700	78
0.76	0.17	6.98	204	18	151	29	441	101	47	665	76

and well preserved. Some samples have strongly argillified glass sherds and were not analyzed. Pumice fragments from Apulian sites are subaphyric to aphyric and show microfenocrysts of sanidine, salitic clinopyroxene, mica, potassic amphibole, with rarer plagioclase, scapolite, nefeline, and garnet. The same phases also occur, with different proportions, in the groundmass of the pottery, as does spatic calcite. Pottery from the La Starza site shows the same features. In these samples pumice fragments generally have a coarser grain-size (1–2 mm vs. 0.5 mm in Apulia) and are more porphyritic, while the matrix of the pottery is more strongly enriched with crystals of sanidine than the matrix of the Apulian samples.

The mineralogy of the pumice is very interesting because of the contemporaneous occurrence of nefeline and scapolite together with potassic minerals (mica and amphibole) that are not very common in the magmatism of Italy or the Mediterranean region. The same mineralogical assemblage is described by Barberi et al. (1981) for the products of Avellino Pumice, a Somma-Vesuvius eruption of Bronze Age date.[4]

Characteristics of the Avellino Eruption

The deposits of the Avellino Pumice have been well studied since the first work of Lirer et al. (1973). The products of this plinian eruption are mainly represented by a pumice fallout sheet dispersed by the prevailing winds in an east–northeast direction (fig. 13.1; Lirer et al. 1973; Rolandi et al. 1993; Cioni et al. 1999). The pumice is characterized by a strong compositional variation, resulting in a sharp color change from white (lower-first layer) to gray pumice (upper-second layer). These deposits show an exponential decrease in thickness with distance, from about 2 m on the slopes of the volcano to 10 cm at a distance of 70 km (La Starza, Ariano Irpino). Coppa Nevigata and the Ofanto Valley are on the fan of the main fallout dispersal, at a distance of about 140 km from Vesuvius. By extrapolating the exponential law of thickness decrease calculated on the more proximal sites, a thickness of fallout deposit of about 3 cm can be estimated for such a distance.

Further Identification

The analyses of the glass in the pumice provides very interesting results. The glass composition is homogeneous and identical to the peak of the gray pumice composition measured in more than 200 samples of pumice from the pyroclastic deposits of the Avellino Pumice (fig. 13.4; Cioni et al. 1999). The analyses in the glass from the pottery revealed a secondary peak coinciding with the mean composition of the white pumice. The magmatic crystals (mainly sanidine and salitic pyroxene) in the matrix of the pottery also have the same composition as those from the pumice (Cioni et al. pers. comm.; Levi et al. 1999). The same results come from the comparison of scapolite microcrysts from the pumice in the pottery and from the Avellino Gray Pumice.

The petrochemical data strongly suggest that the pumice in Apulian and

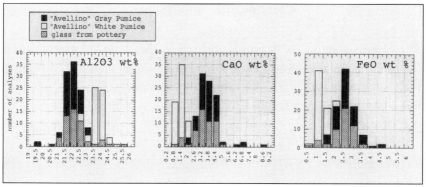

Fig. 13.4. Histograms of chemical composition (Al_2O_3, CaO, and FeO) of Avellino gray and white pumice and the glass from the pottery.

La Starza pottery sherds are very homogeneous and are probably related to the Vesuvian eruption of Avellino Pumice. A Vesuvian origin for the pumice is also indirectly suggested by some leucite-bearing lava fragments occurring in the matrix of the pottery, which are probably related to lithic fragments from the interior of the volcano that are always among the products of strongly explosive eruptions.

Discussions of Results

The XRF data show differences between coastal Apulian sites and La Starza; so if exact provenance cannot be determined, the existence of different local productions is the most probable situation. On the basis of the entire data set we suggest that the finer grain-size for the pumice fragments in Apulian pottery with respect to the pumice in the La Starza samples reflects a primary depositional feature, generally finer grains downwind of the deposit. This fact is in accordance with the position of the archeological sites, and suggests that the pumice of the Apulian pottery was probably collected at a site more distant from Vesuvius than the pumice in the pottery from La Starza, where the deposits of the Avellino eruption are still present. Furthermore, the size of the pumice used as temper allows us to identify different areas of production with respect to the distance from Vesuvius; in the Madonna di Loreto chamber tomb one bowl displays coarser pumice than the others, and can be regarded as an import.

Chronological Implications

The identification of the eruption products in the tempering materials has implications for the discussion of the relative and absolute chronology of the southern Italian Bronze Age; therefore our petrographic and compositional analysis has a much wider importance. The presence of volcanic products demonstrates that the analyzed Protoapennine pottery is more recent than the eruption. We will now underline in a more accurate way the chronological implications that put the Avellino eruption in a wider Mediterranean perspective.

Relative Chronology
The catastrophic volcanic event we are discussing began receiving attention from archaeologists 20 years ago, when it was realized that it covered several archaeological sites, interrupting the development of the local culture of the Campanian plain. This facies has been named after the site of Palma Campania, the first archaeological site where the volcanic destruction was outlined (Albore Livadie and D'Amore 1980). The Palma Campania facies is typical of an advanced moment of the Italian Early Bronze Age (EBA), with strong connections to contemporary archaeological cultures of the Tyrrhenian Sea (Albore Livadie et al. 1996).

The presence of pumice from that eruption in the pottery of the lowest levels of the Apulian site of Coppa Nevigata allows us to expand the fixed point in the chronology to the Adriatic coast, where the cultural development is different. Because of the new data, we can be certain that sites of the so-called Protoapennine cultural facies, such as Coppa Nevigata, Terra di Corte, and Madonna di Loreto, postdate the eruption; until now this was still a matter of discussion.

At the site of Ariano Irpino, 70 km away from Vesuvius, a settlement was founded immediately over the 10-cm thick layer of pumice from the Avellino eruption. The archaeological materials still bear similarities with those of Palma Campania, but also include Protoapennine pottery (Albore Livadie 1990–1991). Moreover, similar products have been identified in the lowest level of the Vivara Island excavation, an important settlement in the Bay of Naples in an area not affected by the Avellino eruption (Cazzella 1994). In the following layer at Vivara, true Protoapennine pottery appears together with fragments of imported Aeolian and Aegean pottery dating to Late Helladic I (LHI).

In summary, the eruption interrupts the Palma Campania cultural facies, preceding not only true Protoapennine sites (Coppa Nevigata) but also intermediate or early Protoapennine cultural aspects (Ariano Irpino, Vivara's lowest level), which are then followed by Protoapennine and LHI pottery. We can say that the eruption occurred more or less at the transition between the EBA (Palma Campania facies) and the Middle Bronze Age (MBA; Protoapennine facies), but probably slightly before. To what extent the complex reorganization of the settlement pattern in Southern Italy, which started in the MBA, was triggered or accelerated by the volcanic catastrophe will continue to be a matter for discussion.

Absolute Chronology

Recent research on dendrochronology and calibrated ^{14}C dates bring coherent data to the discussion. The transition between the north Italian EBA and MBA has been bracketed between 1790 and 1650 cal B.C., based on the site of Laghetto del Frassino (Verona, northern Italy; Martinelli 1996).[5] It is reasonable to accept a date in the middle of the suggested span, about 1720 B.C.[6]

If we consider the radiocarbon dates that refer directly to the eruption,[7] we see that they concentrate around two wiggles of the calibration curve and the portion of the curve between those wiggles (fig. 13.5). The general time-span encompasses the later 19th, the 18th, and most of the 17th centuries, B.C. Two weighed averages produce dates of 3457±66 and 3442±43,[8] 1861–(1740)–1665 and 1876–(1738)–1639 in calibrated years B.C. Such dates, compared with the Laghetto del Frassino sequence, correspond closely to the transition from the EBA to MBA (fig. 13.6).

Two other contexts with radiocarbon dates[9] reinforce the pattern:[10] the northern Italian site of Stanghelle East, from the late EBA/early MBA, whose dates[11] overlap with the dates for the eruption and the Sa Turricula Culture in Sardinia (Ferrarese Ceruti and Lo Schiavo 1991–1992), whose dates are in the same area of the calibration curve as Stanghelle East and the eruption, and last for a short period afterward.[12] This evidence converges to suggest a date for the eruption in the 18th century B.C. This date is coherent with the general pattern; the transition between EBA and MBA in southern Italy should fall between the second half of the 18th and the beginning of the 17th century B.C., as in northern Italy.

The existence of an archaeological layer in Vivara Punta Mezzogiorno, possibly parallel to post-eruptive basal layers of La Starza in Ariano Irpino (Cazzella 1994; Albore Livadie et al. 1996) and preceding evidence for LHI

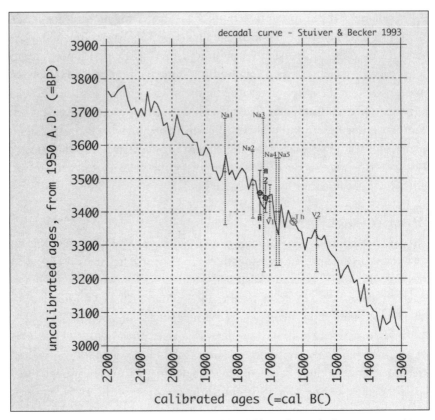

Fig. 13.5. Absolute dates for the Avellino eruption. A1 and A2 are the weighed averages quoted in the text; Na 1–5 are the dates of the Naples Lab; V1 and V2 are dates by Vogel et al. (1990). Dates quoted in n. 7. The recently suggested date for Thera eruption (1628=Th) has been marked.

Aegean contacts, marks an important point in the relative chronology, allowing us to bring into the discussion the much-debated date of the Thera eruption. The Thera eruption occurred before the end of LHI. Traditional chronologists date the eruption in the second half of the 16th century B.C. (see Manning 1995 for references on this viewpoint). The recently proposed date of 1628±1 B.C. (cf. discussion in Kuniholm 1990; Manning 1995) would be about one century later than the date suggested here for the Avellino eruption and convincingly accounts for the existence of a brief gap between the Avellino eruption and LHI (Vivara evidence). Without discussing in detail the complex argument, we propose that the general evidence presented here favors the newly proposed date for the Thera eruption.

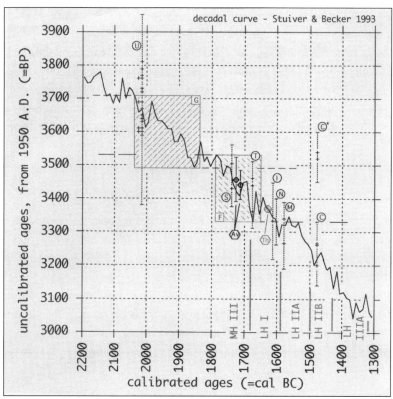

Fig. 13.6. The absolute dates for a selection of archaeological sites and facies of the Italian Bronze Age. The representation is schematic and only the maximum span and central dates (crosses) are indicated. *U*, La Muculufa, EBA; *S*, Stanghelle East; *T*, Sa Turricola facies; *I*, Isolone del Mincio, MBA; *N*, Nuraghe Noeddos, post-Sa Turricola, MBA; *M*, Monte Castellaccio, MBA; *C*, Coppa Nevigata, complexes B–C, MBA; *C**, Coppa Nevigata, complex A (dates in Skeates and Whitehouse 1994a; 1994b). Gray hatched rectangles show the range of the tree-cut phases of the dendrochronological curve Garda I (*G*), EBA (Martinelli 1996) and the possible span for the Laghetto del Frassino curve (*F*). A1 and A2 (weighed averages for the Avellino eruption) have been superimposed, as well as the recently suggested date for Thera eruption (=Th). At the base the ^{14}C Chronology of the Aegean sequence, as proposed by Manning (1995)

We can then reconstruct three cultural phases. An initial post-Avellino eruption phase was transitional between EBA and MBA and lacked LHI material but had pottery transitional between Palma Campania and Protoapennine. A second phase of true MBA, together with LHI pottery, preceded the Thera eruption. A third phase of advanced MBA, post-dated the Thera eruption and still had LHI pottery. The absolute chronology worked out by Manning for the Helladic phases relevant for the present discussion has been inserted at the base of fig. 13.6, and we can see the satisfactory match of the suggested pattern.

We may say that the date of the Avellino eruption for the chronological discussion of the Mediterranean Bronze Age is significant because it bridges the gaps between the dendrochronological sequences, the radiocarbon dates of Central Europe[13] and northern Italy, and the Aegean chronology, currently debated because of the dating of Thera. The extreme coherence of the pattern presented here is a good argument for its reliability.

Conclusions

One of the main problems of the Avellino eruption is its environmental impact. In Apulia destructive effects should have been absent, but we detected some hitherto unsuspected traces of the event. The new raw material, the pumice, was immediately incorporated into a tradition of pottery manufacture that lasted at least 300 years. Obviously, there are other, more important chain-reactions started by the eruption that must be investigated by future research. The full potential of detailed inquiry over such particular events, however, has been outlined through the chronological analysis presented.

REFERENCES

Albore Livadie, C. 1990–1991. "Nuovi scavi alla Starza di Ariano Irpino." *Rassegna di Archeologia* 10:481–91.

Albore Livadie, C., G. Bailo Modesti, A. Salerno, and P.F. Talamo. 1996. "Articolazioni culturali e cronologiche – L'Italia Meridionale — La Campania." In *L'antica età del bronzo (Acts of the Congresso, Viareggio 9–12.1.1995)*, edited by D. Cocchi Genick, 119–34. Firenze.

Albore Livadie, C., and L. D'Amore. 1980. "Palma Campania (Napoli). Resti di abitato dell'età del Bronzo antico." *Notizie degli Scavi di Antichità* 105:59–101.

Amadori, M.L., M. Di Pillo, F. Fratini, S.T. Levi, and E. Pecchioni. 1995. "The Bronze Age Pottery of Coppa Nevigata (FG-Italy): Raw Materials and Production." In *Proceedings of the European Meeting on Ancient Ceramics - Archaeometrical and Archaeological Studies (Barcelona 18–20 November 1993)*, edited by M. Vendrell-Saz, T. Pradell, J. Molera, and M. Garcia, 45–52. Barcelona.

Andronico, D., R. Cioni, A. Sbrana, R. Sulpizio, and R. Santacroce. 1995. "The Geological Evolution of Somma-Vesuvius." *Periodico di Mineralogia* 64:81–2.

Barberi F., H. Bizouard, R. Clocchiatti, N. Metrich, R. Santacroce, and A. Sbrana. 1981.

"The Somma-Vesuvius Magma Chamber: A Petrological and Volcanological Approach." *Bulletin of Volcanology* 44:294–315.

Cazzella, A. 1994. "Cronologia radiocarbonica calibrata e cronologia 'storica' nell'Italia Centro-Meridionale durante l'età del bronzo." In *Radiocarbon Dating and Italian Prehistory*, edited by R. Skeates and R. Whitehouse, 73–83. London.

Cazzella, A., and M. Moscoloni. 1987. "Età del bronzo. La ricerca archeologica." In *Coppa Nevigata e il suo territorio: testimonianze archeologiche Dal VII al II millennio A.C.*, edited by S.M. Cassano, A. Cazzella, A. Manfredini, and M. Moscoloni, 109–90. Roma.

Cioni, R., D. Morandi, A. Sbrana, and R. Sulpizio. 1999. "L'eruzione delle Pomici di Avellino: aspetti stratigrafici e vulcanologici." In *L'eruzione vesuviana delle "Pomici di Avellino" e la facies di Palma Campania (Bronzo antico) (Acts of the Convegno Internazionale, Centro Universitario Europeo per i Beni Culturali, Ravello 15–17 July 1994)*, edited by C. Albore Livadie, 61–92. Bari.

Ferrarese Ceruti, M.L., and F. Lo Schiavo. 1991–1992. "Articolazioni cronologiche e definizione di elementi culturali — La Sardegna." *Rassegna di Archeologia* 10:123–41.

Jones, R.E., and L. Vagnetti. 1991. "Traders and Craftsmen in the Central Mediterranean: Archaeological Evidence and Archaeometric Research." In *Bronze Age Trade in the Mediterranean*, SIMA XC, edited by N.H. Gale, 127–47. Jonsered.

Kuniholm, P.I. 1990. "Overview and Assessment of the Evidence for the Date of the Eruption of Thera." In *Thera and the Aegean World*. Vol. III, *Chronology*, edited by D.A. Hardy and C. Renfrew, 13–8. London.

Levi, S.T., M.L. Amadori, M. Di Pillo, F. Fratini, and E. Pecchioni. 1995. "Archaeometric and Archaeologic Research on the Pottery of Coppa Nevigata (FG-Italy): Production and Provenance." In *The Ceramics Cultural Heritage. Proceedings of the International Symposium: The Ceramics Heritage of the 8th CIMTEC-World Ceramic Congress and Forum on New Material (Firenze 28 June–2 July 1994)*, edited by P. Vincenzini, 423–32. Faenza.

Levi, S.T., R. Cioni, and A. Cazzella. 1999. "Presenza Di Materiale Pomiceo Dell'eruzione Vesuviana Di Avellino Nella Ceramica Dell'età Del Bronzo Di Coppa Nevigata (FG)." In *L'eruzione vesuviana delle "Pomici di Avellino" e la facies di Palma Campania (Bronzo antico) (Acts of the Convegno Internazionale, Centro Universitario Europeo per i Beni Culturali, Ravello 15–17 July 1994)*, edited by C. Albore Livadie, 131–41. Bari.

Levi, S.T., R.E. Jones, M. Sonnino, and L. Vagnetti. 1998. "Produzione e circolazione della ceramica nella Sibaritide protostorica." In *Broglio di Trebisacce 1990–1994. Elementi e problemi nuovi dalle recenti campagne di scavo*, edited by R. Peroni and A. Vanzetti, 175–212. Rossano.

Lirer, L., T. Pescatore, B. Booth, and G.P.L. Walker. 1973. "Two Plinian Pumice Fall Deposits from Somma-Vesuvius, Italy." *Geological Society of America Bulletin* 84:759–72.

Manning, S.W. 1995. *The Absolute Chronology of the Aegean Early Bronze Age*. Sheffield.

Rolandi G., G. Mastrolorenzo, A.M. Barrella., and A. Borrelli. 1993. "The Avellino Plinian Eruption of Somma-Vesuvius (3760 Y. B.P.): The Progressive Evolution from Magmatic to Hydromagmatic Style." *Journal of Volcanology and Geothermal Research* 58:67–88.

Skeates, R., and R. Whitehouse, eds. 1994a. *Radiocarbon Dating and Italian Prehistory*. London.

————. 1994b. "New Radiocarbon Dates for Prehistoric Italy 1." *The Accordia Research Papers* 5:137–50.

Tunzi Sisto, A.M. 1992a. "L'ipogeo di Madonna di Loreto (Trinitapoli, Foggia)." *Rassegna di Archeologia* 10:545–52.

————. 1992b. "Il villaggio preistorico di Madonna di Ripalta." *Rassegna di Archeologia* 10:738–9.

Vanzetti A. 1998. "La data dell'eruzione delle Pomici di Avellino nel quadro della cronologia comparata dell'età del bronzo, tra Egeo e Europa centrale" In *Archeologia e vulcanologia in Campania (Acts of the Convegno, Pompei 21.12.1996)*, edited by P.G. Guzzo and R. Peroni, 167–210. Napoli.

Vogel, J.S., W. Cornell, D.E. Nelson, and J.R. Southon. 1990. "Vesuvius/Avellino, One Possible Source of Seventeenth Century B.C.E. Climatic Disturbance." *Nature* 344:534–7.

NOTES

[1] Among the authors, S.T. Levi performed the general and petrographic classification of pottery; she has further collected and properly edited all the contributions; A. Vanzetti developed the chronological discussion; R. Cioni conducted the detailed study of volcanic materials, in connection with his own geological studies of the Avellino eruption; F. Fratini and E. Pecchioni performed the chemical (XRF analysis) and petrographical characterization (OM analysis) of the pottery. C. Albore Livadie, A. Cazzella, M. Cipolloni, M. Moscoloni, and A. M. Tunzi made this work possible by giving us samples for analyses and supporting us scientifically. Many others contributed to this work with discussions and technical help, including M. L. Amadori, A. Coeli, R. Coeli, S. Conticelli, M. Di Pillo, C. Manganelli Del Fa', and R. Peroni.

[2] Samples were submitted for analysis by A. Cazzella and M. Moscoloni for Coppa Nevigata; A.M. Tunzi Sisto for Terra di Corte and Madonna di Loreto; A.M. Tunzi Sisto and M. Cipolloni for Madonna di Ripalta; C. Albore Livadie for La Starza. We wish to thank all of them heartily.

[3] A high number of imports of whole pots are known in the Italian Bronze Age only in connection with island settlements poor in clay resources (such as the Aeolian islands; Williams 1980), with pots used as containers for traded goods (e.g., pithoi; cf. Levi et al. 1998), or with highly specialized productions (e.g., Mycenaean pottery, cf. Jones and Vagnetti 1991).

[4] Dated to the first half of the second millennium B.C. For a more detailed discussion, see *infra.*

[5] The site contains pottery with characteristics both of the end of the EBA and of the beginning of the MBA. A dendrochronological curve lasting 70 years has been dated by wiggle-matching of the radiocarbon determinations, but the result is somewhere inside the range 1790–1650 cal B.C.

[6] If one looks for sharp lines bordering the periods, we can imagine that the MBA started in

the middle of the Frassino sequence, at age 35 of the dendrochronological curve; the possible date for the beginning is then 1755–1685.

[7] Dates obtained by the team directed by F. Terrasi, working at the Naples laboratory of the Tandem Accelerator, University of Naples "Federico II," presented at the XIII Meeting of UISPP, held in Forlì 8–14 September 1996; dates from Naples are: Zabatta, 3520±160; Lagno Cavone, 3480±100; Pratola Serra, 3450±230; Pozzelle, 3400±160; Frattaminore 3400±160; Vogel et al.1990: RIDDL-1343, Pozzelle, 3430±50; RIDDL-1338, Ottaviano, 3300±80.

[8] Calibration obtained by using the program CALIB, version 3.03c, using the decadal curve by Stuiver and Becker 1993. The first average used only Naples dates; the second also used the oldest of the dates obtained by Vogel et al. (1990: RIDDL-1343). The probabilities (Method B of CALIB) obtained for the averages are: *A1*, 1876–1842 16%; 1827–1789 19%; 1782–1687 56%; 1669–1660 4%; 1648–1639 4%; *A2*, 1859–1847 6%; 1808–1801 4%; 1773–1686 73%; 1670–1659 8%; 1650–1636 9%.

[9] Those dates and the others used in fig. 13.5 are listed in Skeates and Whitehouse (1994a, 1994b).

[10] Two of the dates of the post-eruption levels of Coppa Nevigata are close, but tend to be too early. BO-228: 4010±90 B.P.; BO-229: 3540±60 B.P.; BO-230: 3520±70 B.P. (Skeates and Whitehouse 1994b).

[11] OxA-5494: 3505±55 B.P.; OxA-5495: 3430±55 B.P.

[12] Sa Turricula, R-963a: 3460±50 B.P.; Filiestru Cave, Q-3031: 3440±40 B.P.; Nuraghe Noeddos, Q-3070: 3360±50 B.P.

[13] A discussion of that bulk of evidence is in progress by A. Vanzetti (1998).

14

The A.D. 79 Eruption: Seismic Activity and Effects of the Eruption on Pompeii

Aldo Marturano and Antonio Varone[*]

This chapter reports results of research carried out by geophysicists and archaeologists into the events that preceded, accompanied, and followed the eruption of Vesuvius in A.D. 79. In 1993 debate focused on the links between extraordinary geodynamic events (e.g., earthquakes and eruptions) and changes that occurred to the social fabric and local economy of the area (Anon. 1995). In this interdisciplinary discourse, the House of the Chaste Lovers became the principal bone of contention because many factors (i.e., works in progress and patched-up walls) validated the hypothesis of shocks in the last few years or months. It was proposed that the eruption was preceded by a number of earthquakes, in addition to those earthquakes which—far distant in time—are known to have occurred much earlier in A.D. 62 and A.D. 64. Moreover, various masonry finds appeared to have been displaced from their original positions during the course of the eruption. Excavation was resumed in 1995.

Earlier in the history of this excavation, which began in 1987 (Varone 1993), two distinctive blocks of buildings had been discovered: a southernmost block—corresponding to Numbers 6 and 7; insula 12; Regio IX beside the Via dell'Abbondanza—housing a baker's shop, and a more eastern block where a "rich" dwelling (the House of the Chaste Lovers) was discovered, the main entrance of which was probably by a road to its west. This house, which has been only partially excavated, comprises rooms arranged around a triple

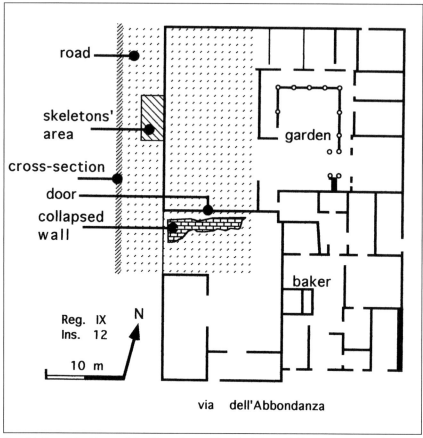

Fig. 14.1. Plan of the House of the Chaste Lovers. The stippled area indicates the extent of the excavations.

colonnade that decorates a well-tended garden. Its western limits and the adjacent road have recently been unearthed (fig. 14.1) and, excavations have now removed the pyroclastic flows to reach the underlying gray pumice layer associated with the plinian phase of volcanic activity. These excavations cast new light on the eruption and its effects.

Pompeii Prior to the A.D. 79 Eruption

A number of precursory earthquakes had occurred prior to the eruption of Vesuvius, but the event of A.D. 62 is the best known and the most severe earthquake, and was followed by another significant event in A.D. 64; these were the only events that may be historically dated with any certainty. There are, however, several historical accounts (e.g., Sen. *Q Nat* 6.1, 27, 31; Plin. *Ep.* 6.16, 20), together with some epigraphical and archaeological evidence (Deutsches Arch. Inst. Rom. et al. 1995), which allow us to argue that several seismic events occurred that were strong enough to damage buildings. On the basis of generalized, sometimes hasty reconstructions, it has been argued that the town was in a state of cultural and economic decay, but it now seems more likely that although the inhabitants were highly suspicious about the numerous shocks that were occurring, they were nevertheless rebuilding. Certainly they couldn't know about the imminent eruption. In A.D. 79 several restorations were being carried out to repair the damage from an earthquake that had occurred not long before the eruption (Varone 1995; Marturano and Rinaldis 1998).

The Plinian Phase

On the morning of 24 August A.D. 79 the eruption of Vesuvius began with a phreatomagmatic (i.e., hydrovolcanic) episode (the opening phase). A basal ash layer characterized this initial phase (Sigurdsson et al. 1985; Barberi et al. 1989), and was produced by lateral blasts and slight water-magma interaction (Lirer et al. 1993). The axis of dispersal of the volcanic products was orientated toward the east. The basal ash layer did not affect Pompeii, but later in the eruption some 240 cm of pumice fall was deposited that was white phonolitic at the base and gray tephritic-phonolitic at the top (Lirer et al. 1973; Civetta et al. 1991; Cioni et al. 1992; Lirer et al. 1993; Cioni et al. 1995). With the passage of time, this phase became characterized by a significant increase in the size of the pumice; in the height of the eruption column; and in the frequency of partial column collapses, which produced pyroclastic flows and surges (Sheridan et al. 1981; Sigurdsson et al. 1985; Carey and Sigurdsson 1987; Lirer et al. 1993). According to estimates based on the letters of Pliny the Younger (Sigurdsson et al. 1985; Carey and Sigurdsson 1987; Cioni et al. 1995), the fallout phase lasted 18–19 hours. This estimate, however, should now be seriously questioned. Stringent philological criteria ascribe a limited chronological validity to the first of the two letters of Pliny the Younger, which Gigante (1989) calls the "Letter for History," but the new stratigraphic evidence agrees very well with some paragraphs currently judged questionable.

Based on the conventional interpretation, Pliny the Elder, the commander of the fleet-endeavored to carry out a highly dubious landing on the Vesuvian coast at the height of the plinian phase. In spite of the terror overwhelming the crew, he decided to set a course for the Stabian area, the region most affected by fallout products. The farther he sailed in this direction, the worse conditions became, since both the caliber of the pumice fall and the percentage of lithic blocks increased during the course of the eruption. Other effects of the eruption were occurring at this time, including partial collapse of the plinian eruption column and associated ash-flows, making the leeward side of the volcano extremely uncomfortable. The Pompeii-Stabiae Directrix lay toward the center of this "hurricane," where visibility was impaired and breathing became difficult.

According to the conventional interpretation, Pliny the Elder must have landed, paid tribute to Pomponianus, and stayed at his villa under the most prohibitive conditions. It seems more likely that he and his crew approached the Vesuvian coast when the plinian phase was almost over. It was sunset, about 6 p.m., when they attempted to dock but failed because of the changed submarine morphology in front of the volcano. Herculaneum had been destroyed by the earlier pyroclastic flows which advanced into the sea for many meters, as suggested by Pliny the Younger, "iam vadum subitum ruinaque montis litora abstantia (Ep. 6.16, 11)." At 6:43 p.m. the sun set beyond the horizon, so that as they sailed along the coast they would have witnessed in the fading light the appalling destruction produced by the eruption. Pliny was dismayed because he knew that he had underestimated the severity of a number of signals, which he had thought indicated normal conditions, without realizing that they were part of an abnormal situation that had been going on for some years. Landing at Stabiae when the eruption was over (around 10 p.m.), he trod on paths dug in pumice deposits 1 m thick and climbed up to the villa, one of many patrician villas overlooking the bay. After bathing and dining, he mistook the modest activity of Vesuvius's "extended flaming foci and high firing column" (Gigante 1989, 75) for fires which peasants had left burning and believed the danger to be over.

According to our reconstruction, the plinian phase lasted six hours and, unless a highly improbable shortening of the plinian phase occurred, by 1 p.m. the eruptive column was fully sustained. In this reconstruction, with estimated volumes of 2.2×10^{12} kg for the white pumice and 6.4×10^{12} kg for the gray pumice, the average rate of fallout products is 200% higher than that proposed by Carey and Sigurdsson (1987; from 8.2×10^7 to 2.4×10^8 for the white pumice and from 1.6 to 4.7×10^8 kg[1] for the gray).

The Flow Phase

During the night strong earthquakes were felt in Stabiae and Miseno that marked the beginning of a new phase. They were stronger than those which had occurred before the eruption, but this time were immediately linked to the activity of Vesuvius. People were better able to protect themselves from the effects of the imminent resumption of activity, "they place pillows on their heads and tie them vigorously with sheets" (Gigante 1989, 77).

Occurring at shallow hypocentral depths (~5 km) with a magnitude of slightly less than 5, these seismic events were responses of the system to the major disequilibrium produced by the earlier intense plinian phase, together with the presence of large quantities of ground water. In the neighborhood of the volcano this disequilibrium caused landslides and earthquakes and in Pompeii the pumice fall contributed to the collapse of buildings.

During deposition of the gray pumice a partial collapse of the plinian column (Sigurdsson et al. 1985; Lirer et al. 1993) generated surges. A "transitional phase" between the magmatic and hydromagmatic phases has previously been proposed at this level in the stratigraphy (Sheridan et al. 1981; Barberi et al. 1989), and, more specifically, following the fallout phase the shift to phreatomagmatic activity was signaled by a layer of accretionary lapilli at the top of the "S6" surge (identified by Sigurdsson et al. 1985; see also Cioni et al. 1990; Lirer et al. 1993). This activity was related to the collapse of the roof of the magma chamber (Barberi et al. 1989) and probably to the partial collapse of the volcano (Lirer et al. 1993). According to Cioni et al., (1990), sedimentological characteristics indicate that deposition was the result of a high-velocity, low density turbulent cloud (Lajoie et al. 1989), but in a more recent paper Cioni et al., (1995) have proposed an alternative model. In this model the turbulent, highly dilute pyroclastic flows marked a drastic change in eruption dynamics, with pumice deposition occurring some 18 to 19 hours after the beginning of the eruption in response to caldera formation related to the collapse of the magma chamber.

As will be discussed later in the chapter no fallout occurred after the gray pumice phase, which can be related to the establishment of the plinian column. Some eruptive units, which may be related to flows deposited after both the plinian phase and a period of relative quiescence lasting roughly 10 hours, have layers of ash containing pisolite in their upper portions. What is more, two ash-fall layers occurred during the final eruptive phase and were deposited at the top of the pumice layer. The first of these layers comprises intercalated ash and pisolites deposited between grains of gray pumice (Yokohama and Marturano 1997), a sedimentology which is indicative of the interaction between the erupting volcano and water-bearing aquifers after the close of the plinian phase. In the Pompeii excavation, this change in eruptive styles can be clearly discerned, and there is evidence of both intense seismic events and the buildup of water between the plinian and flow phases, thus facilitating the development of a phreatomagmatic phase.

Stratigraphy

The excavation of the House of the Chaste Lovers is aligned north to south along the western by-road (figs. 14.2 and 14.3); a 30 m-long, 3 m-high cross-section is exposed and allows the stratigraphy of the fourth phase of the eruption, the flow phase, to be investigated. The pumice fallout layer has not yet been excavated and only the upper gray pumice layer has been investigated. The pavement of the road is roughly 2 m below the current ground surface, and from north to south along the wall major changes in the pumice layer may be observed. At its northern end, the layer is 1 m in thickness, but to the south it barely crops out. This outcrop geology reflects a number of factors: the slope of the road, the sliding patterns created by the partial collapse of buildings, and the extent of pumice penetration in adjacent buildings, which depends on whether indoor rooms or outdoor spaces (e.g., courtyards and gardens) were affected. Within the upper portions of the "A6" pumice, Sigurdsson et al. (1985) defined both fallout phases ("A") and surges ("S"), from which granular sherds of roofing-tiles and bricks from collapsed buildings were recovered. Between the sherds a few centimeters of gray to white fine ash were observed. This gray to white ash also penetrates the lower horizon to a depth of 2–3 cm, thus filling spaces between individual grains of pumice. This is known as the *wa* level. Above, a gray-pinkish ash ("S4") crops out, which in its lowest 3 cm shows a significant fines depletion. Roofing-tiles and wooden trusses, which were originally constructed to support roofs, are bounded by this layer. A layer ("A7") less than 1 cm in thickness and composed of rounded and clear pumice lapilli separates the "S4" and "S5" (5–15 cm thick) levels, which appear to have eroded the underlying substrate. Pieces of plaster and fragments of roofing-tiles are found. Working up through the section, a 4.5 cm-thick layer ("A8") rich in lithics but lacking fines, is found and above this is a series of layers that are designated "S6".

The "S6" layer is around 150 cm in thickness; and comprises several horizons. From the base to the top these are:

A. White to gray pumice lapilli;

B. dune-shaped pumice rich material showing evidence of gliding and containing overlapping roof tiles; toward the top there is a thin band ("C1") in which accretionary lapilli are abundant;

C. several horizons, unrecognized by Sigurdsson et al. (1985): the lower two are separated by an ash, while the upper two are topped by a horizon that is rich in pea stones. Three of the horizons show enrichment of lithics (i.e. debris, lava and dolomite) and fines depletion;

D. a trampled ash horizon.

The details of the succession are not at variance between authors (e.g., Sheridan et al. 1981; Carey and Sigurdsson 1987; Barberi et al. 1989; Cioni et al. 1992; Lirer et al. 1993; Cioni et al. 1996); what do vary are interpretations of the eruption and the modes of transport and deposition. It is our contention (fig. 14.2) that on top of the pumice layer and following an ash fallout phase (*wa*) that characterized the initial interaction with water-bearing strata, an eruptive unit, *eu1* ("S4"), sealed the plinian phase. The subsequent eruptive unit includes both a basal *eu2a* ("A7") and an *eu2b* bed ("S5"). A unit, which we name *eu3* (fig. 14.2), follows and comprises a basal member *a* ("A8") and a median member *b*, both showing characteristics typical of a laminar flow. In contrast, the upper part, *c*, is indicative of more turbulent behavior. The sedimentology of layer *eu3b* is suggestive of debris flow deposition, whereas unit *eu3c* is typical of an ash flow (as defined by Fisher and Schmincke 1984, 298). We interpret *eu3d* as a deposit from a wet eruption cloud. Working up through the succession (fig. 14.2), three units (*eu4*, *eu5*, and *eu6*) duplicate the eruptive style of unit *eu3*, and an ash layer (*eu7*) represents the close of the eruptive sequence.

Although the impact of the eruption on the buildings (breaking roofs, fire, collapsing walls) can only be chronologically reconstructed with certainty once excavation is complete, it should be noted that there is a height difference of some 40–50 cm between the uppermost pumice layers found inside and outside the building. Especially interesting is the difference in the height of the deposits observed at a door opening on the southern side of the building (fig. 14.3). Here a two-winged door remained closed during the eruption and outside the door the uppermost pumice layer is some 50 cm higher than the layer on the inside. The three layers (*eu1*, *eu2*, and *eu3a*) show a clear correlation inside and outside the building, but indoors, between layers *eu1* and *eu2*, there is an additional layer (approximately 10 cm thick) that consists of remobilized light and dark gray ash (*xx*). For some time, therefore, following the deposition of unit *eu1* and during a period of relative quiescence, ash was able to creep into the building as it was dispersed by the wind. Subsequent surge activity completely removed this ash outdoors, but not in more sheltered, indoor locations. Outside the building, the discovery of two skeletons and a collapsed wall are of great importance.

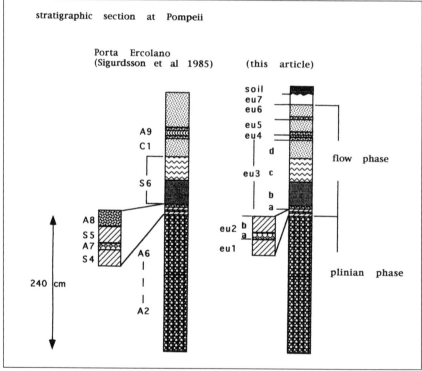

Fig. 14.2. Stratigraphic column from the House of the Chaste Lovers. The stratigraphy recorded by Sigurdsson et al. (1985) is shown for reference.

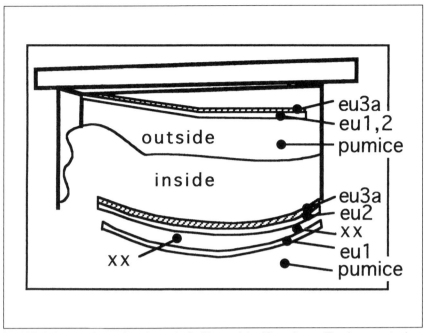

Fig. 14.3. A. Stratigraphy inside and outside the House of the Chaste Lovers. The door remained closed during the eruption. Note level *xx (3A)*, which is found only inside the house. Below is a photograph of the stratigraphy.

Fig. 14.3. B.

The Skeletons

Two skeletons were found to the west of the house. Buildings adjacent to the House of the Chaste Lovers in this area have not yet been excavated, and consequently the width of the by-road may only be inferred from landmarks on the via dell'Abbondanza. Cross-sections in the by-road show a concave pumice layer rising toward the outer wall of the house. As figure 14.4 shows, the skeletons lie in a depression, the axis of which is perpendicular to the concavity.

Skeleton A, which is stratigraphically higher, is offset to the south (fig. 14.5). The right arm of the corpse is bent with the palm of the hand facing up and the left arm lies along the side of the body. The left leg of the corpse is stretched out, the right leg is bent and the sole of the foot lies firmly on the ground. Stratigraphically the talus of the left foot and the pelvis are in deeper layers and, as figure 14.5 shows, the talus is below layer *eu3a* and dips into *eu2b*. Impressions of the pelvis and the lower part of the trunk are also evident in layer *eu2b* and lie in layer *eu3a* and the overlying layer *eu3b*. Basal portions of layers *eu3a* and *eu3b* rest under the back of the right hand, which is bent backward.

Skeleton B lies transversely with respect to both skeleton A and the road (fig. 14.5). The skeleton is lying on its right side, immersed in layer *eu2* (fig.14.6) and the whole left side is neatly bisected, including half the skull, the bones of the left arm, and the left leg (fig. 14.7). The bones of the left foot are still in place, and lean against the wall plunging into the surge that rises slightly toward the wall of the house. The thickness of the surge increases and eventually merges with the body.

In conclusion, we argue that layer *eu3a*, previously considered the product of fallout and named "A8" is the basal portion of layer *eu3*, and is, in fact, a flow. We believe that the victims were killed by surge *eu2*. Skeleton B was only slightly moved by the first flow *eu2*, but was then sharply bisected by the arrival of the thicker basal part of the subsequent pyroclastic flow *eu3a,* which was also capable of transporting large blocks of road metal at high speed and thus cutting roof tiles. As this was occurring, surge *eu2b* prevented the entombed corpse from being dragged along. There is, however, no doubt that skeleton A moved to some extent, since the spine appears to be broken in more than one place and the badly injured skull shows signs of having been damaged by heavy flows.

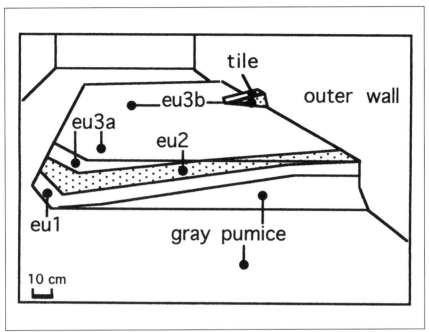

Fig. 14.4. A. Diagram of the stratigraphy with the two skeletons still buried. Observe the concavity of the layers, rising near the house. The highest stratigraphic level shown is *eu3b*. Below is a photograph of the stratigraphy.

Fig. 14.4. B.

Fig. 14.5. Skeleton A: the talus plunges into the stratigraphically lower level, *eu2b*, while *eu3b* lies under the right arm. Skeleton B can be seen lying in a stratigraphically lower position in the background.

Fig. 14.6. Part of Skeleton B totally buried in flow *eu2*. Much of the left side is missing, including half of the skull, the left arm, and the left leg. The left foot remains in place. The right foot, leaning against the wall, is buried in the surge, which rises slightly toward the outer wall of the house.

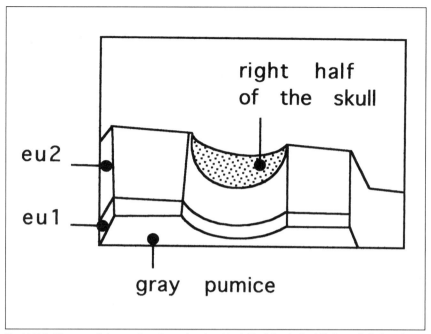

Fig. 14.7. A. Diagram of the stratigraphy under the right half of the skull of Skeleton B. Below the skull is in situ.

Fig. 14.7. B.

The Collapsed Wall

The southern facade of the house, which is perpendicular to the road and overlooks an open space, has been excavated to just above the lintel of the door, giving access to the lower stories of the house. Only part of the wall of the second floor remains in place (fig. 14.8); the collapsed part is buried within the flows of unit *eu3*. This stratigraphy illustrates the "drift capacity" of this unit and has clear implications for understanding the flow movement and the processes by which the skeletons were buried.

The stratigraphy beneath the wall is variable (fig. 14.9). Up to the emplacement of surge *eu2b* no interference is observed. Flows *eu1*, *eu2a* and *eu2b* were deposited over the concave surface of the underlying pumice, but with the deposition of layers *eu3a* and *eu3b* there was, in contrast, a westward thickening of deposits. Fragments of the collapsed wall may be cross-matched with portions of the surviving wall; a window and its grating and the impression of the wooden truss are still perfectly lined up with the masonry and original opening. Clearly the wall was suddenly pushed over by a force acting along its entire length. The collapse was interrupted at various times and at differing heights because the shape of the deposit under the falling wall was being altered by the arrival of the basal part of the flow, i.e., layers *eu3a* and *eu3b*, which filled the space to the south of the wall (fig. 14.10).

Fig. 14.8. The collapsed wall is fully buried in unit *eu3*. The standing wall belongs to the second story of the house.

The easternmost part of the collapsing wall, furthest from the direction of flow, touched the underlying deposit (*eu2*) after about 0.4–0.5 seconds. Therefore, the flow (*eu3*) which slid for nine more meters under the collapsing wall before it landed on the surface, ran at a speed of 65–80 km/h.

The principal characteristics of the flow unit *eu3* may be briefly summarized. Layers *eu3a* and *eu3b* traveled almost simultaneously with only a slight

Fig. 14.9.A. Stratigraphy beneath the collapsed wall, as viewed from northwest. B. Below is a diagram of the stratigraphy. The layer thickness remains constant up to unit eu2, but the basal layers of unit *eu3* are thinner, wedging beneath the falling wall. *Eu3a* granulometric values decline with progression in the same direction.

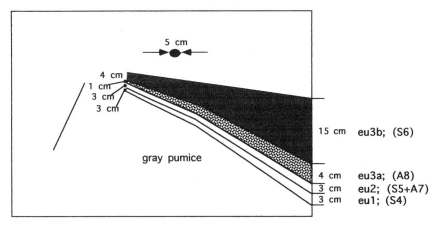

Fig. 14.9. B.

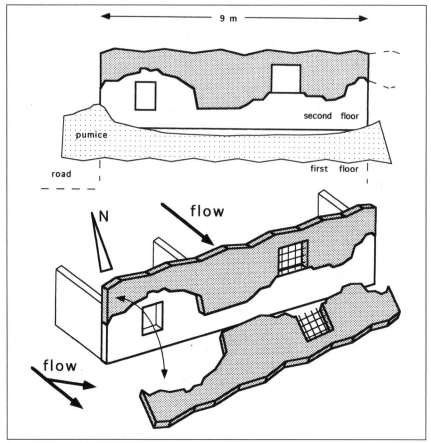

Fig. 14.10. Diagram of the collapsing wall. The parabola of the collapsing wall was halted at different times and height. Under the falling wall, the deposit was changing as a result of the arrival of the basal part of the flow (*eu3a-b*), which extended beyond the corner of the house and filled the outdoor space to the south. The first floor (not painted) is buried in the pumice.

time lag and behaved as a laminar debris flow, but with some local turbulence. As argued above, layer *eu3a*, formerly termed "A8", is a pyroclastic flow and not a product of fallout. Granulometry is yet another peculiarity of this layer beneath the wall because it decreases eastward, towards the terminal part of the deposition. The active thickness of the head of the flow was at least 3 m, i.e., the height of the exposed wall when it arrived. The upper part of the flow (i.e., layers *eu3c* and *eu3d*), which is now found stratigraphically overlying layer *eu3b*, was not deposited at the same time as the basal part of the flow.

Conclusion

On the morning of 24 August A.D. 79 the opening phase of the eruption of Vesuvius was already occurring. A request for help reached Miseno—about 25 km away—about 1 p.m., when the plinian phase was beginning. This intense phase lasted some six hours, and produced 2 m of pumice and lithic fall in Pompeii. There followed an interval of relative quiescence (the transitional phase) before the beginning of pyroclastic flow activity (fig. 14.11). The production of ash was intense and scattered around the volcano, while rocks and debris were probably thrown out into neighboring areas, but this activity was much less powerful than the previous plinian phase. Many inhabitants wandered through Pompeii, perhaps underestimating the danger, and returned to their homes or finally left the city. Some were trapped in rooms on the first floor. In all probability, the distal margin of a surge deposit had already reached the town, but did not cause damage or casualties. By then, Herculaneum, Oplontis, and Villa Regina at Boscoreale were already completely destroyed. The next morning, following a series of strong earthquakes, a black cloud rose above Vesuvius. It was heavily loaded with wet ash and spread at great speed across the slopes of Vesuvius as an avalanche of debris containing fragments from the volcanic edifice as well as new magma. The first of these new surges surprised the inhabitants of

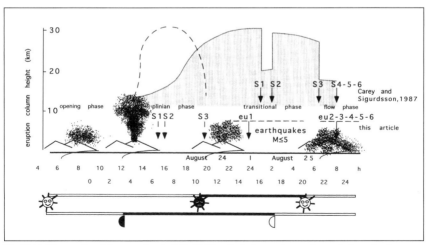

Fig. 14.11. Time scale of the eruption in A.D. 79. The shaded area shows the evolution of column height and the sequence of surges (S1–S6), according to Carey and Sigurdsson (1987).

Pompeii, who were walking about the town unconcerned. They were suffo-
cated by the hot ash and subsequently their corpses were overwhelmed by
the powerful shock wave of the pyroclastic flow. Having reached the top of
the town walls—which were at the same level as the ground surface due to
earlier emplacement of fall deposits (Etani et al. 1995)—the pyroclastic flow
overrode them and spread into the town. Highly mobile, lower density flows
ran high up the sides of buildings and were only slightly impeded by the
walls, which remained in place. Higher density flows were diverted by walls
and channeled along roads. The greater thickness of the flow-layers in the
town, as opposed to those in the surrounding countryside, as well as the different deposition patterns observed at short distances, was caused by buildings interfering with the flow. The impact of these flows was extremely
violent, causing whole facades to collapse and roof trusses and tiles to be
entrained along the course of the flow. The upper margins of the flow rose
hundreds of meters above the town. Deposits related to this horizon are
found at scores of sites many kilometers distant from Vesuvius. It was this
cloud that produced the widespread ash-fall which, according to Gigante
(1989, 87) "enveloped Capri and concealed it."

Following the devastation caused by the first flow (i.e., units *eu3a, b* and
c, inclusive), at least three more flows—albeit significantly less powerful–hit
the walls of the House of the Chaste Lovers. Not only were these less violent,
but they moved across a planar substrate which had been leveled by earlier
flows. Taller and more collapse-resistant buildings, protruding through the
gray "desert," were all that remained to keep watch over ancient Pompeii.
Excavations at the House of the Chaste Lovers are progressing.

REFERENCES

Barberi, F., R. Cioni, R. Santacroce, A. Sbrana, and R. Vecci. 1989. "Magmatic and
    Phreatomagmatic Phases in Explosive Eruptions of Vesuvius as Deduced by Grain-Size
    and Component Analysis of Pyroclastic Deposits." *Journal of Volcanology and Geothermal
    Research* 38:287–307.
Carey, S., and H. Sigurdsson. 1987. "Temporal Variations in Column Height and Magma
    Discharge Rate during the 79 A.D. Eruption of Vesuvius." *Geological Society of America
    Bulletin* 99:303–14.
Cioni, R., L. Civetta, P. Marianelli, N. Metrich, R. Santacroce, and A. Sbrana. 1995.
    "Compositional Layering and Syn-Eruptive Mixing of a Periodically Refilled Shallow
    Magma Chamber. The A.D. 79 Plinian Eruption of Vesuvius." *Journal of Petrology*
    36:739–76.

Cioni, R., P. Marianelli, and A. Sbrana. 1990. "L'Eruzione Del 79 D.C.: Stratigrafia Dei Depositi Ed Impatto Sugli Insediamenti Romani Nel Settore Orientale E Meridionale Del Somma-Vesuvio." *Rivista di Studi Pompeiani* 4:179–98.

———. 1992. "Dynamic of the A.D. 79 Eruption. Stratigraphic, Sedimentological and Geochemical Data on the Successions from the Somma-Vesuvius Southern and Eastern Sector." *Acta Vulcanologica* 2:109–23.

Cioni, R., A. Sbrana, and L. Gurioli. 1996. "The Deposits of A.D. 79 Eruption." In *IAVCEI-CEV, IAVCEI-CMVD, Workshop Handbook, Vesuvius Decade Volcano, September 17–22, 1996,* coordinated by R. Santacroce, M. Rosi, A. Sbrana, R. Cioni, and L. Civetta.

Civetta, L., R. Galati, and R. Santacroce. 1991. "Magma Mixing and Convective Compositional Layering within the Vesuvius Magma Chamber." *Bulletin of Volcanology* 53:287–300.

Deutsches Arch. Inst. Rom. Soprintendenza. Arch. di Pompeii, Osservatorio Ves. 1995. *Archäologie Und Seismologie. La Regione Vesuviana dal 62 al 79 D.C. Problemi Archeologici e Sismologici, Colloquium, Boscoreale, 26–27 November 1993.* München

Etani, H., S. Sakai, and H. Kiriyama. 1995. "Preliminary Report. Archaeological Investigation at Porta Capua, Pompeii." *Opuscula Pompeiana* 5:55–67.

Fisher, R.V., and H.U. Schmincke. 1984. *Pyroclastic Rocks.* Berlin-Heidelberg-Tokyo.

Gigante, M. 1989. *Il fungo sul Vesuvio secondo Plinio il Giovane.* Roma.

Lirer, L., R. Munno, P. Petrosino, and A. Vinci. 1993. "Tephrostratigraphy of the A.D. 79 Pyroclastic Deposits in Perivolcanic Areas of Mt. Vesuvio (Italy)." In *Mount Vesuvius,* edited by B. De Vivo, R. Scandone, and R. Triglia, 133–49. *Journal of Volcanology and Geothermal Research* 58 (1/4).

Lirer, L., T. Pescatore, B. Booth, and G.P.L. Walker. 1973. "Two Plinian Pumice-Fall Deposits From Somma-Vesuvius, Italy." *Geological Society of America Bulletin* 84:759–72.

Marturano, A., and V. Rinaldis. 1998. "The Seismicity Before 79 A.D. Vesuvius Eruption." In *Il Sistema Uomo-Ambiente Tra Passato E Presente,* edited by C. Albore Livadie and F. Ortolani, 237–45. Ravello.

Marturano, A., and V. Rinaldis. 1995. "Il Terremoto del 62 D.C. Un Evento Carico di Responsabilità." In *Archäologie und seismologie: La Regione Vesiviana dal 62 al 79 D.C. Problem Atcheologici e Sismologici,* 131–5. Munchen.

Radice, B. 1969. *The Letters of the Younger Pliny.* New York.

Rosi, M., R. Santacroce, and M.F. Sheridan. 1987. "Volcanic Hazard." In *Somma-Vesuvius,* edited by R. Santacroce 197–220. CNR Quaderni de la Ricerca Scientifica, 114(8).

Sheridan, M.F., F. Barberi, M. Rosi, and R. Santacroce. 1981. "A Model for Plinian Eruptions of Vesuvius." *Nature* 289:282–5.

Sigurdsson, H., S. Carey, W. Cornell, and T. Pescatore. 1985. "The Eruption of Vesuvius in A.D. 79." *National Geographic Research* 1:332–87.

Varone, A. 1993. "New Finds in Pompeii. The Excavation of Two Buildings in Via dell'Abbondanza." *Apollo (London)* 8–12.

Varone, A. 1995. "Più Terremoti A Pompeii? I Nuovi Dati Degli Scavi di Via dell'Abbondanza." In *Archäologie und Seismologie: La Regione Vesuviana dal 62 al 79 D.C. Problemi Archeologici e Sismologici.* Colloquium Boscoreale 26-27 November 1993 29–35. Biering and Munchen.

Yokoyama, T., and A. Marturano. 1997. "Volcanic Products of Vesuvius Eruption in A.D. 79 at Pompeii, Italy, with Special Reference to the Effects on Human Life and Ancient City." *Opuscula Pompeiana* 7.

NOTES

* We are especially thankful to Professor Giuseppe Luongo for his valuable suggestions and useful discussion of the contents of this chapter; to Superintendent Professor Pietro Giovanni Guzzo; the Director of the Soprintendenza Archeologica in Pompeii, Mr. Antonio D'Ambrosio; and Professor Lucia Civetta, head of the Osservatorio Vesuviano. We also wish to thank Mrs. Francesca Tessuto for her skillful and patient work on the excavation site, Mrs. Silvana Siciliano for the translation, and Prof. David Chester for the revision of the English version of our chapter. A first draft of this chapter was submitted to the IAVCEI-97 conference in Puerto Vallarta (Mexico).

15

The Introduction of Applied Sciences in the Study of an Ancient Site: Pompeii

◈

Baldassare Conticello

In 1981 the Archaeological Superintendency of Pompeii was founded, separate from the larger, old, glorious Superintendency of Naples and Caserta, to facilitate the restoration of the Vesuvian area after the great earthquake of 1980, which had damaged archaeological sites in Campania and Lucania. A new, autonomous Institute was established and became operative in 1982. In 1984 a special law brought to the new Institute significant, although largely insufficient, funding.

As director of the new Superintendency, I undertook a difficult, often discouraging, but exciting job of developing a systematic plan in an organic and uniform fashion using, for the first time, an *interdisciplinary approach* for confronting the totality of the problems presented by the excavation, restoration, careful exploitation, computerization, and use of a series of sites: Herculaneum, Oplontis, Pompeii, Boscoreale, and Stabiae. Because of the vastness and completeness of the material, both collected and still to be collected, this approach permitted intervention on archaeological materials on a large scale by *pilot projects*.

True cities—not simply urban settlements—groups of monuments, and single architectural complexes, were to be studied. This new interdisciplinary and systematic approach to the problem of archaeological sites, whose extent is measured in hectares, and which are almost entirely preserved, has permitted me to express my particular *philosophy of antiquity* and its recovery, which must keep in mind the identity of the end-user, the visitor.

The first problem was the minimum necessary depth and intensity of restoration to apply. We had to consider, in fact, that digging necessarily destroys part of the walls or objects brought to light, but we dig in order to bring them back to life. Restoring necessarily brings alteration, but we restore in order to make the past survive. In the light of this incontrovertible fact, one must ask an important question: must monuments, like living beings have a biological life, that runs from birth to death in a predictable number of years, or should monuments and objects be kept alive as long as possible, theoretically *ad infinitum*?

If the second answer is the correct one, it must be acknowledged that frequent restorations cause damage and loss to the monuments and objects, whatever care and sophistication of material and technology are used. With repeated restorations of the same monument or object, its destruction grows exponentially through the loss of surfaces, mortar, plaster, and pigments, even if the structure still seems generally solid and in good condition.

Consequently, priority was given to more in-depth restoration, to avoid the need for further restorations of the same monument. For example, the tops of the walls (the so-called "sacrificial surface") were raised to offer the wind and atmospheric agents a "sacrifice" of the modern walls (which can be rebuilt without problems when they are degraded) to attack before they reach the tops of the ancient walls underneath.

Tubes containing cables were laid in the archaeological area to bring power to the lamps and cameras designed to provide the site in the immediate future with lighting for night visits and for performances in the amphitheater and the theatres. This generally involved going under the sidewalks of the ancient city with tubes large enough to be filled later with other technological devices to avoid damaging the archaeological levels again. The laying of the new cables offered the opportunity to make a series of stratigraphic sondages along the entrances to buildings to investigate the levels beneath the final ones from the period between the earthquake of A.D. 62 and the eruption of A.D. 79, in search of the early settlement of the town, supposedly born in the sixth century B.C. It is, in fact, truly incredible that after some 250 years of exploration, we know almost nothing about the cities of the Vesuvian area from the more than 600 years that preceded the last two decades of their lives.

Ancient Pompeii and other Vesuvian cities are at risk of disappearing in a few years, not only because of precipitation in roofless buildings, but also because of the progressive erosion of the sidewalks.

We did an experiment in Via di Mercurio, close to the Forum, restoring the Roman *cocciopesto* (made of minute terracotta fragments mixed with mortar, sand and volcanic powder), and the underlying earth where it had disappeared, in order to make what have become unattractive canyons safe for guards and visitors to walk upon, and, more importantly, to protect the already preserved portions of the ancient cocciopesto and the stone curbs that are being consumed, and of the walls on which moisture has climbed because of the permeation from sidewalks sunken by rainwater, causing great damage to the plaster wall coverings and to the paintings on them.

The new floor has perfectly sealed the walls of the buildings, preventing the rising humidity from soaking the walls and their paintings. Naturally, the new sidewalks we restored are for the most part clearly modern, and are visibly and appropriately labeled.

Pompeii is a living city which more than two million people a year visit during the day and in which, every night, about 25 guards live, walking up and down on their security rounds, holding a hand lamp. To an observer on a high viewpoint, ancient Pompeii offers the dream-like feeling of a real, inhabited, living town, especially on nights when there is a full moon.

It needs lighting for people's safety and enjoyment, as well as passive security against break-ins. To improve the lighting, the safety, and the use of the archaeological site, we have experimented with a retractable pole with a series of four lamps at the top. This project would provide at night lighting for the guards walking around the site and safety against robbers.

When 500 interconnected poles are set in the 44 excavated hectares of the ancient town, each holding a television camera and four lamps, each lighting 400 square meters of the site at 100 lux. (At the moment only 150 have been acquired, but have not been set by my successor). A control room, already set outside the archaeological site, would command them to rise six meters. From the same centralized control room—when and if my project is completed—all other archeological sites and monuments under the Institute would also be totally monitored.

If, then, we consider that a systematic program (now abandoned) of total weeding was also undertaken—using for the first time in Italian archaeology organic, not poisonous, but only photosynthesis-blocking products—it follows that the general legibility of the ancient structures was greatly enhanced and safely enjoyable. The weeding was undertaken with an eye to the original architecture and city planning: grass was allowed to grow where in antiquity there were gardens (not in the market place, the Forum, as my successor today has done, damaging the appreciation of the square). Where in antiquity there were pavements, weeds were removed, and the soil was recovered with a layer of so-called lava foam (broken pieces of soft volcanic stone).

Thus, we restored the alternation of dark and light, of gray and green, together with restoration, where possible, of the roofs of the buildings, that gives the visitor a comprehensible and correct vision of the cityscape, with the succession of the houses, shops, factories, workshops, temples and public buildings, as contained spaces, and not as containers, or as a succession of undifferentiated courtyards.

Thanks to the accidental presence on our staff of a biologist, we researched the ancient plant materials that came to light during the excavation. The identification of pollens, seeds, and roots was designed to restore neither generic wild flora nor, as in the past, imaginative tree planting (African palm trees in Pompeii?), but rather the same arrangements of plants which the finds have revealed to have been present at the moment of the eruption.

Our goal was replanting the same plants as those growing at the time of the eruption in a particular garden we excavated and preserving all the evidence of the subsoil, arranged according to a precise architecture of gardens that the special excavation conditions permitted. Based on ancient sources and botanic discoveries, seventy new gardens were reconstructed in the site of Pompeii. At the time of my departure from the direction of the Superintendency, about 85% of the excavated area of Pompeii (44 hectares out of 66) was totally cleared of weeds. Now, the weeds have regrown everywhere.

With a special fund personally given to me from the National Research Council, I created in Pompeii a great Applied Research Laboratory, the largest in our administration, for the study of plants, pigments, mortar, wall-detachments, humidity damage to the walls, etc. We also convinced, with great difficulty, the technicians of Pompeii to stop using concrete, which is extremely dangerous for the preservation of the surfaces since it dries and destroys, the stuccoes and painted surfaces and to replace it with the so-called Lafarge mortar that is neutral and not dangerous.

In the three centuries of digging and restoring the ancient Vesuvian towns, each archaeologist in charge of the work has used different methods of preservation of walls, each one easy to distinguish, identify, and attribute, and offering the visitors a kind of ugly patchwork on the ruins. We started to unify these methods as much as possible, deciding to return (when the static imbalance does not necessitate resin injections or insertion of metal supports) to the use of natural materials in restoration, such as wood (laminate, for greater resistance, in platbands), bricks, terracotta tiles, and, in the walls, the traditional Roman building technique using mortar made of plaster, sand, and volcanic pozzolana powder.

We do not believe, in fact, that restoration must be distinguished from the ancient by the use of contrasting materials, recognizable from a distance, as in the past our teachers used to think and to tell us. We are convinced that the harmonization of the materials, the use of ancient techniques, and the rewriting of Roman construction methods, are important and philologically significant steps, on the condition, of course, that the usual elements can be introduced safely, are clearly distinct from the ancient ones at close inspection, and are rebuilt set back from the outer surface of walls and with the insertion of dated labels, etc.

In view of the difficulties encountered by restorers in the past, we began to adopt (that is, to study and test in the laboratory) new technologies for stabilizing the columns and the pilasters by replacing the rigid cores of metal and sand with a thin cord of resin, the elasticity of which can withstand considerable vibrations and transverse movements caused by the frequent earthquakes in the area. The results were a clear, clean, solid presentation of the buildings, partially integrated in their walls and even in the roofs, but new and totally reconstructed. In this work, we used a great deal of photogrammetry and we introduced into archaeology the use of computer simulation, which has given us the opportunity of studying in advance the general vision and the final shapes of each single construction and of a series of buildings aligned along the streets of the town and deciding which one to adopt before moving to the physical restoration of the buildings.

Another important problem for us was how to study the effects of seismic activity on the state of the buildings in ancient times, because this knowledge was extremely important in restoring the buildings damaged in antiquity. We put in charge of this study a great scholar, Dr. Giovanni Ioppolo, recently deceased, who made a series of important observations, published in the fifth monograph of our Institute (1992).

In collaboration with the Seismic Observatory of Vesuvius and the

Institute of Geophysics of the University of Naples, we created a team entrusted with a series of systematic studies of the buildings of Pompeii in search of real, scientific evidence of earthquakes or seismic events besides the known one of A.D. 62 that happened in the area in ancient times. In 1994 we got the first positive results from observations made mostly in the House of Chaste Lovers, excavated by one of the best scholars on Pompeian culture, Dr. Antonio Varone, Vice-Superintendent of Pompeii (see Varone, this volume). The first results were discussed in November 1993 in Boscoreale in the Colloquium "Archaeologie und Seismologie."

We introduced the computer, an IBM 9030—the first Institute to do so in archaeology and in Italy—and used it to record the splendid color-photographs of each painting, of each single object discovered in Pompeii since the beginning of the excavations, both those still in the dig and those taken to the Depot. Each object was classified in the computer by type, material, subject, date and site of discovery, etc., to make their study accessible. We have also introduced in the computer record all the record books of the site, giving scholars the possibility of easily finding information they might need on the buildings and the objects of Pompeii.

The many possibilities offered by the computer gave us the chance to introduce new ways to study and to work with the help of the machine. One of our problems was to fill the empty spaces of a damaged painting with a neutral color that in the past was traditionally a yellow-cream color that was frequently very annoying and inharmonious to the eye. We decided, then, to introduce in the computer all the colors that were contained in the single painting, and to build a new color as a result of the *media ponderata*. The new color was used to fill the empty spaces of the disappeared pigments of a painting in the case of large losses. The optical effect made by this new color on the observer was much less visually annoying than the earlier one.

The town-plan of Pompeii was totally redrawn with the use of aerial photogrammetry, with each single element computerized, to allow future drawings of single parts of the plan directly with the plotter. We also made it possible for the visitor—when the information contained in the machine would be made transferable in a series of terminals placed in the dig—to choose his own trip into the dig, and to ask the machine questions on the topography of the site. A guidebook of Pompeii with two levels of information was already written and transferred to software to offer total information on the history of the city, the excavations, and the art and daily life in Pompeii.

An important problem for us was the reading of the 8,000 carbonized papyri discovered in the 18th century A.D. in the Villa of Papyri in Herculaneum that belonged to the family of Piso, who may have been related to Julius Caesar's family. Most are on philosophical subjects and are attributed to Philodemus from Gadara. These papyri were difficult to read because of the minimal difference between the black of the burned papyri and the dark gray of the ink. Using the computer, we experimented with increasing the contrast between the two colors, which resulted in a red color for the ink and a blue color for the background. With the magnifying capacity of the computer, we were able to make the papyrus on which we did the experiment perfectly readable, even to non-papyrologists.

Immediately before my departure from Pompeii in January 1995, a large international team was established at the Institute, charged with studying the thousands of human skeletons and fragments of human bones discovered mainly in Herculaneum. The aim was to understand everything possible about physical standards, sex, age, activities, illnesses, DNA, and Rh factors. The team never met, however, and is now dispersed, the research abandoned.

My effort during the 10 years I was in charge of the Superintendency was to establish a stable team of scholars working together with me and doing a series of studies using science in the service of archaeology and avoiding and refusing the prejudice that archaeology (and humanities in general) can be penetrated and studied only through keys offered by philosophical, philological, historical, and antiquarian knowledge. We obtained varied success, but we also had no time to accomplish our dream of reunifying the sciences in the interest of human progress.

There is now discussion in the world of scholars about the future of Pompeii because of the continuous degradation of the buildings and of the paintings. Recently, the Director of the British School at Rome, who I personally called to work and to dig in Pompeii, has suggested—I hope only as a provocation—that it would be preferable to rebury the town to preserve it better. He also proposed recreating totally (as in Knossos in the last century) a number of houses and buildings in a less important part of the city of Pompeii, with the aim of offering the visitors better knowledge and appreciation of an ancient Roman town.

Refilling the site would reduce, but not exclude, the destruction of the walls and of the paintings, even if we use a good, neutral material, such as sand, and if we compress the filling, to reduce the risk of penetration of water and humidity. We can cite some of the rooms of the suburban baths of Pompeii. When we started digging the complex, we discovered these rooms had already been excavated and refilled with earth a few years before our total excavation of the baths. The walls were heavily damaged by the humidity of the earth and the splendid Nilotic wall paintings had almost disappeared.

I understand and share the desperate feelings of my British colleague, but I think that our duty cannot be to exclude the citizens and the entire world (two million people a year), from the appreciation, not only of what was at the origin of our knowledge and understanding of classical life but also what was at the beginning of the study of the classical heritage in the 17th century. Neoclassic culture, after all, began from the discoveries of Pompeii and Herculaneum. I personally was greatly successful at restoring, over the course of 10 years, many *insulae* that can live—we now know for sure—for many decades *if there is appropriate maintenance.*

I hope that in the near future the Italian government will understand that investing money—real money, not loose change—in cultural goods and the environment can be highly profitable, not only culturally but also economically, not only in general but to produce specific employment. Since the 1960s, I have expounded in vain this theory and opinion in reports, letters and lectures. Maybe this is the moment of seeing a positive answer that will help to save the archaeological sites, the knowledge, and the appreciation of our past, especially in Pompeii, where Roman evidence is preserved in a splendid and complete way.

Otherwise, we must find international funds to proceed in the restoration—considering the bad condition of the sites—and to resume excavations with the great possibilities offered by the interaction of the applied sciences with archaeology, and this must be done as quickly as possible with the help of all the archaeologists of the world interested in this program. After all, classical culture is the background of our common Western and European civilization, and we all have the duty to contribute to maintain its physical testimony.

REFERENCES

Ioppolo, Giovanni. 1992. *Le Terme del Sarno à Pompei.* Roma.

Deutsches Archäologisches Institut; Romisches Abteilung, Italy; Soprintendenza Archeologica di Pompei; and Osservatorio Vesuviano. 1993. *Archäeologie und Seismologie. La regione vesuviana dal 62 al 79 D.C. Problemi archeologici e sismologici. Colloquium. Bosoreale 26–27 November 1993.* München.

— 16 —

Water Use in Pompeii Between
the Earthquake and the Eruption

Ann Olga Koloski-Ostrow[*]

Water was truly the lifeblood of cities and towns in the Graeco-Roman world. It played a crucial role in shaping urban topography and influenced local history. Water, in fact, provided a source of strength and an underlying structure for ancient urban centers. Pompeii, with its well-excavated and well-preserved houses, public buildings, and street networks, offers an excellent opportunity to explore water use in the urban infrastructure of a first-century Roman city. This chapter offers a partial survey of new research on water technology in Pompeii (see also de Haan and Jansen 1996; Koloski-Ostrow et al. 1997, 189–91; Koloski-Ostrow 2001, 97–104).

The earthquake of A.D. 62, or subsequent smaller earthquakes closer to the time of the eruption itself, caused considerable damage to many superstructures at Pompeii. The archaeological record for this is quite clear (see Varone, this volume). Earlier accounts, however, have suggested that Pompeii's infrastructure (city water supply, drainage systems, sewers) was devastated by these earthquakes. Several lines of evidence presented in this chapter demonstrate that this was not, in fact, the case and that the hydraulic infrastructure in the city continued to function late into its history (de Haan and Jansen 1996, passim).

Aqueducts

Roman aqueducts have been researched for many years, and the distribution of the main water lines have been investigated in various ancient cities (Hodge 1992; Fabre et al. 1992; Evans 1993). During the last few years, G.C.M. Jansen of the University of Nijmegen and engineers at the Technical University of Delft, both in the Netherlands, have given new attention to the layout, distribution, and function of the water pipe system inside Pompeian private houses. The team has found only a few lead pipes remaining in situ, together with 30 bronze taps and 15 lead distribution boxes, making it difficult to obtain a clear picture of the whole domestic system. On the basis of small indications (e.g., indentations in the tufo *impluvia*) and with the help of metal detectors, they reconstructed the integrity of water use in the Roman houses. They have considered how the pipe system operated and revealed to what parts of the house the water was directed and for what it was used: to supply the fountains in the garden, as drinking water, or for domestic uses (Jansen, 2002, passim; Koloski-Ostrow et al. 1997, 188; Jansen 2001, 27–40).

Jashemski has clearly shown dramatic distinctions among gardens in Pompeian houses related to their access to the Augustan aqueduct. Pre-aqueduct houses and the large produce gardens beyond the reach of the aqueduct possessed less elaborate water displays than those housed along the path of the aqueduct. Consider for example, the elegant peristyle garden in the House of the Vettii (VI.15, 1.27) with its 14 fountains or the House of M. Loreius Tiburtinus (II.2, 2) with even more elaborate water displays in its gardens (Jashemski 1996, 51–7; Koloski-Ostrow et al. 1997, 185). Close investigations in these gardens have helped to confirm that the water supply operations were still functioning late in the city's history.

According to new work by de Haan (1996), ancient Pompeii contained at least 30 houses with a private bath-suite, a number far higher than previously realized (de Haan 1996, 59–65; Koloski-Ostrow et al. 1997, 185; de Haan 2001, 41–9). She applies a set of practical questions to the archaeological evidence for the use of water in these private baths: how did the house owners provide their baths with water; how did they get rid of the waste water; how was water for the tub in the caldarium heated; can we make distinctions between groups of private baths based on their need for water (de Haan, forthcoming; Garbrecht and Manderscheid 1994, 1–3).

Fig. 16.1. The *castellum aquae* (water distribution center) at Pompeii. (Photo by Ann O. Koloski-Ostrow)

She has so far determined that there is a direct link between the building of the so-called Serino Aqueduct in Campania in the Augustan period, which presumably also branched off to Pompeii, and the increase in construction of private baths in the last decades of the first century B.C. The more lavish private bath-suites with a great demand for water come into use after this period. Consideration of the private baths in Pompeii also contributes to the ongoing debate about the extent to which facilities in the city still functioned in the post-earthquake period and how water was managed in the last years before the eruption of Mount Vesuvius. De Haan (forthcoming) thinks that many water pipe systems were in good working order up to the end of the city (see also Garbrecht and Manderscheid 1994, 1–3; de Haan 1996, 59–65; Koloski-Ostrow et al. 1997, 185; De Haan 2001, 41–9).

The water supply system at Pompeii was, in fact, quite sophisticated. It consisted of an aqueduct, which survives in fragmentary sections (Pagano 1996, 101–8; Koloski-Ostrow et al. 1997, 182); a so-called *castellum aquae*, or water distribution center (fig. 16.1) at the end of the aqueduct; three large pressure mains; water towers; and secondary and tertiary water mains. The *castellum* divided the arriving water over the three water mains; the water towers enabled water to reach individual customers and public buildings.

Wiggers and his students from the Technical University of Delft, have identified at least 14 water towers (Wiggers 1996, 29–32; Koloski-Ostrow et al.
1997, 183). They were puzzled as to why the Romans did not use just one
major water tower, as we would expect in a modern system. Water from the
aqueduct flowed from tower to tower by means of lead pipes, and the whole
system operated by means of gravity. It seems highly probable that the towers
were connected by one single conduit. Lead boxes used to hold the water
were most likely placed at the top of the towers. Pipe connections to individual houses and other buildings were made through these boxes. Wiggers
and his team have demonstrated that the use of so many towers made it possible to supply water under relatively low pressure to houses and other public
buildings. One tower for the whole town would have meant unreasonably
high pressures in a part of the system.

The multiple water tower system that the Pompeians chose made it easy
to add connections to the network as well as to close them off. If there were
only a single water tower, water would have been temporarily cut off to all
customers when it was necessary to close it for repairs to the whole system.
Clearly the use of multiple towers at Pompeii made repair and reconstruction much easier. Wiggers has noted that the towers could be heightened or
lowered to adjust pressure in the various parts of the town that were serviced
by the aqueduct (Wiggers 1996, 32).

Baths

The construction of the Central Baths unfinished at the time of the eruption
also serves as an indication that the water supply system was in good condition in A.D. 79 and not ruined by earlier earthquake activity. Of the three
large public baths at Pompeii (Forum, Central, and Stabian), it appears that
the Forum Bath was the only one in full operation at the time of the eruption. Nevertheless, other smaller baths (Suburban, baths in the *Praedia* of
Julia Felix, and Sarno Complex) were also fully or partially functioning. In
my work on the Sarno complex I have shown that the cisterns on level 2,
which were originally used to provide water in the multistoried structure,
went out of service with the arrival of water from the Augustan aqueduct
(Koloski-Ostrow 1990, 34–7). The building was clearly undergoing repairs
at the time of the eruption, perhaps from earthquake damage, but these ren-
ovations were to expand the bathing facilities, not to eliminate or diminish

them. Dobbins's investigations on the east side of the Pompeian forum offer further testimony to a city that was more vigorously thriving in its last years than has previously been thought (Dobbins 1994, 629–94).

Public Latrines

Another water facility at Pompeii, which has only recently been included in discussions of urban infrastructures is the public latrine. It is difficult to know the social reasons why the public latrine makes such a striking appearance in the final years of Pompeii. I have argued elsewhere that improved sanitation is undoubtedly an over-simplification of the matter (Koloski-Ostrow 1996, 79–86; Koloski-Ostrow, forthcoming). There were four main new public latrines at Pompeii in the post-earthquake period: in the grand palaestra; in the Stabian Baths; an unfinished latrine in the Central Baths; and the well-preserved forum latrine, also unfinished at the time of the eruption of Vesuvius in A.D. 79. These new, handsome public facilities provide new evidence of a changing cityscape and of new uses of the waterworks. Pompeii's public latrines serve as an example, like newly improved amphitheaters and baths springing up throughout the empire in this period, of the largess of the Roman military state coming to Pompeii at a time of social and civic disruption.

Conclusions

This new research on water begins where earlier projects have left off. These new studies no longer overlook the small-scale aspects of water management, water supply systems, and drainage within Roman towns. New research on the distribution and use of water throughout the city and in particular, within individual houses has produced new insights about ancient city life. Jansen has studied sanitation and disposal of wastewater in several Roman cities, including Pompeii, and has discovered that almost every house at Pompeii and Herculaneum has a private toilet, contrary to the common opinion that most Romans used public latrines (Jansen 1992, 449–68; Jansen 1997, 121–34). Her research method has been to evaluate the complete water management system within the city, not only the separate parts of it.

Scholars are also forging an enormously helpful interdisciplinary collaboration. By incorporating differences in ground levels in computerized

simulations of Pompeii, Herculaneum, and other Roman cities, Jansen
has been able to trace lines for disposal of wastewater. Such computerized
images help explain why sewers are so rare in Pompeii and are absolutely
required at Ostia. Incorporation of environmental data (nature of soil, the
local topography, disposition of water supply) has greatly enhanced the
research strategies of a number of projects (Crouch 1993; 1996, 137–43).

In conclusion, I would express the strong hope that the results of both
large-and small-scale water projects, such as those presented at the *Cura
Aquarum* conferences at Pompeii in 1994 and in Sicily in 1998, will continue to consider the ecological, historical, social, economic, and political
factors that affected water use and distribution in individual Roman cities.
In this way, we can truly begin to be enlightened by new aspects of Roman
daily life in the shadow of Vesuvius.

REFERENCES

Crouch, D. 1993. *Water Management in Ancient Greek Cities*. New York and Oxford.

———. 1996. "Priene's Streets and Water Supply." In *Cura Aquarum in Campania:
Proceedings of the Ninth International Congress on the History of Water Management and
Hydraulic Engineering in the Mediterranean Region* (*Pompeii 1–8, October 1994*), edited by
N. de Haan and G.C.M. Jansen, 137–43. *BABesch* Suppl. 4. Leiden.

Dobbins, J.J. 1994. "Problems of Chronology, Decoration, and Urban Design in the Forum
at Pompeii." *AJA* 98:629–94.

Evans, H.B. 1993. *Water Distribution in Ancient Rome: The Evidence of Frontinus*. Ann Arbor.

Fabre, G., J-L. Fiches, P. Leveau, and J-L. Paillet. 1992. *Le Pont du Gard. L' eau dans la ville
antique*. Paris.

Garbrecht, G., and H. Manderscheid. 1994. "Die Wasserbewirtschaftung römischen
Thermen: Archäologische und hydrotechnische Untersuchung." In *Mitteilungen des
Leichtweiss-Instituts für Wasserbau der Technischen Universität Braunschweig, 118 A-C*, 1–3.
Braunschweig.

de Haan, N. 1996. "Die Wasserversorgung der Privatbäder in Pompeji." In *Cura Aquarum in
Campania: Proceedings of the Ninth International Congress on the History of Water
Management and Hydraulic Engineering in the Mediterranean Region* (*Pompeii 1–8, October
1994*), edited by N. de Haan and G.C.M. Jansen, 87–91. *BABesch* Suppl. 4. Leiden.

———. 2001. "*Si aquae copia patiatur*: Pompeian Private Baths and the Use of Water." In
Water use and Hydraulics in the Roman City, edited by A.O. Koloski-Ostrow, 41–9.
Colloquia and Conference Papers Series, Archaeological Institute of America 3. Dubuque.

———. Forthcoming. "Römischer Privatbäder, Entwicklung, Verbreitung und Sozialer
Status." Ph.D. diss., University of Nijmegen.

de Haan, N., and G.C. M. Jansen, eds. 1996. *Cura Aquarum in Campania: Proceedings of the Ninth International Congress on the History of Water Management and Hydraulic Engineering in the Mediterranean Region (Pompeii 1–8, October 1994)*. *BABesch* Suppl. 4. Leiden.

Hodge, A.T. 1992. *Roman Aqueducts and Water Supply*. London.

Jansen, G.C.M. 1992. "Water Systems and Sanitation in the Houses of Herculaneum." *Mitteilungen des Leichtweiß-Instituts für Wasserbau der Technischen Universität Braunschweig* 117:449–68.

———. 1997. "Private Toilets at Pompeii: Appearance and Operation." In *Sequence and Space in Pompeii*, edited by S.E. Bon and R. Jones, 121–34. Oxbow Monographs 77. Oxford.

———. 2001. "Water Pipe Systems in the Houses of Pompeii: Distribution and Use." In *Water Use and Hydraulics in the Roman City*, edited by A.O. Koloski-Ostrow, 27–40. Colloquia and Conference Papers Series, Archaeological Institute of America 3. Dubuque.

———. 2002. *Water in de Romeinse stad Pompeji, Herculaneum, Ostia*. Leuven.

Jashemski, W.F. 1996. "The Use of Water in Pompeian Gardens." In *Cura Aquarum in Campania: Proceedings of the Ninth International Congress on the History of Water Management and Hydraulic Engineering in the Mediterranean Region (Pompeii 1–8, October 1994)*, edited by N. de Haan and G.C.M. Jansen, 51–7. *BABesch* Suppl. 4. Leiden.

Koloski-Ostrow, A.O. 1990. *The Sarno Bath Complex*. Rome.

———. 1996. "Finding Social Meaning in the Public Latrines of Pompeii." In *Cura Aquarum in Campania: Proceedings of the Ninth International Congress on the History of Water Management and Hydraulic Engineering in the Mediterranean Region (Pompeii 1–8, October 1994)*, edited by N. de Haan and G.C.M. Jansen, 79–86. *BABesch* Suppl. 4. Leiden.

———, ed. 2001. *Water Use and Hydraulics in the Roman City*. Colloquia and Conference Papers Series, Archaeological Institute of America 3. Dubuque.

———. Forthcoming. *The Archaeology of Sanitation in Roman Italy: Water, Sewers, and Latrines*. Chapel Hill.

Koloski-Ostrow, A., N. de Haan, G. de Kleijn, and S. Piras. 1997. "Water in the Roman Town: New Research from *Cura Aquarum* and the *Frontinus Society*." *JRA* 10:181–91.

Pagano, M. 1996. "Note su alcuni acquedotti romani in Campania." In *Cura Aquarum in Campania: Proceedings of the Ninth International Congress on the History of Water Management and Hydraulic Engineering in the Mediterranean Region (Pompeii 1–8, October 1994)*, edited by N. de Haan and G.C.M. Jansen, 101–8. *BABesch* Suppl. 4. Leiden.

Wiggers, J.B.M. 1996. "The Urban Water Supply of Pompeii." In *Cura Aquarum in Campania: Proceedings of the Ninth International Congress on the History of Water Management and Hydraulic Engineering in the Mediterranean Region (Pompeii 1–8, October 1994)*, edited by N. de Haan and G.C.M. Jansen, 29–32. *BABesch* Suppl. 4. Leiden.

NOTES

* I wish to express my sincere thanks to the late Professor Miriam Balmuth for the invitation to give this preliminary report at the international colloquium, "Cultural Responses to the Volcanic Landscape," held at Tufts University on 16–17 November 1996. I am grateful to the editors of this volume for many helpful suggestions and corrections. Any remaining errors are mine alone. I am most appreciative for the many permissions and kindnesses extended to me during the preparation of this chapter by the Superintendency at Pompeii. I am deeply indebted to several Dutch scholars and engineers (named individually in the text of this chapter) and to participants of the 1994 conference held at Pompeii, *Cura Aquarum in Campania*, for sharing their ideas with me and for allowing me to discuss several international projects in this article which will help us understand water use in the ancient city.

PART III

RESPONSES IN ANCIENT LITERATURE

Volcanic Echoes in Ancient Near Eastern Texts

◈

Karen Polinger Foster*

Volcanism in the Near East and Aegean

The Near East and Aegean include two major groups of active and inactive volcanoes (Simkin and Siebert 1994; Daubeny 1848). The first comprises volcanoes stretching across the Mediterranean through Anatolia and into the Caucasus. Their locations mark where the northward-moving African tectonic plate grinds beneath the relatively stationary Eurasian tectonic plate, with strong subduction under the Hellenic arc (Aegean) and the Calabrian arc (southern Italy) responsible for many of the world's best-known eruptions. The second group encompasses the continental, rift-induced volcanoes of Syria, the Arabian peninsula, Iran, and Afghanistan, as well as the island volcanoes dotting the Indian Ocean.

In searching for volcanic echoes in ancient Near Eastern texts, let us start by considering the region's largest eruption of the past 100,000 years, the ca. 1525/24 B.C. explosion of the Cycladic island volcano of Thera (modern Santorini) (Hardy et al. 1990; Stiros and Jones 1996; McCoy and Heiken 1990; Forsyth 1997, 1–11). Over the course of a million years, a dozen large-scale eruptions had transformed Thera into the shape of a backward C enclosing one or possibly two calderas. By the mid-second millennium B.C., at the height of the Aegean Bronze Age, the volcano had been quiescent for 15,000 years, and the island was home to thriving towns and ports.

An earthquake, caused by tectonic shifting beneath the Aegean Sea, awakened the volcano. Shortly thereafter, a precursory ash fall heralded the plinian phase of the eruption, during which a column of pulverized magma shot 30–35 km into the air. When the sea flowed over the magma exposed in the vent, the hydrovolcanic interaction greatly increased the violence of the eruption. Fresh volcanic material surged out laterally, succeeded by horizontal flows of gas-rich clouds laden with ash, pumice, and blocks. A current point of debate, whose chronometric implications are discussed below, involves the amount of sulfur released into the atmosphere during this phase, as significant sulfuric aerosols lower global temperatures, stunting growth and resulting in thin post-eruption tree rings (Baillie 1995; Charlson and Wigley 1994; Simkin 1994; Hay 1996; Manning 1999). The entire volcanic event lasted at least 18 hours, more likely several days. The accompanying disturbances surely included periods of daytime darkness, wind, lightning, rain, and deafening noise, experienced far across the Mediterranean.

Tons of ejected debris completely buried Thera's settlements. One of these, on the southern coast near the modern village of Akrotiri, was discovered in 1967 by Spyridon Marinatos (Marinatos 1968–1976; Doumas 1983, 1992; Sherratt 2000). As at the famous cities at the foot of Vesuvius, thick volcanic deposits had effectively preserved a wealth of architecture, wall paintings, and small finds. Unlike their Roman counterparts, however, the Therans seem to have safely fled the island. Some of them returned briefly after the initial phase to clear debris and sort goods and furnishings, abandoning the effort when the ash began to fall in earnest.

Excavation of this "Pompeii of the ancient Aegean" has given rise to an important new field of Bronze Age art and archaeology. Thanks to its volcanic burial, Thera presents an ensemble unique among Aegean sites for its contextual integrity. Here, for instance, with wall paintings still on their original walls, we may begin to understand more fully the fundamental interdependence of Aegean architecture and painting. To take one example, in a small room in the Delta complex, a continuous mural of rock formations, with lilies growing from the clefts and swallows flying overhead, provides a theatrical backdrop for an ecstatic drama enacted in a space specially designed for epiphanic ritual (Foster 1995).

Volcanologists have assigned the Bronze Age eruption of Thera, a 6.9 on the Volcanic Explosivity Index (VEI), a logarithmic scale similar to the Richter scale used for earthquakes (Simkin and Siebert 1994, 23–6). VEI ratings take into account volume of tephra, cloud column height, eruption type, duration, and other factors. Thera's VEI rating was determined from ejecta volume measurements (30 km³), as well as from data gathered from comparable, well-documented eruptions such as Tambora (VEI 7) and Krakatau (VEI 6.3), both 19th-century eruptions in the Indonesian archipelago. Thera's VEI 6.9 puts it at the upper end of the scale, a paroxysmal, Ultra-Plinian event with substantial tropospheric and stratospheric injection.

Given the eruption's magnitude, it is not surprising that it has often been seen as the historical nugget embedded in such later accounts as the Atlantis legend, the story of Deucalion and the flood, episodes in the tale of the Argonauts, the passages about the fate of the Phaeacians in the *Odyssey*, and the parting of the Red Sea (Luce 1969; Friedrich 2000; Buckland, et al. 1997; Greene 1992). Appraisal of this material for possible Theran connections lies beyond the scope of my present study. Rather, I am concerned with investigating Egyptian and Mesopotamian texts, not only for Thera-specific references, but also for any use of volcanic imagery in general, a subject that hitherto has received scant attention.

Searching for Volcanic Echoes

Many scholars have remarked upon the apparent lack of notice accorded the Thera eruption in contemporaneous sources, explaining the silence by the fact that Thera exploded inopportunely during periods remarkable for their paucity of historical records. In Egypt, this is the end of the Second Intermediate Period and the rise to power of the Theban brothers Kamose and Ahmose, who conquered the Hyksos and founded the 18th Dynasty of the New Kingdom. In Mesopotamia, this is the end of the Old Babylonian period, with the Hittites' sack of Babylon about 1595 B.C. ushering in a century with almost no historical records. As for neighboring Minoan Crete, the Linear A documents, still undeciphered, seem in any case to pertain mainly to economic matters.

Admittedly, these are discouraging circumstances. Yet I would suggest that perhaps we have been unrealistically expecting the texts to take a predetermined narrative shape, on the order of recording that at a certain time an island blew apart in a cloud of fire and dust. But what do written reports of later volcanic eruptions throughout the world actually say about these kinds of events? What do oral histories preserve? How do artistic and literary figurative expression treat volcanoes? Finally, what role did observation of volcanoes and other unusual natural phenomena play in ancient Near Eastern thought?

For our purposes, the reports made after the comparable eruptions of Tambora in 1815 and Krakatau in 1883 are especially relevant. Numerous journals, ships' logs, and letters consistently mention the following phenomena: daytime darkness two days later and 500 km distant; total darkness for two days 160 km away; detonations heard 4653 km across the Indian Ocean; and severe earthquakes over a wide area (Simkin and Fiske 1983). In nonliterate societies, one finds the same emphasis, in which a major volcanic eruption is principally remembered as a legendary "Time of Darkness" or "Great Darkness," when flares and torches were useless (Blong 1982; Bullard 1984). Oral histories in volcanic regions often fix dates from these periods, noting the interval between the desolation caused by "what fell from the sky" and the seemingly miraculous increase in the land's fertility (Blong 1982, 168–70). The glassy, sterile particles in volcanic ash break down to release potassium, phosphorous, and other essential nutrients, resulting in soils of unsurpassed fertility and explaining why 10% of the world's population currently lives within dangerous radius of active volcanoes (Time-Life Books 1982, 47, 115; Chester 1993).

With the 18th and 19th centuries' appreciation of volcanoes as explicable phenomena (Bullard 1962; Murphy 1978; Jenkins and Sloan 1996; Sigurdsson 1999; Scarth 1999; de Boer and Sanders 2002), rather than as manifestations of "diseas'd nature" (Shakespeare, *Henry IV*, Part 1, Act 3, Scene 1, lines 27–8) or divine displeasure, interest grew in correlating eruptions with climatic and visual aftereffects. Benjamin Franklin, for instance, correctly attributed the frigid winter of 1784 to significant eruptions in Japan and Iceland, while New England's "Year Without a Summer" occurred in 1816, following Tambora (Stommel and Stommel 1983; Simkin and Fiske 1983). With the wisdom of scientific hindsight, various volcanic culprits may now be fingered for past occurrences. The massive eruption of Kuwae in the South Pacific, for example, was quite probably responsible for the strange atmospheric portents witnessed during the Turkish siege of Constantinople in 1453, which despairing observers believed fulfilled an ancient prophecy concerning the fall of Byzantium (Simarski 1996).

Though no longer mythopeically deemed the flaming abode of writhing giants, volcanoes have continued to elicit creative responses in the modern era, from the smoking folly built in the princely garden at Wörlitz to the exploding island staged for the Versailles inaugural tableaux (Thacker 1979, 217–8, 222; Mukerji 1997, 210; Greene 1992). Writers and artists regularly used volcanic imagery, much of it Vesuvian as Pompeii and Herculaneum became fixtures on the Grand Tour (Murphy 1978; Jenkins and Sloane 1996). In chapter 104 of Herman Melville's novel *Moby Dick*, for instance, Ishmael calls upon "Vesuvius' crater for an inkstand," a fittingly cosmic image for his epic tale. Volcanic aerosols, particularly those engendered by Tambora and Krakatau, resulted in such European and North American sights as green suns, blue moons, and blazing sunsets. Inspired by the after-effects of Krakatau, Alfred, Lord Tennyson wrote:

> Had the fierce ashes of some fiery peak
> Been hurl'd so high they ranged about the globe?
> For day by day, thro' many a blood-red eye...
> The wrathful sunset glared (*St. Telemachus*, lines 1–5).

The best-known American painter of volcanoes and their aftereffects was Frederic Edwin Church, whose 1860s views of the South American erup-tions of Cotopaxi and Sangay were considered signs of the New World's tri-umph over the "errors of human history . . . an eternal cosmic Genesis," while in his 1861 "Our Banner in the Sky," a volcanic sunset with crimson-streaked sky and twilight stars, betokened divine support for the Union cause in the Civil War (Fiske and Nielsen 1985; Dee 1992; Huntington 1966; Kelly 1988).

With regard to Thera itself, no eruption from Classical times to the latest one in 1950 has approached the scale of the Bronze Age cataclysm. Nevertheless, accounts of these smaller events provide a valuable basis for extrapolation (Doumas 1978; Fouqué 1998; Vougioukalakis n.d.). In 197 B.C., the geographer Strabo wrote that "fires broke forth from the sea and continued for four days, so that the whole sea boiled and blazed." The A.D. 1650 eruption occasioned reports of thunderous noises and fires visible from Crete. During a minor eruption in 1867, an English journalist on Crete saw smoke by day and fires by night along the northern horizon.

The aftereffects of at least one of these more recent Thera eruptions seem to have been noted in Mesopotamia. In the winter and early spring of 197 B.C., the Babylonian astronomical diaries record exceptionally bad weather: storms, heavy rains, flooding, dense fog, and solar and lunar halos—all post-volcanic phenomena (Sachs and Hunger 1989, SE 114). The diaries also seem to preserve other volcanic echoes, among them the 183 B.C. eruption of

Vulcano, which caused overcast skies and severe cold in Babylon (Sachs and Hunger 1989, SE 129). Though it is tempting to attribute in like manner the lengthy invisibilities of Venus recorded in the Old Babylonian period to the Bronze Age eruption, the material is too textually corrupt to permit any reliable association (Reiner and Pingree 1975, 21–3, contra Baillie 1995, 86).

Ancient Near Eastern interest in what today we term "earth science" was not confined to celestial and climatic matters, but also devolved upon geology, including petrological oddities like meteorites and suggestively shaped flint nodules (Meijer 1992; Bjorkman 1973; Ünal 1977). This continued into the Islamic period, with regular documentation of earthquakes and related events in 7th through 18th century Arabic sources (Poirier and Taker 1980). As for volcanic vocabulary, no generic term for volcano has been identified in ancient Egyptian or Mesopotamian languages, a linguistic situation paralleled in Greek and Latin (Johnston, this volume; Polimenakos 1996; Foster 1999, 33–4). The same is true for Arabic, where *burkan* comes into use only in the mid-19th century, as a loan-word from *vulcano*. The Akkadian "Starry Mountain" is the volcano Kawkab in northeastern Syria, perhaps so named because of the way its lava flows emanate in a ray-like pattern from its summit, or for its starbright effusions (Catagnoti and Bonechi 1992; Dillemann 1962; Foster and Ritner 1996, 4).

In ancient Near Eastern art, volcanic representation takes pride of place as the world's first known landscape. A seventh-millennium wall painting from the Anatolian site of Çatal Hüyük depicts a closely rendered, Strombolian-type eruption, with ash clouds rising above spasmodically ejected bombs and blocks (Mellaart 1967, 176–7; Simkin and Siebert 1994, 180). More recently published volcanic scenes from the site seem unlikely to be authentic (Mellaart 1993; Collon 1990). Thereafter, mountains figure prominently in landscapes, especially in glyptic, but it is difficult to recognize unambiguous volcanic referents because of the apparent disjunction (for the most part) between Mesopotamian pictorialization and literary/mythological imagery (Postgate 1994; Michalowski 1986; Mindlin et al. 1987; Vogelzang and Vanstiphout 1996; Oppenheim 1978). Promisingly volcanic scenes include mountains with incorporated figures, sometimes engulfed in fire; mountains with spiralform flames shooting out; and showers of stones raining upon mythological landscapes (Foster 1999, 35–7). The most compelling image occurs on the Old Babylonian plaque discussed below.

Volcanic Echoes from Mesopotamia

We turn now to Mesopotamian literature in search of volcanic echoes. From the end of the third millennium on, numerous texts mention bizarre atmospheric phenomena, glowing mountains, pulverization of mountains by human and divine agents, and daytime darkness, all associated with dire meteorological events and destructions (Foster and Ritner 1996, 7–8, 12–4). Remarkable items fall from the sky: fire and potsherds, dust and hot bits of burnt clay, stones and fiery glare, clay pellets, and small cakes (Foster 1991; Dennis 1992). Is this hyperbole for literary effect, or is there some physical basis? I, for one, agree with A.R. Millard (1987, 67): "What can have inspired the poets to write of something so peculiar...the answer is Reality!"

J.V. Kinnier Wilson has advanced the idea that two components of Mesopotamian reality were the great Saidmarreh landslide of about 9500 B.C. and naturally ignited seepages of gas and oil, accompanied by noxious fumes (Kinnier Wilson 1979). The landslide, located in the Zagros foothills due east of Babylon, must have occasioned deafening noise and an enormous quantity of dust, but did memory of it persist until its incorporation in Sumerian literature 7,000 years later? Be that as it may, certain descriptive passages do not fit within the parameters of either of these geological realities. Kinnier Wilson calls them "misunderstandings and confusion," citing as good examples rains of stone and fire, as well as a destroyed mountain made incongruously into "a kind of paradise area, full of growth and fertility" (Kinnier Wilson 1979, 109–12).

I suggest that volcanic eruptions and their aftereffects provide a convincing, comprehensive basis for much discourse previously deemed "misunderstandings" or anomalies. The daytime darkness, solar and lunar halos, strangely luminous cloud formations, and fiery glares at sunset are phenomena entirely consistent with volcanic aftereffects. I would hazard that some of the most spectacular sights were caused by Thera, the principal volcanic event of its place and time, and passed down in the conservative omen and ritual text tradition. The eccentric rains, including "stones of a fiery glare," flaming potsherds, and cakes (pumice?) would likewise seem in line with volcanic ejecta, cast figuratively in more familiar domestic terms. And the land's resurgent fecundity is typical of fresh volcanic soils the world over.

I further propose that volcanic imagery underlies the fundamental trope for a major work of Sumerian literature, the 700-line narrative poem known as *Lugal-e* (Foster 1999; Jacobsen 1987, 233–71; Bottéro and Kramer 1989, 338–77; van Dijk 1983 [text edition]). The text was composed toward the end of the third millennium, with the earliest known manuscripts dating to the first half of the second millennium. *Lugal-e* tells how the warrior-god Ninurta vanquishes Azag, a powerful entity the text never specifically identifies, but rather describes in such a way as to leave no doubt, in my view, as to Azag's true identity. Azag is a being of the mountains, engendered on Earth by Sky, massively strong and solidified, possessing a dreadful aura. Through copulation with (or in) a mountain, Azag produces numerous progeny, which elect the "plant-stone" as their king. Azag also has many stone allies, all but one of them igneous rocks. In short, Azag is none other than a volcano, whose eruption and associated phenomena are poetically metamorphosed into a cosmic battle waged against Ninurta (Foster 1999).

In their first confrontation, Azag and its stone allies rout Ninurta. The sun vanishes, the moon does not appear, and the "day was made (black) like pitch." Then Azag "gashed the earth's body . . . bathed the sky in blood . . . and till today black cinders are in the field." As Azag "rains down clay pellets for rain," Ninurta rallies, defeating Azag so thoroughly that it can never reproduce again. The triumphant Ninurta ordains: "From this day on, may (the name) Azag not be spoken . . . let 'zalag stone' be its name . . . may thus its extinction be bitter."

Lugal-e concludes with two geological musings. In the first, the poet describes how Ninurta sets about reorganizing the hydrogeography of the Tigris, creating properly flowing watercourses and foothills, apparently using Azag's remains, as one would expect in a post-volcanic landscape. The foothills are to be particularly fertile, a possible recognition of the fecundity of volcanic soils. The second, a section perhaps originally from another Sumerian work, takes the form of Ninurta's sentencing of Azag's defeated stone allies and progeny, beginning with the elected king, the "plant-stone." Ninurta metes out judgments to the rest: lava, basalt, granite, diorite, limestone, alabaster, hematite, steatite, flint, and a host of other stones. Finally, the god Enlil promises his son Ninurta that his mountain-enemy will never be restored.

When considered from a volcanic perspective, the narrative structure and complex imagery of *Lugal-e* coalesce for the first time, I believe, into a meaningful mythohistorical and descriptive whole. As just one example, let us take the recalcitrant problem of identifying the "plant-stone." If, as I see it,

Azag is a volcano, then its foremost progeny must be an igneous rock not otherwise cited among Azag's allies. "Plant" implies that the lithic king is green. From earliest times, the Mesopotamians knew and prized such a stone: green obsidian from Nemrut Dagh in eastern Anatolia (Moorey 1994, 37, 63–71; Mellaart 1975, 91; Foster 1999, 31–3; Bouška et al. 1993, 95–101; Williams-Thorpe 1995; Wright 1969; Roaf 1990, 34). Obsidian, a volcanic glass that fractures conchoidally into hard, sharp blades, was used in the ancient Near East exactly as Ninurta decrees. The god condemns the fallen "plant-stone" to be forever pared off, to grind its teeth (retouched serrations) on its own offspring, to pierce carnelian, to work other stones. "Plant-stone" also occurs in nonliterary texts, including lists of beads, jewelry, and booty presented to the Assryian king Assurnasirpal and lists of materials intended for boring and drilling, all in line with its being obsidian (Foster 1999, 31–2, 39).

An Old Babylonian clay plaque from Khafajeh has often been considered the likeliest pictorialization of Azag (Roaf 1990, 77). Ninurta (if it is he), bow slung over his shoulder, confronts a remarkable opponent, hands bound behind its back. Its head, radiating fire, bears a mask featuring a frontal Cyclopean eye, a broad triangular nose, and a trapezoidal mouth. Naked from the waist up, revealing rolls of fat under a swelling breast, the being wears boots and an ankle-length skirt of overlapping elements flaring outward at the hem. The god grasps one of the flaming rays, plunging his sword into his foe's mid-section. In many significant aspects, the plaque's iconography accords perfectly with the Azag imagery in *Lugal-e*: a being of dreadful aura, neither male nor female, its face masked, and lava-like lower reaches, killed by a sword-thrust to its liver as Enlil advises. Other, more generic interpretations are also possible, as is often the case in Mesopotamian art.

We may pose three final questions about the volcanic echoes in *Lugal-e*. Where are the mountains in the poem and are they in fact volcanic? Were the Sumerians familiar with them? Is Azag meant to be a particular volcano? *Lugal-e* specifies the Tigris as the river whose headwaters Ninurta reconfigures after Azag's demise (Heimpel 1987). It follows that the setting must be the mountains of eastern Anatolia, in the vicinity of Lake Hazar, where the Tigris rises amidst a half dozen active volcanoes and volcanic rock formations. From the Neolithic on, Mesopotamians valued this area, especially for its obsidian. Distinctive artifacts and architecture of the ca. 3200 B.C. Late

Uruk culture of Sumer have been found at several sites in the Upper Tigris basin, apparently Sumerian commercial, military, or administrative outposts (Roaf 1990, 53–65; Algaze 1993). Even after obsidian demand diminished in later periods, the region remained an important destination on the Mesopotamian map. In the late third millennium, the Akkadian king Naram-Sin claims to have reached the source of the Tigris, a royal feat emulated over a thousand years later by Shalmaneser III and other Assyrian kings (Lehmann-Haupt 1906, 31–44; Luckenbill 1926, 246–9; Grayson 1991, 61 and 1996, 92–6; Frayne 1993, 86).

In answer, then, to the first two questions, I suggest that the *Lugal-e* battleground lies within range of the headwaters of the Tigris, a volcanic area certainly known to the Sumerians. Of the surrounding active volcanoes, which might Azag be? Two hundred kilometers due east of Lake Hazar soars Nemrut Dagh, not only the most continuously-eruptive Anatolian volcano of the past 10,000 years, but also the Sumerians' source of green obsidian (Simkin and Siebert 1994, 43; Degens et al. 1984; Landmann et al. 1996). If the "plant-stone" of *Lugal-e* and other texts is green obsidian, could Azag be Nemrut Dagh? In the Tigris watershed and in Nemrut Dagh, poetic imagination would have found an eminently conducive environment for developing the extended volcanic trope of *Lugal-e*.

Volcanic Echoes from Egypt

Turning to Egypt, we have an extraordinary text from the reign of Ahmose, founder of the 18th Dynasty. This is a stele erected at Thebes to record a highly destructive storm and to commemorate the pharaoh's rebuilding program. In 1967 and 1968, Claude Vandersleyen published fragments of the stele, which had been used as broken fill in the Karnak Temple's Third Pylon (Vandersleyen 1967 and 1968). Vandersleyen's familiarity with weather patterns in modern Egypt, as well as general Egyptological unfamiliarity with Thera (whose excavation had just begun), led him to interpret the text so it referred to a localized Theban storm. Relying on his translations, Ellen Davis concluded in 1990 that this local storm could not be related to the Thera eruption, promising though the stele otherwise seems (Davis 1990).

Robert Ritner and I have recently reexamined this so-called Tempest Stele (Foster and Ritner 1996; for a response, whose proposals we find unconvincing, see Wiener and Allen 1998). Three passages explicitly extend the devastation to the whole country, twice using the expression, the "Two Lands," standard Egyptian formulation for the Nile Valley and Delta areas. While sudden, violent storms recur in ancient Egyptian life and literature, only the Ahmose stele details, in nonhyperbolic prose, such a severe catastrophe over the length and breadth of Egypt. The pharaoh cites deafening noise, enveloping darkness, torrents, houses washed into the river and bobbing like boats, and chapels, tombs, and temples damaged, collapsed, or reduced to "that which was never made." Ahmose also notes that the darkness was in the "western region," precisely where the Egyptians placed the Aegean Keftiu (Wachsmann 1999, 298; Darnell 1991, nn. 82, 84). He attributes the storm to divine displeasure, yet declares "how much greater this is than the wrath of the great god, than the plans of the gods." The stele finishes by telling how Ahmose "began to reestablish the Two Lands."

Could these be echoes from Thera? The phenomena described are strikingly consistent with eruption report language, as discussed above. This brings us to an all-important question: when did Thera explode? The short answer is, we do not yet know for certain. At present, the two main chronometric proposals are a century apart (numerous articles in Bietak 2003; Wiener 2003). The later, Short Chronology date is based chiefly on ceramic sequences, stratified Theran pumice, and Egyptian synchronisms, yielding 1530–1520 B.C. as the most likely decade. The earlier, Long Chronology date is based largely on evidence from dendrochronology and ice cores, pointing to the mid-17th century B.C. for hemisphere-wide cooling, atmospheric disturbances, and volcanic ash fall. Over the past few years, support for the Long Chronology has steadily eroded, in the face of such findings as the fact that the volcanic glass in the Greenland ice cores turns out not to have come from Thera (Zielinski and Germani 1998; Wiener 2003; Bietak 2003). It appears ever more probable that an undocumented, cataclysmic eruption occurred somewhere in the world about 1650 B.C., perhaps in Indonesia, the Pacific, or the Americas, but not in the Aegean.

How does the 16th-century date work in terms of Ahmose's witnessing the Thera eruption and its aftereffects? According to high Egyptian chronology, Ahmose ruled 1550–1525 B.C.; low chronology puts him at 1539–1514 B.C. The stele was carved before his year 22, since his name was written differently the last three years of his reign. By Ahmose's year 11 at the earliest and 18 at the latest, he had conquered the Hyksos capital of Avaris in the eastern Delta. Manfred Bietak's recent discoveries at Avaris (Tell

el-Dab'a) include the remains of a palatial complex most probably begun by
Ahmose, with subsequent structures built not later than Thutmosis III (ca.
1479–1425 B.C.). Fresco and painted stucco relief fragments found in and
around these buildings give an idea of their sophisticated, complex decorations, whose style and technique are unmistakably Aegean, with clear parallels to Theran and Minoan work (Bietak 1996; Davies and Schofield 1995;
Cline 1998; Bietak 2000; also numerous articles in Sherratt 2000).

Numerous lumps of water-worn pumice from Thera have been recovered
from the workshops of palace G, in the palace itself, and in the domestic
quarter, all datable to the Thutmosid phase of the complex. Though pumice
from various Mediterranean volcanoes must always have been collected
along the coast of Egypt, the standard abrasive was quartz sand, more readily
and reliably available (Lucas and Harris 1962, 73). If large amounts of
Theran pumice had washed up during the Second Intermediate Period, in
accordance with the Long Chronology eruption date, one would expect to
find it in Hyksos levels. Yet this does not seem to be the case, as Bietak and
others have pointed out. Theran pumice "appears suddenly" at Avaris and
neighboring sites, as well as in northern Sinai, "in one [post-Hyksos] horizon
and not before" (Bietak 1996, 124; Stanley and Sheng 1986; see also Cline
1998, 215).

Furthermore, pumice lumps turn up in graves at Thebes, Maiyana, and
Kahun dating to the terminal Second Intermediate Period/early 18th
Dynasty (Foster and Bichler 2003). If this too is Theran pumice, its presence
in modest burials of the Ahmosid/Thutmosid age, as far upstream as Thebes,
would have important implications for the eruption-date debate. Until now,
the large sample size required for reliable instrumental neutron activation
analysis has precluded work on these and other museum pumice specimens.
Thanks to techniques recently developed in Vienna and Oxford, it may soon
be possible to analyze these pieces to ascertain if indeed these graves contained Theran pumice (Bichler et al. 1997; Peltz et al. 1999; Peltz and
Bichler 2001).

In sum, the following sequence of events may be provisionally suggested,
using the low Egyptian chronology currently favored. By year 11 at the earliest (1528 B.C.) and year 18 at the latest (1521 B.C.), Ahmose had conquered Avaris and begun building a palatial complex there, complete with
frescoes and stucco reliefs apparently painted by Minoan artists. Given the
very close stylistic parallels to some Theran material, the volcano must have

erupted about the time the Avaris frescoes were executed. Substantial pumice rafts soon drifted across the Mediterranean to the beaches of northern Egypt, whence the desirable stones made their way into numerous contexts, from Avaris workshops to the cosmetic goods in Theban and other graves. In or before Ahmose's year 22 (1517 B.C.), the pharaoh erected at least one monument to commemorate an extraordinary natural and national catastrophe, which may well have been the Thera eruption. In year 22, the royal treasurer recorded the opening of a new quarry for major projects, perhaps connected with the post-Theran, Egypt-wide restorations (Sethe 1906, 24–5; Harvey 1994). Three years later, Ahmose died. As for the frescoes at Avaris, the artists used lime plaster (standard for the Aegean), which inadequately bonded to the Egyptian mudbrick surfaces. Before the reign of Thutmosis III, possibly within a short time of their application, the paintings sloughed off the walls and had to be discarded.

As of this writing, there is a growing body of new scientific and archaeological evidence for 1525/1524 B.C. as the time of the eruption (Wiener forthcoming). This date would dovetail neatly with the chronological window afforded by the Tempest Stele. We know that Ahmose conquered the Hyksos and established the 18th Dynasty of the New Kingdom. Did he also lead Egypt through the greatest volcanic event of the Bronze Age world?

Conclusions

Volcanic landscapes seem to have played significant roles, hitherto unexamined, in historical, descriptive, and literary texts from the ancient Near East. In my view, volcanoes, eruptions, volcanic aftereffects, and associated phenomena provide a compelling basis for a new understanding of many texts, as well as artistic imagery. Volcanic echoes may be found in Mesopotamian material ranging from the Babylonian astronomical diaries to the Sumerian narrative poem *Lugal-e*. In ancient Egypt, the Tempest Stele of Ahmose may well stand as an eyewitness account of the Thera eruption of ca. 1525/1524 B.C., the region's largest eruption of the past 100,000 years.

REFERENCES

Algaze, G. 1993. *The Uruk World System: The Dynamics of Expansion of Early Mesopotamian Civilization*. Chicago.

Baillie, M.G.L. 1995. *A Slice Through Time: Dendrochronology and Precision Dating.* London.

Bichler, M., H. Egger, A. Preisinger, D. Ritter, P. Stastny. 1997. "NAA of the 'Minoan Pumice' at Thera and Comparison to Alluvial Pumice Deposits in the Eastern Mediterranean Region." *Journal of Radioanalytical and Nuclear Chemistry* 224:1–2, 7–14.

Bietak, M., 1996. *Avaris, the Capital of the Hyksos: Recent Excavations at Tell el-Dab'a.* London.

———. 2000. " 'Rich Beyond the Dreams of Avaris: Tell el-Dab'a and the Aegean World. A Guide for the Perplexed.' A Response to Eric H. Cline." *BSA* 95:185–205.

Bietak, M., ed. 2003. *The Synchronization of Civilisations in the Eastern Mediterranean in the Second Millennium B.C. Proceedings of the SCIEM 2000 EuroConference, Haindorf, 2–7 May 2001.* Vienna.

Bjorkman, J.K. 1973. *Meteors and Meteorites in the Ancient Near East.* Tempe, Ariz.

Blong, R.J. 1982. *The Time of Darkness: Local Legends and Volcanic Reality in Papua New Guinea.* Canberra.

Bottéro, J., and S.N. Kramer. 1989. *Lorsque les dieux faisaient l'homme: Mythologie mésopotamienne.* Paris.

Bouška, V., Z. Borovec, A. Cimbalnikova, I. Krous, A. Layčakora, and M. Pačesova. 1993. *Natural Glasses.* New York.

Buckland, P.C., A.J. Dugmore, and K.J. Edwards. 1997. "Bronze Age Myths? Volcanic Activity and Human Response in the Mediterranean and North Atlantic Region." *Antiquity* 71:581–93.

Bullard, F.M. 1962. *Volcanoes in History, in Theory, in Eruption.* Austin.

———. 1984. *Volcanoes of the Earth.* Austin.

Catagnoti, A., and M. Bonechi. 1992. "Le volcan Kawkab, Nagar et problèmes connexes." *N.A.B.U.,* June: 50–3.

Charlson, R.J., and T.M.L. Wigley. 1994. "Sulfate Aerosol and Climate Change." *SciAm* 270:2, 48–57.

Chester, D. 1993. *Volcanoes and Society.* London.

Cline, E.H. 1998. "Rich Beyond the Dreams of Avaris: Tell el Dab'a and the Aegean World: A Guide for the Perplexed." *BSA* 93:199–219.

Collon, D. 1990. "Subjective Reconstruction? The Çatal Hüyük Wall-Paintings." *HALI* 12:5, 119–23.

Darnell, J.C. 1991. "Supposed Depictions of Hittites in the Amarna Period." *Studien zur altägyptischen Kultur* 18:113–40.

Davies, W.V., and L. Schofield, eds. 1995. *Egypt, the Aegean and the Levant: Interconnections in the Second Millennium B.C.* London.

Davis, E.N. 1990. "A Storm in Egypt during the Reign of Ahmose." In *Thera and the Aegean World III.* Vol. 2, *Earth Sciences,* edited by Hardy, D.A., J. Keller, V.P. Galanopoulos, N.C. Flemming, and T.H. Druitt, 232–5. London.

Daubeny, C. 1848. *A Description of Active and Extinct Volcanoes.* London.

de Boer, J.Z., and D.T. Sanders 2002. *Volcanoes in Human History.* Princeton.

Dee, E.E. 1992. *Frederic Edwin Church: Under Changing Skies.* Philadelphia.

Degens, E.T., H.K. Wong, S. Kempe, and F. Kurtman. 1984. "A Geological Study of Lake Van, Eastern Turkey." *Geologische Rundschau* 73:701–34.

Dennis, J. 1992. *It's Raining Frogs and Fishes: Four Seasons of Natural Phenomena and Oddities of the Sky.* New York.

Dillemann, L. 1962. *Haute mésopotamie orientale et pays adjacents*. Paris.

Doumas, C. 1983. *Thera: Pompeii of the Ancient Aegean*. London.

————. 1992. *The Wall-Paintings of Thera*. Athens.

Fiske, R.S., and E. Nielsen. 1985. "Church's Cotopaxi: A Modern Volcanological Perspective." In *Creation & Renewal: Views of Cotopaxi by Frederic Edwin Church*, edited by K. Manthorne, 1–6. Washington, D.C.

Forsyth, P.Y. 1997. *Thera in the Bronze Age*. New York.

Foster, K.P. 1991. "Ceramic Imagery in Ancient Near Eastern Literature." In *Materials Issues in Art and Archaeology*, Vol. II, edited by P.B. Vandiver, J. Druzik, and G.S. Wheeler, 389–413. Pittsburgh.

————. 1995. "A Flight of Swallows." *AJA* 99:409–25.

————. 1999. "Volcanic Landscapes in *Lugal-e*." In *Landscapes: Territories, Frontiers and Horizons in the Ancient Near East. Papers Presented to the XLIV Rencontre Assyriologique Internationale, Venezia, 7–11 July 1997*. Vol. III, *Landscapes in Ideology, Religion, Literature and Art*, edited by L. Milano, S. de Martino, F.M. Fales, and G.B. Lanfranchi, 23–39. Padova.

————. 2001. "Dionysos and Vesuvius in the Villa of the Mysteries." *AntK* 44: 37–54.

Foster, K.P., and M. Bichler. 2003. "Theran Pumice from Egyptian Graves?" In *METRON: Measuring the Aegean Bronze Age. Proceedings of the Ninth International Aegean Conference, New Haven, 18–21 April 2002*, edited by K.P. Foster and R. Laffineur, 431–9. Liège.

Foster, K.P., and R.K. Ritner. 1996. "Texts, Storms, and the Thera Eruption." *JNES* 55:1–14.

Fouqué, F. 1998. *Santorini and Its Eruptions*. Translated and annotated by A.R. McBirney. Baltimore.

Frayne, D. 1993. *The Royal Inscriptions of Mesopotamia: Sargonic and Gutian Periods (2334–2113 BC)*. Toronto.

Friedrich, W.L. 2000. *Fire in the Sea: The Santorini Volcano, Natural History and the Legend of Atlantis*. Cambridge.

Grayson, A.K. 1991. *The Royal Inscriptions of Mesopotamia: Assyrian Rulers of the Early First Millennium B.C.* Vol. I, *(1114–859 BC)*. Toronto.

————. 1996. *The Royal Inscriptions of Mesopotamia: Assyrian Rulers of the Early First Millennium B.C.* Vol. II, *(858–745 BC)*. Toronto.

Greene, M.T. 1992. *Natural Knowledge in Preclassical Antiquity*. Baltimore.

Hardy, D.A., J. Keller, V.P. Galanopoulos, N.C. Flemming, and T.H. Druitt, eds. 1990. *Thera and the Aegean World III*. Vol. 2, *Earth Sciences*. London.

Harvey, S. 1994. "Monuments of Ahmose at Abydos." *Egyptian Archaeology* 4:4.

Hay, W.W. 1996. "Tectonics and Climate." *Geologische Rundschau* 85:409–37.

Heimpel, W. 1987. "The Natural History of the Tigris According to the Sumerian Literary Composition *Lugal-e*." *JNES* 46:309–17.

Huntington, D.C. 1966. *The Landscapes of Frederic Edwin Church: Visions of an American Era*. New York.

Jacobsen, T. 1987. *The Harps That Once...: Sumerian Poetry in Translation*. New Haven.

Jenkins, I., and K. Sloan. 1996. *Vases and Volcanoes: Sir William Hamilton and His Collection*. London.

Kelly, F. 1988. *Frederic Edwin Church and the National Landscape*. Washington, D.C.

Kinnier Wilson, J.V. 1979. *The Rebel Lands: An Investigation into the Origins of Early Mesopotamian Mythology*. Cambridge.

Landmann, G., A. Reimer, and S. Kempe. 1996. "Climatically Induced Lake Level Changes at Lake Van, Turkey, During the Pleistocene/Holocene Transition." *Global Biogeochemical Cycles* 10:797–808.

Lehmann-Haupt, C.F. 1906. *Materialien zur älteren Geschichte Armeniens und Mesopotmiens*. Berlin.

Lucas, A., and J.R. Harris. 1962. *Ancient Egyptian Materials and Industries*. London.

Luce, J.V. 1969. *The End of Atlantis: New Light on an Old Legend*. London.

Luckenbill, D.D. 1926. *Ancient Records of Assyria and Babylonia*. Vol. I. Chicago.

Manning, S.W. 1999. *A Test of Time: The Volcano of Thera and the Chronology and History of the Aegean and East Mediterranean in the Mid-Second Millennium B.C.* Oxford.

Marinatos, S. 1968–1976. *Excavations at Thera*. Vols. I–VII. Athens.

McCoy, F.W., and G. Heiken. 1990. "Anatomy of an Eruption." *Archaeology* 43:3, 42–9.

Meijer, D.J.W., ed. 1992. *Natural Phenomena: Their Meaning, Depiction and Description in the Ancient Near East*. Amsterdam.

Mellaart, J. 1967. *Çatal Hüyük: A Neolithic Town in Anatolia*. London.

––––––. 1993. "Déscriptions (picturales) d'éruptions récentes du Hasan Dağı par les hommes du néolithique à Çatal Hüyük." *LAVE* 42:17–30.

Michalowski, P. 1986. "Mental Maps and Ideology: Reflections on Subartu." In *The Origins of Cities in Dry-Farming Syria and Mesopotamia*, edited by H. Weiss, 126–56. Guilford.

Millard, A.R. 1987. "The Sign of the Flood." *Iraq* 49:63–9.

Mindlin, M., M.J. Geller, and J.E. Wansbrough, eds. 1987. *Figurative Language in the Ancient Near East*. London.

Moorey, P.R.S. 1994. *Ancient Mesopotamian Materials and Industries*.

Mukerji, C. 1997. *Territorial Ambitions and the Gardens of Versailles*. Cambridge.

Murphy, A. R. 1978. *Visions of Vesuvius*. Boston.

Oppenheim. A.L. 1978. "Man and Nature in Mesopotamian Civilization." In *Dictionary of Scientific Biography*, Vol. 15, edited by R. Adams and L. Zejszner, 634–66. New York.

Peltz, C., P. Schmid, and M. Bichler. 1999. "INAA of Aegean Pumices for the Classification of Archaeological Findings." *Journal of Radioanalytical and Nuclear Chemistry* 242:2, 361–77.

Peltz, C., and M. Bichler. 2001. "Classification of Archaeologically Stratified Pumice by INAA." *Journal of Radioanalytical and Nuclear Chemistry* 248:1, 81–7.

Poirier, J.P., and M.A. Taker. 1980. "Historical Seismicity in the Near and Middle East, North Africa, and Spain from Arabic Documents (VIIth – XVIIIth Century)." *Bulletin of the Seismological Society of America* 70:2185–210.

Polimenakos, L.C. 1996. "Thoughts on the Perception of the Earthquake in Greek Antiquity." In *Archaeoseismology*, edited by S. Stiros and R.E. Jones, 253–7. Athens.

Postgate, J.N. 1994. "Text and Figure in Ancient Mesopotamia: Match and Mismatch." In *The Ancient Mind: Elements of Cognitive Archaeology*, edited by C. Renfrew and E. B.W. Zubrow, 176–84. Cambridge.

Reiner, E., and D. Pingree. 1975. *The Venus Tablets of Ammisaduqa*. Malibu.

Roaf, M. 1990. *Cultural Atlas of Mesopotamia and the Ancient Near East.* New York.

Sachs, A.J., and H. Hunger. 1989. *Astronomical Diaries and Related Texts from Babylonia.* Vienna.

Scarth, A. 1999. *Vulcan's Fury: Man Against the Volcano.* New Haven.

Sethe, K. 1906. *Urkunden der 18.Dynastie,* Vol. IV/1. Leipzig.

Sherratt, S., ed. 2000. *The Wall Paintings of Thera: Proceedings of the First International Symposium.* Athens.

Sigurdsson, H. 1999. *Melting the Earth: The History of Ideas on Volcanic Eruptions.* New York.

Simarski, L.T. 1996. "Constantinople's Volcanic Twilight." *Aramco World* 47:6, 8–13.

Simkin, T. 1994. "Distant Effects of Volcanism: How Big and How Often?" *Science* 264:913–4.

Simkin, T., and R.S. Fiske. 1983. *Krakatau 1883: The Volcanic Eruption and Its Effects.* Washington, D.C.

Simkin, T., and L. Siebert. 1994. *Volcanoes of the World: A Regional Directory, Gazetteer, and Chronology of Volcanism during the Last 10,000 Years.* Tucson.

Stanley, D.J., and H. Sheng. 1986. "Volcanic Shards from Santorini (Upper Minoan Ash) in the Nile Delta, Egypt." *Nature* 320:733–5.

Stiros, S., and R.E. Jones, eds. 1996. *Archaeoseismology.* Athens.

Stommel, H., and E. Stommel. 1983. *Volcano Weather: The Story of 1816, the Year Without a Summer.* Newport.

Thacker, C. 1979. *The History of Gardens.* Berkeley.

Time-Life Books. 1982. *Planet Earth: Volcano.* Alexandria.

Ünal, A. 1977. "Naturkatastrophen in Anatolien im 2.Jahrtausend v. Chr." *Belleten* 163:447–72.

Vandersleyen, C. 1967. "Une tempête sous le règne d'Amosis," *Revue d'Égyptologie* 19:123–59.

———. 1968. "Deux nouveaux fragments de la stèle d'Amosis relatant une tempête." *Revue d'Égyptologie* 20:127–34.

van Dijk, J. 1983. *LUGAL UD ME-LAM-bi NIR-GAL.* Leiden.

Vogelzang, M.E., and H.L.J. Vanstiphout, eds. 1996. *Mesopotamian Poetic Language: Sumerian and Akkadian.* Groningen.

Vougioukalakis, G. n.d. *Santorini. Guide to "The Volcano" (Palea and Nea Kameni): Volcanic Activity in Historic Times.* Santorini.

Wachsmann, S. 1998. *Seagoing Ships & Seamanship in the Bronze Age Levant.* College Station, Tex.

Wiener, M.H. 2003. "Time Out: The Current Impasse in Bronze Age Archaeological Dating." In *METRON: Measuring the Aegean Bronze Age. Proceedings of the Ninth International Aegean Conference, New Haven, 18–21 April 2002,* edited by K.P. Foster and R. Laffineur, 363–99. Liège.

———. Forthcoming. "Chronology Going Forward (With a Query about 1525/24 B.C.)" In *Manfred Bietak Festschrift.*

Wiener, M.H., and J.P. Allen. 1998. "Separate Lives: The Ahmose Tempest Stela and the Theran Eruption." *JNES* 57:1–28.

Williams-Thorpe, O. 1995. "Obsidian in the Mediterranean and the Near East: A
  Provenancing Success Story." *Archaeometry* 37:217–48.
Wright, G.A. 1969. *Obsidian Analysis and Prehistoric Near Eastern Trade.* Ann Arbor.
Zielinski, G.A., and M.S. Germani. 1998. "New Ice-Core Evidence Challenges the 1620s
  B.C. Age for the Santorini (Minoan) Eruption." *Journal of Archaeological Science*
  25:279–89.

ACKNOWLEDGMENTS

* I would like to thank particularly Miriam S. Balmuth for inviting me to take part in the
  Tufts colloquium; fellow participants and audience members for stimulating discussion of
  my presentation; Patricia A. Johnston for patient editing; Benjamin R. Foster for assistance in cuneiform matters and for furnishing many essential references; Robert K. Ritner
  and John C. Darnell for Egyptological advice; members of the 1997 Yale graduate sem-
  inar on Egypt and the Aegean for working through much of this material with me;
  Gregory A. Zielinski and Jonathan Lees for geological guidance; Alice L. Slotsky for examining the Babylonian astronomical diaries for volcano weather; Franz Rosenthal for
  checking Arabic lexicography for volcanic terminology; Douglas Keenan for references to
  Lake Van sediment studies; and Malcolm Wiener for chronological counsel. The present
  article brings together, with a different focus and updated discussion, portions of my
  recently completed volcanic trilogy, which begins with the Thera eruption and concludes
  with Vesuvian imagery in the Villa of the Mysteries at Pompeii (Foster and Ritner 1996;
  Foster 1999; Foster 2001).

— 18 —

Volcanoes in Classical Mythology

◈

Patricia A. Johnston

The mythology of Greece and Rome contains numerous allusions to volcanic activity and its causes. A brief survey of these allusions, with particular regard to the mythological explanations in classical literature, may give us insight into why these societies reacted (or did not react) as they did to the volcanic presence.

The mythological explanations can be broken down into three categories. The first of these held that eruptions are caused by a Titan or Giant who was cast into Tartarus after an unsuccessful attempt to overthrow Zeus and his reign, and that the volcano Etna was then placed on top of him to pin him down. In this version, the eruptions are the result of the still-smoldering fire from Zeus' lightning bolt, which occasionally erupts from the mountain, spewing destruction far and wide.

The second mythological explanation was that the Greek god of fire, Hephaistos (Vulcan in Latin), had his workshop at the base of a volcano. He was assisted by divine blacksmiths, the giant, one-eyed Cyclopes, who, under Vulcan's direction, produced the weapons with which Zeus controls the universe. The location of Vulcan's workshop is most often identified as Mt. Etna, but tradition allows for other workshop sites including Lemnos, where Hephaistos landed when he was thrown from Olympus. Lipari (in Callimachus) and Vulcano (in Vergil) were also designated as sites for his workshop. Cicero (*Nat. D.* 3.22) identifies four different gods named Vulcan and correspondingly four different sites for the workshop. In the *Iliad*, however,

Hephaistos' workshop is on Mt. Olympus. In Homer's *Odyssey* (9.105 ff.), the homes of the Cyclopes are in caves at the top of steep mountains, but no actual geographical location is indicated.

A third important mythological aspect of volcanoes is that they were believed to provide a path into the Underworld, either through the craters themselves or through the numerous crevices in the volcanic terrain. Persephone was thought to have been abducted through a crevice (e.g., at Cyane, at Syracuse, in Plato, *Phaedrus* 113b8–c1). Empedocles claimed to have made visits to the Underworld, from where he purportedly acquired much of his knowledge of magic, and is reported to have ended his life by leaping into Etna. Vergil's Aeneas (*Aen.* 6) was said to have descended to the Underworld at Lake Avernus, now an extinct volcano.

The Giant Beneath the Volcano

Hesiod provides one of our earliest implicit literary references to volcanoes, using much of the detail found in later descriptions. In the *Theogony*, he recounts at length the struggle between Zeus and the Giant Typhoeus (Typhon in Latin), a creature of great physical strength and fiery nature. During this struggle earth, heaven, the seas, and the Underworld tremble, burn, and are in near chaos, as Zeus wields all his power, including his own burning bolts of lightning against this monstrous creature. When Typhoeus is finally stricken and defeated by Zeus' lightning, the earth itself melts:

> like tin
> when smiths use bellows to heat it in crucibles,
> or like iron, the hardest substance there is,
> when it is softened by fire in mountain glens
> and melts in bright earth under Hephaistos' hands.
> So the earth melted in the incandescent flame.
> And in anger Zeus hurled him into Tartaros' pit (Hes., Theog.
> 861–867, trans. S. Lombardo and R. Lamberton 1993).

Pindar, in the early fifth century, gives a similar explanation of volcanic activity, but he adds that Typhon's enormous body extends from beneath Etna to the shores of Cumae (*Pyth.* 1.15). There he "flings forth the most terrifying founts of fire...as he lies bound between those dark-leafed peaks and the ground below, while all his out-stretched back is goaded by his craggy couch" (*Pyth.* 1.25–8, trans. J. E. Sandys 1978).

In Callimachus's *Hymn to Apollo* (4.41 ff.), the thunder of Ares' shield is compared to an eruption of Etna, when the Giant under Etna, here said to be Briares, shifts to his other shoulder. In Callimachus' version, both the shifting Giant and Vulcan's workshop are said to be under Etna.[1]

Vergil's earliest allusion to volcanoes occurs in the fourth book of the *Georgics*, which is concerned with the art of beekeeping (*Geo.* 4.170–5). There he compares the teamwork of the tiny, well-organized bees to the skillful movements of Zeus's divine smiths as they forge his weapons. In this account, the forge is located inside Mt. Etna: "Etna moans as the anvils are piled inside her (*gemit impositis incudibus Aetna,* 4.173)." In *Aeneid* Book 3, however, Vergil continues the tradition that a Titan lies beneath Mt. Etna, but here the Titan is named Enceladus (3.578), a name that is descriptive of the terrible noise (ὁ κέλαδος) an eruption would make. In *Aeneid* Book 9, Pindar's Typhon reappears, but now he is placed under another volcano, on Ischia (Inarime, 9.716).

In the Book 3 of the *Aeneid*, an eruption of Etna takes place just as the Trojans, having eluded the dangers of Scylla and Charybdis, sail into a harbor on the coast of Sicily which is "unstirred by the wind" (3.570). The noise and drama of Etna's eruption contrast starkly with the stillness of the harbor; the sky is black with pitch and glowing ash, and balls of flame shoot up and "lick" the constellations (*sidera lambit,* 3.574). Etna, we are told, is "vomiting up" (*eructans,* 3.576) boulders and liquid rocks. These boulders, like the very "entrails of the mountain" (*avulsa...viscera montis,* 3.575) are said to have been "ripped out" in the course of this violent regurgitation. "According to rumor," Aeneas tells Dido and her guests, "the scorched body of Enceladus is restrained here." The fire itself, according to the tradition, was kindled by the initial bolt of fire which cast the Giant down to Tartarus; it lives on, smoldering and periodically bursting into flame. "Etna," Aeneas continues, "which lies on top of him, exhales flames when the subterranean fires erupt, and every time he adjusts his body, the whole of Sicily trembles and rumbles and the sky grows dark with smoke (*Aen.* 3.578–82)."

The combined physiology of a quasi-human Mt. Etna and of the Giant Enceladus produce what I shall refer to as the "Enceladian Etna," one part (Etna) 'licking' the stars and vomiting its innards while the other part (the Giant) shifts his uncomfortable position. There is a later parallel in Book 9 to this notion, where Vergil briefly describes the *durum cubile,* the hard bed on which Typhoeus lies beneath Ischia (*Aen.* 9.715–6). In Book 3, however, the description of Enceladian Etna anticipates the appearance on the following day of the Cyclops Polyphemus, huge, angry, and blinded. Achaemenides, an abandoned companion of Odysseus (who, in the *Aeneid,* escapes with the Trojans) describes the drunken Polyphemus in terms similar to Aeneas' anthropomorphic description of Enceladian Etna erupting. Polyphemus was blinded by Odysseus and his men, while he was asleep in his cave (*iacuit per antrum/ immensus* 3.631–2), glutted with food, including a number of Odysseus' companions, and wine. As he fills the cave with his enormous size, he vomits (*iacuit...eructans,* 3.631–2) gore and pieces of his victims mingled with crusts of bread and blood-red wine. The accounts of Etna erupting and Polyphemus vomiting have been carefully juxtaposed to show both the Cyclops and the volcano as destructive, hideous monsters, regurgitating their innards and bringing utter ruin (*horrificis...ruinis*) to all who come too near to them.

Vulcan's Workshop

In Greek myth and literature, Hephaistos was a divine craftsman, and the god of metal workers. His name, which is etymologically connected to the Greek verb λέγειν, "to burn," is often used interchangeably with the Greek word for fire. Handbooks for Greek literature and mythology tend to emphasize the constructive aspect of this deity. The activity in Hephaistos' workshop is depicted on the cloak that Jason wears as he goes to meet Hypsipyle on Lemnos in Apollonios of Rhodes' *Argonautica* (1.730): "On the cloak were the Cyclopes seated at their imperishable work, forging a thunderbolt for King Zeus; by now it was almost finished in its brightness and still it wanted but one ray, which they were beating out with their iron hammers as it spurted forth a breath of raging flame (trans. Seaton 1988)." These weapons enable Zeus to control gods and mortals, and thus maintain order in the universe. So great is the power of fire that Zeus conceals it from mortals, until Prometheus steals it and gives it to them (Hesiod, *Works and Days,* 51). For the Greeks, fire represents not only a powerful tool for mortals but is equally important as the key to knowledge and foresight. 'Foresight' is of course the meaning of Prometheus' name. At the beginning of Aeschylus' *Prometheus Bound,* Hephaistos is directing the Giants Brontes,

Bia, and Steropes while they chain Prometheus to the Caucasian cliffs, from where his eternally regenerating innards will be consumed by vultures. While he is being chained, Prometheus muses how his theft has benefited mortals: "I found them witless and gave them the use of their wits and made them masters of their minds" (Aesch. *PV* 442–3). After naming the benefits, particularly the intellectual ones, of his gift, he concludes: "All arts that mortals have come from Prometheus," (*PV* 506), that is, through his gift of fire.

This constructive aspect of fire tended to be highlighted in Roman literature as well. Handbooks on Roman mythology tend to list Roman *Vulcanus* as the equivalent to the Greek *Hephaistos*. The name Vulcanus, however, does not appear to have roots in either the Greek or Latin languages, but it seems to come from early Italic, possibly Etruscan roots. Etruscologists derive the name from the god Velkhan, who was primarily a god of destructive fire, although Stoltenberg (1957), following Altheim (1930), also calls him "the god of heavenly fire of the sun with its light and warmth," the god of productive fire, and the god of the hearth. It is possible that this last-named aspect of Velkhan has some bearing on the scene in the *Aeneid Book* 8, where Vulcan arises at dawn to make new armor for Aeneas. He is compared to the housewife getting up at dawn to begin her chores, whose first act is to resuscitate the fire on the hearth; she awakens (*suscitat*) the ashes and *sopitos...ignis*, literally, "fire that has been lulled to sleep" (i.e., the embers). "So, too," writes Vergil, "the Lord of Fire (*ignipotens*)...arose from his soft bed to forge the weapons" (408–15)."

Another Etruscan god of fire, whom Etruscologists even more often equate with Roman Vulcan, is Sethlans, the Etruscan deity associated with the productive use of fire (Stoltenberg 1957, 66–71; Georgiev 1979, 126).[2] As the embodiment of one or both of these Etruscan fire-gods, Vulcan seems to have been worshipped at Rome from the earliest known periods; his temple, according to Vitruvius (1.7.1), was supposed to stand outside the city, because of his association with destructive fire. Pallotino has, on several occasions, pointed out an interesting reference in Pliny the Elder's *Natural History* (35.157) to a sixth-century B.C. sculptor from Veii named Vulca, who was commissioned by Tarquinius Superbus during the sixth century to work on a statue of Capitoline Zeus (Bonfante, 20, 34 n. 78; Livy 1.53.3; Pliny *HN* 35.157; von Vacano, *ANRW* 1.4 1973; Brendel, 463 n. 27; Pallotino 1945, 163). Can a sculptor's name so similar to Vulcan be only a coincidence? Probably not. This god may have been associated with metalworking and fire from a very early time, not only among the Greeks and Romans, but also among the pre-Roman inhabitants of Italy (Meiggs 1960, 177, 336–43).[3] His epithets shows that he has power over fire itself, which in Aeschylus' *Prometheus Bound* becomes the key to intelligence and forethought; he is *ignipotens, Anax Aetnaeos*, and the weapons he forges are irresistible.

Other Vergilian characters share some of Polyphemus' volcanic characteristics (Hardie 1982, 90–7,189–90; Buchheit 1963, Sullivan 1972, 186–91; Glenn 1971, 129–55; LaPenna, 3–30), the best example being Cacus (*Aen.* 8.190 ff.), the monstrous shepherd who is terrorizing the future site of Rome when Hercules arrives there with the cattle of Geryon. Cacus is so taken by the beauty of these cattle that he steals some of them while Hercules sleeps. When Hercules awakens and fails to discover where they have gone, the cattle in Cacus' cave low to their departing fellow-cattle, with the result that Hercules finds and frees them, and then kills Cacus. Cacus, like Polyphemus, is a shepherd, huge and something less than human (Cacus is referred to as both *semihomo*, 'half-man', 8.194, and *semiferus,* 'half-beast', 8.267). Both dwell in caves, and getting into or out of their caves requires some kind of ruse. Odysseus and his men tied themselves to the blinded Polyphemus' rams to escape, and Cacus almost succeeds in tricking Hercules by reversing the direction of the cattle's footsteps (*Aen.* 8. 210–1). Cacus, it is interesting to note, is a son of Vulcan:

> huic monstro Volcanus erat pater: illius atros
> ore vomens ignis magna se mole ferebat. (*Aen.* 8.198–9)

> Vulcan was this monster's father: he walked
> as a huge mass, vomiting black fire from his mouth.

Vomiting black fire is mentioned when he is fighting with Hercules (*incendia vana vomentum,* 259) and again when he is dead:

> nequeunt expleri corda tuendo
> terribilis oculos, vultum villosaque saetis
> pectora semiferi atque exstinctos faucibus ignis.
> (*Aen.* 8.265–267)

People cannot get enough of gazing at the terrible eyes, face, and shaggy chest of this half-wild creature and the fire extinguished from his jaws.

Cacus dwells in a cave to which the sun has no access, and after Hercules rips open the cave and exposes it to the light of day, it is as if he has laid bare the depths of the Underworld itself:

> non secus ac si qua penitus vi terra dehiscens
> infernas reseret sedes et regna recludat
> pallida, dis invisa, superque immane barathrum
> cernatur, trepident immisso lumine Manes. (*Aen.* 8.241–6)[4]

> Just as if the earth, gaping open to its very depth because of some
> great force, should uncover its deepest sites and the pale realms,
> hateful to the gods, and a great pit should be viewed from above,
> and the Dead should tremble at the new light.

Thus Cacus may be said, like Typhoeus and Enceladus, to inhabit a dwelling which extends down into Tartarus. His fiery breath and the dark caverns in which he dwells place him, like Polyphemus, in the metaphorical world of Enceladian Etna. His relationship to Vulcan renews our awareness that the god of fire is ever-changeable—recall *Aeneid* Book 2, where Vulcan, as the embodiment of fire, is seen destroying Troy, *Volcano superante domus, iam proximus ardet/ Ucalegon* (311).

Vergil elsewhere depicts volcanic activity as evidence of Vulcan's well-run workshop at the heart of the volcano. Whereas in *Aeneid* Book 3 the Cyclops Polyphemus and Enceladian Etna are juxtaposed, in *Aeneid* Book 8 (as in *Geo.* 4.170–5), the Cyclopes and the volcano have been integrated. In both *Aeneid* Book 8 and *Georgic* Book 4, the Cyclopes instigate volcanic activity by heating iron, beating it into shape, and tempering it in cool water, making the flames, sound, and steam produced by a volcano. This activity produces goods which can be productive or harmful, but always with a purpose, as opposed to the brutal, widespread destruction erupting from an angry imprisoned monster in the other explanation of volcanic activity. The Cyclopes not only forge the lightning bolts with which Zeus imposes order on the world; they also make unusual products that affect the behavior of mortals and the course of human affairs, not always for the better, such as the arms of Achilles (*Il.* 17.462), Aeneas' arms (*Aen.* 8.407), and the walls of Elysium (*Aen.* 6.630).

In Book 8 of the *Aeneid*, in a scene closely modeled on the arms-making scene in Homer's *Iliad* (17.462), Venus persuades Vulcan to make a new set

of arms for Aeneas. The limping god goes to his workshop to resuscitate the
fires there. Here, however, Vergil chooses a new location for Vulcan's workshop. He delays naming the island initially, but finally describes the setting,
"An island of steaming rocks stands tall between Sicania and Aeolian Lipari"
(416–7) and identifies the activity that takes place there: "beneath it the
Etna-like (*Aetnaea*) caves thunder, hollowed out by the noisy Cyclopes'
forges. Mighty blows on the anvils repeatedly echo with moans, again and
again, and Chalybaean iron hisses in vats and fire breathes heavily in the fur-
nace." (*Aen.* 8.417–21)

Then he gives the location of the island:

> insula Sicanium iuxta latus Aeoliamque
> erigitur Liparen fumantibus ardua saxis,
> quam subter specus et Cyclopum exesa caminis
> antra Aetnaea tonant, validique incudibus ictus
> auditi referunt gemitus, striduntque cavernis
> stricturae Chalybum et fornacibus ignis anhelat.
> (*Aen.* 8.416–421)

> A steep island of smoking rock arises between
> Sicily and Aeolian Lipari; under this island the
> caves and grottoes hollowed out by the Cyclopes' forges
> thunder and moan with the mighty blows on the anvils and
> hot metal of the Chalybes hisses in the hollows and the
> fire in the furnaces heavily pants.

Vergil postpones providing the island's name until line 422, "*Volcani
domus et Volcania nomine tellus,*" thus surprising his reader with the information that Etna is no longer the designated site for the workshop. In *Georgics*
4.173, the Cyclopes' forge is in Etna (*gemit impositis incubibus Aetna*). Here
he uses the adjective *Aetnaea (antra)*, but clearly designates the island Volcano
rather than the island Sicily as the location of these "Etna-like caves."

There appears to be no generic word in Latin for "volcano" or "volcanic."
It is therefore conceivable that Vergil may here be using the adjective *aet-
naeus*, which does appear in Greek, but with specific reference to the volcano, Mt. Etna (e.g., Eur. *Cyc.* 20: τήνδ᾽ ἐς Αἰτναίαν πέτραν) to create a
generic term meaning something like "volcanic." Another way to interpret

Aetnaea antra would be to understand that all the volcanoes in the Liparean islands are interconnected by subterranean caves (as Mynors 1990, 280–1 appears to do, *ad Geo.* 4.170–5).

The "moans" (*gemitus*) from within the volcano again tend to give it a certain human quality, as the details of Etna's tortured "body" does in *Aeneid* Book 3, where the Giant Enceladus and Etna become one. The "panting" of the fire in line 420 (*anhelat*) suggests the sound of the Cyclopes' bellows in the *Georgics* simile, where the honeybees, tiny crafting creatures, and the Cyclopes, huge crafting creatures, are compared.

The passage describing the workshop in *Aeneid* 8 indicates that at that particular time, the Cyclopes were working on an *informatum...fulmen*, a bolt not yet completed, for Jupiter, which already bears colorful detail, thus recalling the description of the workshop's activities in Apollonius of Rhodes' *Argonautica*. Their project is interrupted by Vulcan's arrival and instructions to set aside this *fulmen* while they forge new weapons for Aeneas. Here the description of the Cyclopes' teamwork is almost a verbatim repetition of the *Georgics* 4.171–5:

....alii ventosis follibus auras
accipiunt redduntque, alii stridentia tingunt
aera lacu; gemit impositis incudibus *antrum*;
illi inter sese multa vi bracchia tollent
in numerum, versantque tenaci forcipe *massam*.
(*Aen.* 8.444–53)

Some accept and remit the air with wind-filled bellows,
others dip the hissing bronze in water; the cave moans as the
anvils are beaten, while [the Cyclopes] mightily raise their
arms in rhythm and turn the lump of metal with clinging tongs.

Three words differ from the *Georgics* passage. *Taurinis* (*Geo.* 4.171) here becomes *ventosis*. *Aetna* (*Geo.* 4.173) here becomes *antrum,* and *ferrum* (*Geo.* 4.175) here becomes *massam*. The substitution of *massam* for *ferrum* may not be significant, particularly since the introduction of the *Georgics* simile already includes *massis: ac veluti lentis Cyclopes fulmina massis/ cum properant,* "just as when the Cyclopes forge thunderbolts from flexible lumps" (presumably, lumps of iron; *Geo.* 4.170). Vergil may have intended for *ventosis* to emphasize the windiness already closely associated in the *Aeneid* with this location, since Vulcano is one of the Aeolian islands and Aeolus, who controls the winds, set them free in this area at the beginning of the *Aeneid,* blowing the Trojans off course to Carthage.[5] The change from *Aetna* to *antrum* would also be appropriate in *Aeneid 8,* since Vergil has moved the site of Vulcan's forge away from Etna.

Modern vulcanologists distinguish different types of volcanic activity and volcanoes. Some erupt dramatically and seriously damage the surrounding terrain and its inhabitants, as Vesuvius did in A.D. 79. Others, like Stromboli, erupt with great frequency, shooting sparks and debris into the area as frequently as every 15 minutes, but do relatively little damage, since the debris settles back into their cones. Still others, like Solfatara, vent only gases and mud. With each major eruption, however, the character of a volcano can change dramatically; a volcano with an unobstructed vent, for example, can become obstructed, forcing the magma to work its way out through different channels. (Santacroce, this volume; Bullard 1984, 184–255). The activity of any given volcano can vary considerably, so that references to the same volcano can signify very different kinds of activity. Vergil seems to be attempting to draw distinctions between the various volcanoes he names in the *Aeneid*; one behaves more like the Enceladian-type of volcano, suggesting an angry Giant beneath it, while another suggests there is something constructive going on within, such as the workshop of Vulcan. The differences in the personalities of the Cyclopes whom Vergil associates with these particular volcanoes—the hard-working, creative smithies on the one hand, and cruel Polyphemus on the other—serve to underscore that difference.

Entrances to the Underworld

The third common association of volcanoes in classical mythology was with pathways into the Underworld. Traditions indicate a number of different locations where the descent was made. Odysseus, who goes to the edge of the Underworld but does not actually enter, is said to have gone to the land of the Cimmerians. This is thought to have been somewhere in the vicinity of the Crimea, but neither the location nor the identity of the Cimmerians is certain. Herakles descends at the edge of Ocean (i.e., the edge of the known world), which is somewhere beyond the southern tip of Spain.

Persephone, according to the *Hymn to Demeter* (15–6), was in the plain of

Nysa when Hades rose out of the earth and grabbed her. Nysa is the name of a series of mountain ranges sacred to Dionysus, located far to the east in Bactria, far from the usual setting of her abduction in Sicily. Pindar and all subsequent classical writers have her descend in Sicily. Pindar refers to the power of Aetnaean Zeus (*Ol.* 6.96), and Plato (Kingsley 1995, 133, 240)[6] says she was abducted beside the Cyane fountain at Syracuse when the earth split open and she was carried down by her abductor (Zuntz 1971, 70–4). Ovid elaborates this identification in his *Metamorphoses* (5.359) where Pluto ascends from the Underworld through Etna. Goaded by Cupid's arrow, he grabs Persephone at Enna, carries her past Paternò to Cyane, and there descends.

The fifth century Presocratic philosopher Empedocles, who moved from his native Acragas in Sicily (about 443 B.C.) to the coast of mainland Italy, claimed to have made many trips to the Underworld. Among many accounts of his death, perhaps the best known is the one that says he died by throwing himself into Mt. Etna (Diog. Laert. 8.69; cf. Strabo 6.2.8 and 10; Luc. DM 6(20).4; *Suda*, s.v. Εμπεδοκλης Μετωνος; Kingsley 1995, 235 ff.). His detractors said he did this in an attempt to destroy any trace of his body, and thus to defraud his followers by making everyone believe he had become a god. One of the bronze sandals he wore, however, was ejected by the volcano and thus what had really happened was exposed. While Van Gröningen suggests that the bronze sandals were a substitute for leather because of Empedocles' horror of animal sacrifice (Van Gröningen 1956, 47–61), and others have suggested that it was an attempt to place himself as it were on a bronze pedestal while still alive, or to establish a symbol of his divinity,[7] Kingsley has identified a passage in a magical papyrus showing that "a bronze sandal in antiquity was a symbol connected specifically with Underworld ritual and magic." The papyrus, moreover, makes it clear that one and only one sandal was to be worn. This single bronze sandal was apparently a symbol of Hekate, who granted access to the Underworld (Kingsley 1995, 238).

Other sites for contact with the Underworld include Taenarum, on the southern tip of the Peloponnesian Peninsula, and Lake Avernus. Taenarum is the site through which Herakles traditionally dragged Cerberus from the Underworld. Vergil's Orpheus also enters through Taenarum (*Geo.* 4.467) but exits at Lake Avernus in Italy (*Geo.* 4.493), the same site where Vergil's Aeneas both enters (*Aen.* 6.240–1) and appears to exit (*Aen.* 6.893). Line 242, which is omitted by most editors, specifically names Avernus. Vergil says that Aeneas and the Sibyl exited through the Gates of Ivory.

Conclusion

Greek and Roman mythology explained volcanic eruptions as being caused by a restless, angry Giant pinned down by the weight of the volcano or as an indication of the activity in Vulcan's workshop. The volcanic landscape also provides pathways into the Underworld. The association of volcanoes with the gods and their activities made the ever-present threat of this phenomenon understandable and probably helped justify the decision to settle in a landscape that was threatening but where the fertile soil had much to offer. Volcanoes will always inspire a reverence of some sort. Some peoples anthropomorphize them, as at Popocatepetl (Plunket and Urunuela, this volume). Others see them as suitable for divine sites, as the cathedrals of Cappadocia indicate (Burri, Massoli-Novelli and Petitta, this volume). The strong association with the Underworld heightened the terror, sanctity, and awe of volcanoes for Greeks and Romans, and all these elements are found in their mythological accounts of this phenomenon. Greek and Roman mythology tends to treat them in varying combinations of these two categories.

REFERENCES

Altheim F. 1930. *Griechische Götter in alten Rom.* Giessen.

Buchheit V. 1963. *Vergil über die Sendung Roms: Untersuchungen zum Bellum Poenicum und, zur Aeneis. Gymnasium Beiheft* 3. Heidelberg.

Bullard, F.M. 1984. *Volcanoes of the Earth.* 2nd ed. Austin.

Capdeville, Gérard. 1995. *Volcanus. Recherches Comparatistes sur les Origines du Culte de Vulcain.* Rome.

Chester D.K., A.M. Duncan, J.E. Guest, P.A. Johnston, and J.J.L. Smolenaars. 2000. "Human Response to Etna Volcano during the Classical Period." In *The Archaeology of Geological Catastrophes,* edited by W.J. McGuire, D.R. Griffiths, P.L. Hancock, and I.S. Stewart. London.

Freeman, E. 1891–1894. *History of Sicily,* 2 vols. Oxford.

Galinsky, K. 1972. *The Herakles Theme: Adaptations of the Hero in Literature from Homer to the Twentieth Century.* Totowa, NJ.

Georgiev, V.I. 1979. *La Lingua e L'Origine degli Etrusci.* Roma.

Glenn, J. 1971. "Mezentius and Polyphemus." *AJPh* 92:129–55.

Hardie, P.R. 1982. *Virgil's Aeneid: Cosmos and Imperium.* Oxford.

Johnston, P.A. 1996. "Under the Volcano: Volcanic Myth and Metaphor in Vergil's *Aeneid.*" *Vergilius* 42:55–65.

Kingsley, P. 1995. *Ancient Philosophy, Mystery, and Magic: Empedocles and Pythagorean Tradition.* Oxford.

Leonard, W.E., and S.B. Smith, eds. 1942. *Lucretius: De Rerum Natura.* Madison, Wis.

Lombardo, S., and R. Lamberton, trans. 1993. *Hesiod: Works and Days and Theogony.* Indianapolis and Cambridge.

Mair, A.W., and G.R. Mair. 1977. *Callimachus: Hymns and Epigrams.* Cambridge, Mass.

Meiggs, R. 1960. *Roman Ostia.* (Oxford).

Mynors, R.A.B. 1990. *Virgil: Georgics: Edited with Commentary.* Oxford.

Pallotino, M. 1945. *La Scuola de Vulca.* Roma.

Rose, H.J., et al., eds. 1964. *The Oxford Classical Dictionary,* Oxford.

Sandys, J.E., trans. 1978. *Odes of Pindar.* Cambridge, Mass.

Seaton, R.C., trans. 1988. *Apollonius Rhodius.* Cambridge, Mass.

Stoltenberg, H.L. 1957. *Etruskische Gottnamen.* Leverkusen.

Sullivan, F.S. 1972. "Volcanoes and Volcanic Characters in Vergil." *CPh* 67:186–91.

Taylor, L.R. 1912. *The Cults of Ostia.* Bryn Mawr Monographs XI. Bryn Mawr.

Van Gröningen, B.A. 1956. "Le Fragmente B111 d'Empédocle," *Classica et Mediaevalia* 17:47–61.

Zuntz, G. 1971. *Persephone: Three Essays on Religion and Thought in Magna Graecia.* Oxford.

NOTES

[1] Frazer, 1, 197 notes that a similar belief is common among the people of East Timor and the Tongans. Callimachus, *Hymn* 4.141 places both the giant Briares and the workshop under Aetna. In the fifth and sixth centuries, according to Strabo, the area between the Bay of Naples and Sicily were believed to be linked by a single network of underground passages and channels of fire; hence Pindar describes Typhon (*Pyth* 1.15) as being "pinned down at one end by Sicily and by the area around Cumae at the other" (cf. Kingsley 1995, 100; 134 n. 4). Ovid, *Metamorphoses* 5.346–53, has Typhoeus pinned down under the whole of Sicily.

[2] For the Etruscan names, see Altheim 1930, 172; H.J. Rose (1964, 1131) notes that he had a considerable cult at Ostia, where he seems to have been the chief god; cf. R. Meiggs, (1960, 337).

[3] Although regarding the cult of Vulcan at Ostia important there, including at an early time, suggests that Vulcan came to Ostia from Rome rather than the reverse. Taylor (1912, 14), calls the preeminence of the cult of Vulcan "the most distinctive feature in the history of Ostia's religion."

[4] Hercules kills Cacus when he is returning from his battle with Geryon, a battle which has been shown to be another version of Hercules's visit to the Underworld and his victory there. Hercules is a model for Aeneas, who has also recently returned from the Underworld. Galinsky and others have argued that the struggle between Hercules and Cacus foreshadows the coming struggle between Aeneas and Turnus (cf. Galinsky 1972, 126–52, 143–5).

[5] In the *Georgics* IV simile, the close ties between men and cattle are emphasized; in addition, at the conclusion of that poem, a hive of bees is born out of a cow's corpse, thus making the choice of *taurinis* more appropriate there.

[6] The bronze sandal points to Hekate and, through her, to the mysteries of Persephone. The craters and volcanic phenomena of Sicily, including Etna itself, were not just viewed as entrances to the Underworld but were associated specifically with the mythology and the mysteries of Persephone.

[7] cf. Empedocles Fr. 112 D-K, 4–6: "All hail, O friends! But unto ye I walk/ as god immortal now, no more as man,/ on all sides honored fittingly and well,/ crowned both with fillets and with flowering wreaths." Cited by W. E. Leonard and S. B. Smith, ad *Lucretius* 1.729–30.

Earthquakes and Volcanic Eruptions in Latin Literature: Reflections and Emotional Responses

❖

Johannes Jacobius Luis Smolenaars

Artificis naturae ingens opus aspice.
"Look upon the colossal work of the artist Nature." (*Aetna* 601)

The anonymous poet of the *Aetna* concludes his profession of love for the subject of his poem, the volcano, with a satire on modern tourists who travel the world to visit such "miracles" as Thebes, Athens, and Troy in ashes, and to view the famous paintings and sculptures of the Greeks. In his opinion, we should abandon these ignoble cares and rather look upon "the colossal work of the artist Nature" (*Aetna* 601), by which he refers to Mount Etna. Earlier in the poem, he champions the study of science even more explicitly:

> Not cattle-like to gaze on the world's marvels merely with the eye, not to lie outstretched upon the ground feeding a weight of flesh, but to grasp the proof of things and search into doubtful causes. All this is the mind's divine and grateful pleasure. (*Aetna* 224–51; trans. J.W. Duff and A.M. Duff 1961)

The poet's "proclamation of the majesty of physical research" (*Aetna* 252–5) is most exceptional in ancient doxography; more often science is seen solely as a means to much higher aims, such as freeing mankind from a fear of the gods, punishment after death, or from the belief that volcanic eruptions are an act of god.

The various theories on the causes of earthquakes and volcanic eruptions which appear in Greek and Latin doxography are concerned with air or wind, the sea or water, and underground fire. Since Thales of Miletus (sixth century B.C.), a long line of Greek and Latin philosophers have offered theories on volcanic activity, some based on direct observation and others purely speculative. Plato may have seen Etna erupt during his first visit to Sicily (388–387 B.C.). He suggests in the *Phaedo* that an enormous river of fire (*Pyriphlegethon*) raging in the depths of the earth feeds the volcanic craters. He was the first to refer to a lava flow in his description of the subterranean regions:

> many streams of liquid mud of varying density, like the rivers
> of mud that flow before the lava in Sicily, or like the lava itself.
> (*Phd.* 112D)

Aristotle traces the origin of underground fire to particles of air which burst into flames as a result of the friction caused by the wind. Others, considering the earth as a living creature, explain its convulsions—volcanic manifestations—as analogous to flatulence and spasms in the human body.

The greater part of Greek theory on the subject has been handed down to us by the Latin authors Lucretius, Seneca, and Pliny the Elder (author of the influential *Naturalis Historia,* which was completed in A.D. 77). Following the principles of Epicurean philosophy, the poet Lucretius discusses a series of possible explanations in his didactic poem *de rerum natura* (6.535–702), including the fall of masses of earth into a subterranean lake and subterranean winds upsetting the balance of the earth (described below). The study of volcanic activity gained in popularity when earthquakes caused great destruction in Campania (A.D. 62–64), and Vesuvius buried Pompeii and Herculaneum (A.D. 79). The dissertation by Seneca (5 B.C.–A.D. 65) on the theories of his predecessors in Book 6 of his *Naturales Quaestiones* was triggered by these frightful earthquakes that occurred between A.D. 62 and 64. He was the first to adduce the principle of gas pressure as an explanation for the force of volcanic eruptions.

The anonymous poet of *Aetna* unfortunately believed Vesuvius to be extinct, from which we may safely conclude that this enthusiastic poem was composed before A.D. 63. At the request of the historian Tacitus, Pliny the Younger wrote a detailed description of the eruption in A.D. 79 which caused the death of his uncle Pliny the Elder, commander of the fleet at

Misenum at the time. In his account (*Epist.* 6.16 and 20; discussed below), Pliny the Younger presents the first detailed eyewitness description of a cataclysmic ("plinian") eruption. Latin epic poetry, nonetheless, persisted in attributing volcanic manifestations to such superhuman forces as giants buried under volcanoes as a punishment or Vulcan producing weapons for Jupiter in his workshop. After Virgil (70–19 B.C.), however, these mythological descriptions were often cleverly phrased in the language of science; see, for instance, Claudian's presentation of Ceres (below). Likewise, in the emotional and poetic responses of Statius and Martial to the A.D. 79 eruption of Vesuvius any distinction between mythological and scientific beliefs seems deliberately blurred. These poets would certainly have smiled at the seriousness of the cautionary voice of the poet of the *Aetna* not to believe what the poets tell us:

> principio ne quem capiat fallacia vatum
> sedes esse dei tumidisque e faucibus ignem
> Vulcani ruere et clausis resonare cavernis
> festinantis opus. (*Aetna* 29–33)

> First, let no one be deceived by the fictions poets tell—that Aetna is the home of a god, that the fire gushing from her swollen jaws is Vulcan's fire, and that the echo in that cavernous prison comes from his restless work. (trans. J.W. Duff and A.M. Duff 1961)

At the close of antiquity, the wedding of science and poetry was completed by the poet Claudian (ca. A.D. 400) in his grotesque mythological picture of the goddess Ceres climbing Mount Etna in order to fire her torches (*Rape of Proserpina* 3.392–9); it is her knowledge of scientific theory that enables the goddess to continue the mythological search for her daughter in the darkness of the night:

> Postquam perventum scopuli flagrantis in ora,
> protinus arsuras aversa fronte cupressus
> faucibus iniecit mediis lateque cavernas
> texit et undantem flammarum obstruxit hiatum,
> compresso mons igne tonat claususque laborat
> Mulciber: obducti nequeunt exire vapores.

coniferi micuere apices crevitque favillis
Aetna novis: strident admisso sulphure rami.

When she had climbed to the mouth of the burning rock,
straightway, turning aside her head, she thrust the kindling cypresses
into its inmost depths, thus closing in the cavern on all sides and
stopping up the blazing exit of the flames. The mountain thunders
with repressed fire and Vulcan is shut in a grievous prison; the
enclosed smoke cannot escape. The cone-bearing tops of the
cypresses blaze and Etna grows with new ashes; the branches crackle,
kindled with the sulphur. (trans. M. Platnauer 1922)

Poetic Accounts Versus Geological Evidence

Both geological evidence and early historic records suggest that Mount Etna
has been frequently active back to at least 700 B.C. (Chester and Duncan, this
volume). Eruptions of Vesuvius have also left traces in several deposits between
the Avellino eruption some 3,850 years ago and the eruption of A.D. 79, but
none of these are documented in dependable historical records. The study by
Stothers and Rampino (1983), an important contribution to the history of
Mediterranean volcanoes, provides a complete list of ancient written sources
on eruptions. Unfortunately, establishing the dependability of these descriptions in every individual author was considered "beyond the scope of this
article (Stothers and Rampino 1983, 6358)," which in some cases was detri-
mental to the conclusions involved. For instance, the authors place too much
confidence in the descriptions of Vesuvius by the epic poet Silius Italicus in
Punica, where the nobles of Capua show Hannibal Mount Vesuvius:

monstrantur Vesuuina iuga atque in uertice summo
depasti flammis scopuli stratusque ruina
mons circum atque Aetnae fatis certantia saxa. (12.152–4)

They showed Hannibal Mount Vesuvius, where fire has eaten away
the rocks at its summit, and the wreckage of the mountain lies all
around, and the discharge of stones seeks to rival the death dealt by
Etna. (trans. J.D. Duff 1961)

Stothers and Rampino take Silius' description (together with *Pun.* 8. 653) as evidence of an eruption in 216 B.C. But it is most unlikely that Silius, 300 years after these supposed events, is describing the aspect of the mountain in 215 B.C., as these authors seem to believe (Stothers and Rampino 1983, 6360). The description of the rocks as "eaten away" rather recalls Strabo's description of Vesuvius long before the eruption of A.D. 79:

> These masses of rock look as though they had been eaten out by fire; and hence one might infer that in earlier times this district was on fire and had craters of fire, and then, because the fuel gave out, was quenched. (*Geography* 5.8; trans. Jones 1928)

In Strabo's day (about A.D. 20), the summit was barren and ash-colored. So perhaps Silius, writing around A.D. 90, is picturing Vesuvius as it was before A.D. 79, but this assumption certainly does not confirm his testimony concerning an eruption in 216 B.C. In fact, it is much more likely that Silius' depiction harks back to the havoc wreaked by the eruption of August 25, A.D. 79, which he may have observed first-hand during his annual visit to Vergil's tomb on September 21 (see Martial 11.48). In his commentary on Silius, Spaltenstein first assures us that "Silius n' a pas besoin de penser à la catastrophe de l' année 79," but then is surprised that Silius does not refer explicitly to "cet événement terrible et contemporain." In my view, Silius actually has in mind the 79 A.D. eruption and pictures the supposed eruption in 216 B.C. in accordance with his own recent observations.

Since no violent eruption of Mt. Etna is reported between 122 and 49 B.C. (see Chester and Duncan in this volume), and Vesuvius was dormant during that same period, Lucretius, who died ca. 55 B.C., never lived to see any violent eruption. Therefore, his treatise on volcanic phenomena is purely theoretical, based on earlier (Greek) theories and accounts, and possibly on the reports by the survivors of the violent eruption of Etna in 122 B.C. But Vergil's statement at the end of *Georgics* I (given below), that he actually witnessed (*vidimus*) a major eruption of Mt. Etna at the time of Julius Caesar's assassination on March 15, 44 B.C., may well be accurate, although one could argue that *vidimus* ("we saw") is didactic rather than autobiographical (as does Thomas 1968). Historical records of unusual atmospheric phenomena in 44–42 B.C. in such sources as Pliny the Elder, Plutarch, and Dio Cassius point to a huge eruption in 44 B.C. (Stothers

and Rampino 1983, 6358; see also Ramsay and Lewis 1997) also referred
to in the poetry of Tibullus and Ovid. Admittedly, lists of similar prodigies
became a standard element in the literary tradition but, as Karin Polinger
Foster (this volume) points out, omens like solar and lunar halos are often
echoes of actual volcanic activities. Moreover, further evidence of a major
44 B.C. eruption, possibly Etna, comes from a time record of acidity in a
Greenland ice core (Stothers and Rampino 1983, 6360). Finally, it seems
most unlikely that Virgil fabricated a volcanic eruption in order to drama-
tize Caesar's death; his contemporaries would not be easily convinced.
Vergil may rather have linked these historical events, just as the volcanic
activity of the Popocatépetl (1995) was supposed to announce the collapse
of the PRI government in Mexico. Taken together, these arguments appear
to indicate that, regardless of whether he was an eyewitness or not, Vergil's
account of this eruption in *Georgics* does reflect actual historical events:

> quotiens Cyclopum effervere in agros
> vidimus undantem ruptis fornacibus Aetnam
> flammarumque globos liquefactaque uoluere saxa! (1.471–3)

> How often *we saw* Aetna flood the Cyclopes' fields, when streams
> poured from her rent furnaces, and she whirled balls of flame and
> molten rocks! (trans. Fairclough 1961)

Likewise, we may be tempted to read Vergil's personal experiences in his
description of the uncanny phenomena following Aeneas' sacrifice to
Hecate, goddess of the Underworld, which took place in the dead of night
near Lake Avernus in *Aeneid* 6.255–8:

> sub pedibus mugire solum et iuga coepta moveri
> silvarum, visaeque canes ululare per umbram
> adventante dea.

> The ground rumbled underfoot, the wooded ridges began to quiver,
> and through the gloom dogs seemed to howl as the goddess drew nigh.
> (trans. Fairclough 1961)

Here the unseen presence of Hecate, coming to open the way to the Underworld, is announced by phenomena that, according to ancient science, were related to earthquakes and would be described by modern vulcanologists as precursory seismic activity. Vergil's clever combination of the mythological content (Hecate's approach) and the language of science was understood by Seneca, who justly sees *mugire* ("bellow") as the result of winds which create a disturbance underground (*Q Nat.* 6.13.5). However, since no seismic phenomena are reported in this particular region after the second millennium B.C., Vergil cannot actually have seen with his own eyes the phenomena described here. He therefore seems to be assuming, by analogy with the *Campi Phlegraei* (the "Burning Fields") and the *Solfatara* in his day, that the region around Lake Avernus had been more volcanically active a thousand years ago, at the time of Aeneas' descent into the underworld. Such an assumption would have been corroborated by bradyseismic and fumarolic activity, as well as by the hot springs feeding the Claudian *Thermae* at the east edge of Lake Avernus, now arbitrarily known as "Tempio di Apollo."[1]

The Earliest Pioneers of Geology

Ancient theories on volcanic phenomena may seem naive and slightly bizarre when seen through the eyes of modern science, mainly because the doxographers had no knowledge of chemistry or magmatic and geothermal theory. Seneca's statement, however, may serve as a warning against any condescension:

> opiniones veteres parum exactas esse et rudes. Circa verum adhuc errabatur; nova omnia erant primo temptantibus; postea eadem illa limata sunt....Plurimum ad inveniendum contulit qui speravit posse reperiri. Cum excusatione itaque veteres audiendi sunt. (*Q Nat.* 6.5.2)

> I must say that the old theories are crude and inexact. Men were still in error about the truth. Everything was new for men who were making the first attempts. Later these theories were refined...The man who had the hope that the truth could be found made the greatest contribution to discovery. And so the ancients must be listened to, indulgently (trans. T.H. Corcoran 1962)

Lucretius and Virgil never witnessed any violent volcanic eruption in the Campi Phlegraei caldera, nor did any Roman before A.D 62. Some men of science recognized the presumably volcanic origin of Mt. Vesuvius and the Phlegraean Fields, such as Strabo, quoted above, and the poet of the *Aetna:*

> testisque Neapolin inter
> et Cumas locus ex multis iam frigidus annis,
> quamvis aeternum pingui scatet ubere sulphur. (*Aetna* 431–3)

> Another witness is the region between Neapolis and Cumae (i.e., Solfatara), now cooled for many a year, though sulphur wells forth unceasingly in rich abundance. (trans. A.M. Duff and J.W. Duff 1961)

There was no suspicion of any serious threat from Vesuvius or the Phlegraean Fields, however, as is also clear from Seneca's introduction to his treatise on earthquakes, which was triggered by the events of A.D. 62. The actual observation of volcanism in ancient doxography is generally limited, but, as Chester and Duncan illustrate, we do have a few interesting exceptions.

The *Aetna* poet made a thorough study of the volcano, as is evident from his detailed observations on the characteristics of lava stone in lines 402–25. Seneca, in a letter to his friend Lucilius, who was touring Sicily, requested a full account of this visit and also asked Lucilius, "to climb Aetna at my special request. Certain naturalists have inferred that the mountain is wasting away and gradually settling, because sailors used to be able to see it from a greater distance (*Ep.* 79.2–4)." The idea is that Lucilius' observations on the spot will help to establish whether the height of the mountain is indeed decreasing. I find it difficult to understand why Seneca asks his friend to undertake this specific investigation, i.e. to measure:

> quantum ab ipso ore montis nives absint, quas ne aetas quidem solvit;
> adeo tutae sunt ab igne vicino. (*Ep.* 79. 2–4)

> just how far distant the snow lies from the crater,—I mean the snow which does not melt even in summer—so safe is it from the adjacent fire. (trans. A.M. Duff and J.W. Duff 1961)

Presumably Seneca asked Lucilius to measure the distance between the crater and the snow line, supposedly unaffected by the fire inside the volcano (*ab igne vicino*), because he had at his disposal earlier data that could now be compared with the findings of Lucilius' research.

Lucretius' Theories on Volcanic Activities

Let us take a brief look at the theories of the most original Roman poet and philosopher on this subject, T. Lucretius Carus, a fervent adherent of Epicurean atomism.

Epicurean Principles

In most early theories, earthquakes and eruptions are triggered by the action of wind, water, and fire, acting individually or in combination. Most of these theories assume that the earth is *not* a solid mass, but has deep inside it hollow caverns, rivers, and lakes. Take, for example, Lucretius *De Rerum Natura*:

> Nunc age, quae ratio terrai motibus extet
> percipe et in primis terram fac ut esse rearis
> supter item ut supera ventosis undique plenam
> speluncis multosque lacus multasque lacunas
> in gremio gerere et rupes deruptaque saxa;
> multaque sub tergo terrai flumina tecta
> volvere vi fluctus summersaque saxa putandumst.
> undique enim similem esse sui res postulat ipsa. (6.535–42)

> Come now and hear what is the law of earthquakes. And first of all let yourself suppose that the earth below, just as above, is full on all sides of windy caverns, and that it bears in its bosom many lakes and many pools and cliffs and sheer rocks; and that many rivers hidden beneath the back of the earth roll on amain their waves and submerged stones. For clear fact demands that it should be in all parts like itself. (trans. Bailey 1963)

In line 542 Lucretius applies a very important principle from Epicurean philosophy, that of the "equal distribution" (Greek *isonomia*), the assumption that things invisible, such as atoms and the parts below the surface of the earth, can be inferred from our own experience of the visible. Since the surface of the earth displays cavities and other irregularities—as we can ourselves see—the parts below must be similar, "for clear fact demands that it should be in all parts like itself."

Earthquakes

Lucretius explains the phenomenon of earthquakes (6.535–607) by means of four causes, all of which may be operative at any time, though in each particular case only one will be the true cause. In his first two explanations (6.543–56) he attributes earthquakes to the collapse of the roof and sides of the subterranean caves. This collapse either causes a dislodgment of the surface of the earth (6.543–51) or agitates and oscillates the water of a subterranean lake if the rubble falls into that lake (6.552–6) (see Bailey 1963).

According to his third explanation, subterranean wind blowing against the sides of the caves causes the surface of the earth to move in that same direction. The consequent lateral impulsion of the earth, upset its balance:

> Praeterea ventus cum per loca subcava terrae
> collectus parte ex una procumbit et urget
> obnixus magnis speluncas viribus altas,
> incumbit tellus quo venti prona premit vis. (6.557–60)

> Moreover, when the wind gathering throughout the cavernous places of the earth blows strong from one point, and with all its weight presses on the lofty caves with mighty strength, the earth leans over to where the swooping force of the wind presses it. (trans. Bailey 1963)

Finally, in the fourth explanation (6.577–600), earthquakes may be caused by the direct force of the wind. Erupting from the caverns inside the earth, wind may breach the surface of the earth and burst out. This explanation implies the compression of enclosed wind (cf. Sen. Q Nat. 6.13). Lucretius concludes his paragraph on earthquakes (6.601–7) with a sarcastic reference to those who stubbornly believe that our world is indestructible, protected by some eternal force, while the actual dangers that the earthquakes represent should persuade them to think otherwise:

proinde licet quamvis caelum terramque reantur
incorrupta fore aeternae mandata saluti:
et tamen interdum praesens vis ipsa pericli
subdit et hunc stimulum quadam de parte timoris,
ne pedibus raptim tellus subtracta feratur
in barathrum rerumque sequatur prodita summa
funditus et fiat mundi confusa ruina.

Let them then believe as they will that heaven and earth will be indestructible, entrusted to some everlasting protection; and yet from
time to time the very present force of danger applies on some side
or other this goad of fear, lest the earth, snatched away suddenly
from beneath their feet be carried into the abyss, and the sum of
things, left utterly without foundation, follow on, and there be a
tumbling wreck of the whole world. (trans. Bailey 1963)

Epicurean philosophy is convinced of the ultimate destruction of the earth
and indeed of the universe; this tumbling wreck of the whole world is prefig-
ured by the phenomenon of earthquakes. The lesson to be drawn from volcanic
phenomena is that our world is not eternal, that we should accept its ultimate
destruction, announced by the occurrence of earthquakes, and that this certainty should replace our fears and take away our false hopes for eternity. For
Lucretius, science is certainly not an end in itself, but rather a means to higher
goals: the happy life, free from disturbing hopes and fears. In a similar but more
explicit manner, the Stoic philosopher Seneca also hopes that his theories on
volcanism will provide solace to the distressed, and allay their great fear:

If I must fall, let me fall with the world shattered, not because it is
right to hope for a public disaster but because it is a great solace in
dying to see that the earth, too, is mortal. (*Q Nat.* 6.2)

Volcanic Eruptions

Next, Lucretius discusses the causes of volcanic eruptions (6.639–702).
Since Vesuvius was still hiding its violent nature, he, like Vergil, took Mount
Etna as his model, writing:

Nunc ratio quae sit, per fauces montis ut Aetnae
expirent ignes interdum turbine tanto,
expediam; neque enim mediocri clade coorta
flammea tempestas Siculum dominata per agros
finitimis ad se convertit gentibus ora,
fumida cum caeli scintillare omnia templa
cernentes pavida complebant pectora cura,
quid moliretur rerum natura novarum. (*DRN* 6.639–46)

Now what is the reason that through the jaws of Mount Etna flames
breathe forth in so great a hurricane, I will unfold. For indeed the
flaming storm gathered with no moderate force of destruction and ruled
tyrant through the fields of the Sicilians and turned to itself the gaze of
neighboring nations, when they saw all the quarters of the heavens
smoke and sparkle, and filled their breasts with shuddering anxiety for
what new change nature might be planning. (trans. Bailey 1963)

The particular explosion referred to here was probably the major eruption
of 122 B.C. (Chester and Duncan, this volume; but see Stothers and Rampino
1983, 6360). If so, it was not witnessed by Lucretius himself.

The first part of Lucretius' explanation (6.682–93) is similar to his theory
on earthquakes. The volcano has hollow caves beneath it, which are full of
air; when agitated this air becomes wind. This wind, which grows hot as a
result of motion, heats and melts the rocks. Because the crater of the volcano
affords a narrow outlet (*fauces*, literally "throat"), it is not an earthquake but
an eruption which is caused.

In the second part (6.694–700), Lucretius answers the difficult problem
of accounting for the enormous quantities of flames, smoke, ashes and rocks.
Is there some supply from outside the volcano? He argues that the crater is
connected with the sea, and that each wave which comes in brings sand and
rocks and wind, which ultimately blows everything out through the crater.
Thus some of the material which the crater emits is brought in from outside:

praeterea magna ex parti mare montis ad eius
radices frangit fluctus aestumque resorbet
ex hoc usque mari speluncae montis ad altas
perveniunt subter fauces. (*DRN* 6.694–7)

> Moreover, in great part the sea makes its waves break and sucks in its backwash at the roots of that mountain. From this, sea caves stretch underneath right to the lofty jaws of the mountain. (trans. Bailey 1963)

This "Neptunist" theory has no parallel in Greek doxography, but is not unique in Latin theory. Ovid in *Metamorphoses* 15.340–55, sticks closely to Greek theory by having the philosopher Pythagoras illustrate the principle of ever-changing forms of nature by means of the supposed beginning and ending of Aetna's fire, but Seneca in his letter to Lucilius quoted above also discusses the possibility that Etna is being consumed and yet remains the same size; like Lucretius, he suggests that the mountain is fed by other, external, material (*Ep.* 79).

5 February A.D. 62.

The violent earthquake on February 5, A.D. 62 prompted the philosopher Seneca to write his treatise on earthquakes, *Naturales Quaestiones:*

> Pompeios, celebrem Campaniae urbem ... consedisse terrae motu, vexatis quaecumque adiacebant regionibus, Lucili, virorum optime, audivimus, et quidem hibernis diebus, quos vacare a tali periculo maiores nostri solebant promittere. Nonis Februariis hic fuit motus ...qui Campaniam, numquam securam huius mali, indemnem tamen et totiens defunctam metu, magna strage vastavit. (*Q Nat.* 6.1)

> Lucilius, my good friend, I have just heard that Pompeii, the famous city in Campania, has been laid low by an earthquake which also disturbed all the adjacent districts. ...In fact, it occurred in days of winter, a season which our ancestors used to claim was free from such disaster. This earthquake was on the Nones of February .... It caused great destruction in Campania, which had never been safe from this danger but had never been damaged and time and again had got off with a fright. (trans. T.H. Corcoran 1962)

The purpose of Seneca's Book Six is to "find solace for distressed people and to remove their great fear." Seneca's Stoic solace is that death is the same everywhere, that "all places have the same conditions and if they have not yet had an earthquake, they nonetheless can have quakes," with the exception of Egypt, where the mud is too compact. "If you wish to fear nothing, consider that everything is to be feared" (*Q Nat.* 6.1–2). For some time after A.D. 62 the earth continued to tremble, as we infer from Tacitus' *Annals* 15.33–4 (A.D. 64), where Nero, aspiring to be a world-famous singer, chooses the theatre at Naples for a tryout:

> There an incident took place, sinister in the eyes of many, providential and a mark of divine favor in those of the sovereign; for after the audience had left, the theatre, now empty, collapsed without injury to anyone. (Tac. *Ann.* 15.34, trans. Jackson 1951)

Suetonius tells the same story, but adds the cause of the theatre's collapse:

> And he made his début at Naples, where he did not cease singing until he had finished the number which he had begun, even though the theatre was shaken by a sudden earthquake shock. (Suet. *Ner.* 20, trans. Rolfe 1960)

A further testimony to this event is offered by a Pompeian inscription offering thanks for Nero's safety in the earthquake:

> pro salute Ner[onis] in terr[ae motu]. (*CIL* IV.3822)

25 August A.D. 79: Vesuvium Fuisse Postea Cognitum Est

Seventeen years later, at about midnight on August 25, A.D. 79, glowing avalanches and their pyroclastic flows ('nuées ardentes') came roaring down the slopes of Mount Vesuvius. The eruption threw six cubic kilometers of ash and pumice into the sky. We have an accurate eyewitness description of this cataclysmic eruption by Pliny the Younger, recorded at Tacitus's request 27 years after the disaster (*Epist.* 6.16 and 20). A few quotations from these famous letters will suffice to show Pliny the Younger to be both a man of science and a great dramatist, while encouraging a further reading of these "crucial documents in volcanology" (Krafft 1993, 41).

Letter 6.16 to Cornelius Tacitus

It is true that he [my uncle] perished in a catastrophe which destroyed the loveliest regions of the earth, a fate shared by whole cities and their people, and one so memorable that it is likely to make his name live forever. . . . On 24 August, in the early afternoon, my mother drew his attention to a cloud of unusual size and appearance. . . . . It was not clear at that distance from which mountain the cloud was rising [it was afterwards known to be Vesuvius]; its general appearance can best be expressed as being like an umbrella pine, for it rose to a great height on a sort of trunk and split off into branches. . . . Sometimes it looked white, sometimes blotched and dirty, according to the amount of soil and ashes it carried with it. (trans. Radice 1969)

Letter 6.20 to Cornelius Tacitus

For several days past there had been earth tremors which were not particularly alarming because they are frequent in Campania; but that night the shocks were so violent that everything felt as if it were not only shaken but overturned. . . . We also saw the sea sucked away and apparently forced back by the earthquake: at any rate it receded from the shore so that quantities of sea creatures were left stranded on dry sand. On the landward side a fearful black cloud was rent by forked and quivering bursts of flame, and parted to reveal great tongues of fire, like flashes magnified in size. . . . A dense black cloud was coming up behind us, spreading over the earth like a flood. . . . Then darkness came on once more and ashes began to fall again, this time in heavy showers. We rose from time to time and shook them off, otherwise we should have been buried and crushed beneath their weight. . . . At last the darkness thinned and dispersed into smoke or cloud; then there was genuine daylight, and the sun actually shone out, but yellowish as it is during an eclipse. We were terrified to see everything changed, buried deep in ashes like snow-drifts. (trans. Radice 1969)

Poets also recorded their emotional responses to the A.D. 79 disaster. In his moving lament for his father, Statius, a professional poet in Naples, calls upon Parthenope, patron of Naples, to lift up her head from the ashes and mourn over her great departed son:

> Exsere semirutos subito de pulvere vultus,
> Parthenope, crinemque adflato monte sepultum
> pone super tumulos et magni funus alumni. (*Silv.* 5.3.103–6)

> Lift up, Parthenope, lift up thy head half-buried from the dust that suddenly whelmed thee, lay thy tresses merged beneath the mountain's exhalations upon the tomb of thy great departed son. (trans. Mozley 1955)

We may infer that Statius' father died shortly after the eruption, which, although preceded by numerous ground shocks, came as a total surprise (*subito de pulvere*). Statius' use of *adflato monte* refers to pneumatic theories, such as Lucretius' fourth explanation. In the same lament, we are informed that Statius' father had resolved to sing of the A.D. 79 eruption, which is attributed here to Jupiter as a deliberate "act of god":

> iamque et flere pio Vesuvina incendia cantu
> mens erat et gemitum patriis impendere damnis,
> cum pater exemptum terris ad sidera montem
> sustulit et late miseras deiecit in urbes. (5.3.205–8)

> And already was it thy purpose to bewail in pious chant the conflagration of Vesuvius, and expend thy tears on the ruin of thy native land, when the Father caught up the mountain from the earth and lifted it to the skies, then hurled it far and wide upon the hapless cities. (trans. Mozley 1955)

Toward the end of his verse-epistle to Vitorius Marcellus (*Silv.* 4.4), Statius links the date and location of his composition (*sonabam* is epistolary imperfect) with Vesuvius' outburst of anger, and wonders whether the imaginative powers of future generations will be capable of understanding the destruction that took place here, once the devastated landscape will have been rehabilitated:

Haec ego Chalcidicis ad te, Marcelle, sonabam
litoribus, fractas ubi Vesvius egerit iras
aemula Trinacriis volvens incendia flammis.
mira fides! credetne virum ventura propago,
cum segetes iterum, cum iam haec deserta virebunt,
infra urbes populosque premi proavitaque tanto
rura abiisse mari? necdum letale minari
cessat apex, procul ista tuo sint fata Teate,
nec Marrucinos agat haec *insania* montes. (*Silv.* 4.4.78–86)

So sing I to you, Marcellus, on the Cumaean shores where Vesuvius
spews out its wrath, part assuaged, whirling firebrands to rival Aetna's
flames. It is very hard to credit! Will the coming generations of men
believe—when the crops return, when these deserts have turned
green—that cities and people are crushed underneath and that their
ancestors' fields have disappeared in such a great inundation? The
peak has not yet ceased to threaten destruction. Far be that fate from
thy Teate, nor may such madness seize the Marrucinian hills. (trans.
Coleman 1988)

Lines 78–80 call to mind Vergil's *sphragis* ("signature") at the end of *Georgics*
IV, contrasting the poet's idle life with Octavian's great victories in the East:

Haec super arvorum cultu pecorumque canebam
et super arboribus, Caesar dum magnus ad altum
fulminat Euphraten bello victorque volentis
per populos dat iura viamque adfectat Olympo. (*Geo.* 4.559–62)

Thus I sang of the care of fields, of cattle and of trees, while great
Caesar thundered in war by deep Euphrates and gave a victor's laws
unto willing nations, and essayed the path to Heaven. (trans. Thomas
1968)

Since Statius contrasted his own life with that of his addressee earlier in
the poem (line 67), his obvious reference *(haec... canebam...dum)* to Virgil's
lines *(haec...sonabam...ubi)* seems to emphasize the futility of his poetry
when compared to the savage destruction wrought by Vesuvius called
Vesaevus, in 4.8.5, probably after its wild *(saevus)* character.

Conclusion

The melancholy reflected in Martial's wistful memories of the happy past
enjoyed by this region, written nine years after the eruption, provides a fitting climax to this selection of emotional poetic responses:

> Hic est pampineis viridis modo Vesbius umbris,
> Presserat hic madidos nobilis uva lacus:
> Haec iuga, quam Nysae colles, plus Bacchus amavit,
> Hoc nuper Satyri monte dedere choros
> Haec Veneris sedes, Lacedaemone gratior illi,
> Hic locus Herculeo numine clarus erat
> Cuncta iacent flammis et tristi mersa favilla:
> nec superi vellent hoc licuisse sibi. (4.44)

> This is Vesbius, green yesterday with viny shades; here had the noble
> grape loaded the dripping vats; these ridges Bacchus loved more than
> the hills of Nysa; on this mount of late the Satyrs set afoot their
> dances; this was the haunt of Venus, more pleasant to her than
> Lacedaemon; this spot was made glorious by the fame of Hercules. All
> lies drowned in fire and melancholy ash; even the High Gods could
> have wished this had not been permitted them. (trans. Ker 1961)

The lovely picture of Vesuvius in the first part of the poem recalls the
famous Pompeian fresco showing the wine god Bacchus at the foot of the
mountain. Martial's *Veneris sedes* refers to Pompeii, the spot favored by the
Goddess of Love and patron of the Roman people. *Hic locus* refers to
Herculaneum, made famous by the mighty Hercules. All the places so dear
to these powerful gods have now been destroyed. Like Statius, Martial attributes the devastation of this region to the gods, but in his opinion, these gods
now may well wish that this power had not been given to them. The observation that the gods deeply regret the destruction caused by their own hands
serves to emphasize the enormity of the disaster, havoc beyond belief. The
Jewish or Christian writer of graffito *CIL* 4.4976, "*Sodoma Gomora,*" would
have disagreed with this observation. He would have considered this act of
god a justified retribution exacted from Pompeii, a just reward for the
depravity of this "Sodom and Gomorra."

REFERENCES

Bailey, C. 1963. *Titi Lucreti Cari: De Rerum Natura. Libri Sex.* Oxford.

Bömer, F. 1969–1986. *P. Ovidius Naso Metamorphosen.* Heidelberg.

Chester D.K., A.M. Duncan, J.E. Guest, P.A. Johnston, and J.J.L. Smolenaars. 2000. "Human Response to Etna Volcano during the Classical Period." In *The Archaeology of Geological Catastrophes*, edited by W.J. McGuire, D.R. Griffiths, P.L. Hancock, and I.S. Stewart, 179–88. Geological Society Special Publication 171. London.

Chester D.K., A.M. Duncan, J.E. Guest, and C.R.J. Kilburn. 1985. *Mount Etna: Anatomy of a Volcano.* London.

Corcoran, T.H., trans. 1962. *Seneca: Naturales Quaestiones.* Cambridge.

Coleman, K.M. 1988. *Statius, Silvae* IV. Oxford. Translated by H.R. Fairclough 1974. Cambridge, Mass.

Duff, A.M., and J.W. Duff, trans. 1961. *Anon: Aetna.* Cambridge.

Duff, J.D., trans. *Silius Italicus: Punica.* Cambridge.

Fairclough, H. Rushton, trans. 1961. *Virgil: Georgics.* Cambridge.

Geikie, Sir Archibald. 1897. *The Founders of Geology.* New York.

Gilbert, O. 1907. *Die Meteorologischen Theorien des Griechischen Altertums.* Leipzig.

Jackson, J., trans. 1951. *Tacitus: Annals.* Cambridge.

Johnston, P.A. 1996. "Under the Volcano: Volcanic Myth and Metaphor in Vergil's *Aeneid.*" *Vergilius* 42:55–65.

Jones, Horace L., trans. 1928. *Strabo: Geography.* Cambridge.

Ker, Walter C.A., trans. 1961. *Martial: Epigrams.* Cambridge.

Krafft, M. 1993. *Volcanoes: Fire from the Earth.* New York.

Mozley, J.H., trans. 1955. *Statius I: Silvae; Thebaid I–IV.* Cambridge, Mass.

Platnauer, M., trans. 1922. *Claudian: Rape of Proserpina.* Cambridge.

Radice, B., trans. 1969. *Pliny's Letters.* New York.

Ramsay, J.T., and A. Lewis. 1997. *The Comet of 44 B.C.* Atlanta.

Rolf, J.C., trans. 1960. *Suetonius.* Cambridge.

Smolenaars, J.J.L. 1997. "Lake Avernus, the 'Birdless Place': Poetic License or Carbon Dioxide?" *Classica Cracoviensia* 3:145–56.

Spaltenstein, F. 1986. *Commentaire des Punica de Silius Italicus.* Geneva.

Stothers, R.B., and M.R. Rampino. 1983. "Volcanic Eruptions in the Mediterranean before A.D. 630 from Written and Archeological Sources." *Journal of Geophysical Research* 88:6357–71.

Thomas, R.F., trans. 1968. *Virgil: Georgics, I: Books I–II; II: Books III–IV.* Cambridge.

NOTES

[1] Regarding Lake Avernus in *Aeneid* 6.236, see Smolenaars 1997, 145–56.

— 20 —

Conclusion

◈

Mirium A. Balmuth, David K. Chester, and Patricia A. Johnston

Vulcanologists and geologists have focused on the phenomenon of volcanic activity, in part to be able to forecast, assist, and protect populations subject to the threat it poses. Archaeologists and classicists have tended to focus on the subsequent physical remains of eruptions and on the intellectual response to them, as reflected in the literature and in religious and mythological traditions.

The field of volcanology has been transformed in the last 10 years, from being firmly anchored within geology to developing a truly interdisciplinary and international focus. Under the forthcoming United Nation's plan for the first decade of the 21st century, the International Strategy for Disaster Reduction, or ISDR (Hamilton 1999; United Nations 1999), it is highly probable that interdisciplinary research, involving archaeology, literary studies, and history will become an even more prominent part of the volcanology. Research of this kind holds not only an intrinsic fascination, but also the power to inform studies of risk assessment and emergency planning by providing long-term perspectives on how peoples and cultures have lived near volcanoes and responded to their eruptions. Chapters in the present volume by Roberto Santacroce et al., Angus Duncan and David Chester, Giovanni Orsi and his Neapolitan colleagues, together with work on reconstruction of preindustrial responses to loss and damage by Etna, are not isolated examples of the use of historical and archaeological information, but are part of a rapidly evolving approach, indeed a developing consensus, which holds to a conviction that comprehensive hazard planning must be informed by an understanding of both the cultural milieu and the history and archaeology of volcanic regions (Chester et al. 1999; Dibben and Chester 1999; Luhr and Simkin 1993; Chester 2005).

One example of the present day importance of such studies emerges from Haraldur Sigurdsson's recently published and highly acclaimed *Encyclopedia of Volcanology* (Sigurdsson 2000). This volume contains the usual chapters on processes, planetary volcanism, hazards, prediction and mitigation, and extensive coverage of topics which include, inter alia: the soils of volcanic regions, volcanic materials, tourism; archaeology, art, literature, and film. Even ten years ago, the inclusion of such material in a major volcanological textbook would have been unthinkable. The snapshot of the scope and content of volcanology at the beginning of the 21st century provided by the *Encyclopedia*, demonstrates just how far research has developed since the International Decade for Natural Disaster Reduction was inaugurated in 1990, but it is not an isolated example (Fisher et al. 1997; Ingleton 1999).

A major concern for scholars studying volcanic landscapes is to persuade populations to take the threat of eruptions seriously. Varone and Marturano demonstrate that this tendency was clearly evident in Pompeii, whose population in A.D. 79 assumed too soon that the threat had passed. Plunket and Uruñuela found a similar pattern of behavior from the first century B.C., in populations living in the shadow of Popocatépetl. Since 1996, when they first presented the work published in this volume, 10 more households have been studied, focusing heavily on the domestic rituals structured by a general Mesoamerican cosmovision and expressed via images and concepts related to the volcanic landscape. In their studies of the abandonment of this Pre-Columbian village and the detailed analysis of the specific contexts of artifacts left behind by the population, they have found a large degree of variability. Some families relocated gradually to the valley floor as volcanic activity increased. The courtyards of their houses were swept and the dishes were washed and placed upside down around the edges of the patio to keep them clean; jars and other large vessels were put in the corner storage areas. At one house, the incense burner was lit and placed before the household shrine. These houses look almost as if the family members had just finished cleaning up before retiring for the night. A second, less common scenario suggests a more abrupt abandonment by families busy with daily chores: dishes of food were left outside the buildings next to the hearth, the grinding stone was left face up, and household shrines were not in use. The variability found at the Tetimpa houses demonstrates the decision-making processes of individual families as they watched Popocatépetl become increasingly violent.

It is hoped that studies in this collection of the use of volcanic materials for human habitation, such as those by DeRita and Giampaolo, Balmuth; Ginesu and Sias; and Burri, Massoli-Novelli and Petitta will lead to future investigations into reference materials which will further strengthen interaction between disparate research fields. Such materials could equate the traditional terminology of Roman archaeologists with the technical nomenclature used by geologists and vulcanologists; provide a technical description (inclusions, color, texture, etc.) of the stone types and a fuller list of the monuments where they were used, so that the serious student can use the published information as a guide when viewing the actual monuments in, Rome, Sardinia, and Turkey.

The study of ancient pottery is another important means of tracking the spread of volcanic eruptions and the use of the erupted materials by populations. In the study of ancient potteries, petrographers (Pecchioni, Elena and Fabio Fratini; Levi et al. in this volume) have emphasized the importance of distinguishing between the composition of the raw materials and the manufacturing techniques. The differences in composition, particularly chemical composition, give rise to some ambiguities; sometimes they can be due to different production areas or to different manufacturing technologies. Difficulties arise when attempts are made to define the reference groups. The main purpose of future research must be to determine how differing raw materials and manufacturing technologies contributed to the final composition of the ceramic paste. This approach may be useful when investigating ceramic pastes' composition and when determining provenance.

In order to determine the raw materials and the possible mixture of temper used in the manufacturing of the ceramic paste, different kinds of analyses (mineralogical, petrographic, and chemical) are generally carried out on both the ceramics and on the lithological components located near archaeological sites. Leri et al. (in this volume) have adopted techniques of geochemical analysis. These have involved taking into account the determination of the chemical composition of (both) the bulk sample and the matrix. This is accomplished by the use of EMP analysis. Such data, however, must also be utilized with the petrographic, XRD, and XRF techniques.

We hope this volume will encourage future interdisciplinary exchanges on the themes outlines in this volume. It has been our experience that geologists, classicists, and archaeologists can work together fruitfully on topics of shared interest and that dialogue is mutually productive.

REFERENCES

Chester, D.K. 2005. "Volcanoes and Society." In *Volcanoes and the Environment*, edited by J. Marti and G.J. Ernst Cambridge.

Chester, D.K., C. Dibben, R. Coutinho, A.M. Duncan, P.D. Cole, J.E. Guest, and P.J. Baxter. 1999. "Human Adjustments and Social Vulnerability to Volcanic Hazards: the Case of Furnas Volcano, São Miguel, Azores." In *Volcanoes in the Quaternary*, edited by C. Firth, and W. J. McGuire, 189–207. Geological Society London, Special Publication 161. London.

Dibben, C., and D.K. Chester. 1999. "Human Vulnerability in Volcanic Environments: The Case of Furnas, São Miguel, Azores." *Journal of Volcanology and Geothermal Research* 92: 133–50.

Fisher, R.V., G. Heiken, and J.B. Hulen. 1997. *Volcanoes: Crucibles of Change*. Princeton.

Hamilton, R. 1999. "Natural Disaster Reduction in the 21st Century." In *Natural Disaster Management,* edited by J. Ingleton, 304–7. Leicester.

Ingleton, J., ed. 1999. *Natural Disaster Management*. Leicester.

Luhr, J.F., and T. Simkin. 1993. *Parícutin: The Volcano Born in a Mexican Cornfield*. Phoenix.

Sigurdsson, H. 2000. *Encyclopedia of Volcanoes*. San Diego.

United Nations. 1999. *International Decade for Natural Disaster Reduction: Successor Arrangement*. New York.

Glossary of Volcanological and Geological Terms

D.K. Chester and A.M. Duncan

Aa lava. A Polynesian word, aa lava is characterized by a rough rubbly surface of angular jagged fragments with sharp spines. The morphology contrasts with that found on *pahoehoe* lava flows.

Accretionary lapilli. Spherical or nearly spherical masses of cemented ash, ranging from a few millimeters to several centimeters in diameter, also known as *pisolites*. These form as moist aggregates of ash in eruption clouds and can result either from rain falling through an eruption cloud, or in wet hydrovolcanic (i.e., phreatomagmatic) eruptions. See *hydrovolcanic*.

Acid lava (acid igneous rocks). The terms acidic and basic are used to describe rocks with, respectively, high and low percentages of silica. These terms were coined in the 19th century when silica was thought to form from silicic acid. Although these terms are still in use, alternatives are *silica-rich*, *felsic* or *silicic* for acid, and *silica-poor*, or *mafic* for basic.

Airfall volcanic deposits (more properly known as **tephra fall deposits**). Volcanic fragments which are transported in an eruption column and fall to the earth's surface. The largest fragments occur closest to an eruption site, becoming progressively finer with distance. Winds may significantly influence the nature of dispersal and consequent sedimentation. See *tephra*.

Amphibole (hornblende). A hydrous ferromagnesian silicate mineral.

Andesite. A medium dark-colored volcanic rock containing 57–63% of SiO_2 by weight. It is of so-called intermediate composition, more silica-rich than basalt and less silica-rich than dacite and rhyolite. Andesite is the principal constituent of the orogenic volcanic series (see *plate tectonics*) and is associated with plinian eruptions which produce large eruptions columns, much tephra fall, pyroclastic flows and surges.

a.s.l. Above sea level.

Basalt. Dark colored volcanic rock containing 45–52% SiO_2 by weight. Basalt is of basic composition and is less silica-rich than intermediate rocks, like andesite, and much less silica-rich than acidic rocks, such as rhyolite. Basalt is strongly associated with Hawaiian and strombolian-style eruptions, which produce large volumes of lava and relatively little pyroclastic material. See also *flood basalt*.

Basic lava (basic rocks). See *basalt*.

B.P. B.P. means years before present and the convention is used in connection with radiocarbon dates. Radiocarbon (^{14}C) dates are recorded with reference to a zero year (A.D. 1950), using the original ^{14}C half-life of 5570±30 years. Dates can easily by converted to the new revised 5730±40 half-life by multiplying by 1.03.

Bradyseismic event. Increased seismic activity which accompanies deformation of the ground surface.

b.s.l. Below sea level.

Caldera. A large volcanic depression formed by collapse. A caldera is more or less circular in outline and its diameter is many times greater than any included vent. A nested caldera shows different generations of smaller calderas within a larger caldera. The adjective "resurgent" is used to designate a caldera whose floor initially subsided, but was later uplifted on one or more occasions.

Clinopyroxene. A ferromagnesian silicate mineral.

Composite volcano. A volcano typically forming a cone-shaped construct built from lava flows and layers of pyroclastic material. An alternative term is *stratovolcano*. In contrast, a *shield volcano* is a convex construct with gentle slopes, typically formed from basaltic lava flows.

Continental sediment. Continental sediments or sedimentary rocks, have their origin on land and contrast with those formed in marine environments. See *sediment*.

Crystal fractionation. A mechanism by which the composition of magma changes by the physical separation of early formed crystals. This typically occurs in magma reservoirs.

Debris avalanche. A large mass of material falling or sliding rapidly under the force of gravity. The term is used to describe the mass of sediments the fall of which creates large amphitheatre-shaped hollows on the sides of volcanoes.

Diopside. A member of the pyroxene mineral family found in mafic rocks.

Directed blast. An explosive volcanic blast with a lateral component. Directed blasts are triggered by gas pressure exceeding the load of the overlying rocks, or a sudden removal of these rocks by some outside agency such as a landslide. The most famous recent example occurred during the eruption of Mount St. Helens (U.S.) in 1980.

Dome. A steep-sided mass of viscous acidic or intermediate lava extruded from a volcanic vent. Domes are often circular in plan view and spiny, rounded, or flat on top. Surfaces are often rough and blocky as a result of fragmentation of the cooler, outer crust during the growth of the dome.

Downthrown. Downthrown is a term used in connection with faults, planar or curved fractures in the Earth's crust across which there has been relative displacement. Movement is predominantly vertical and one side is raised or *upthrown* relative to the other which is *downthrown*.

Dyke (also **dike**). A type of igneous intrusion. Magma ascends through a vertical or sub-vertical fissure. When it cools, it becomes a vertical sheet of rock with roughly parallel sides. In contrast, a *sill* is a horizontal or sub-horizontal intrusion. See *igneous intrusion*.

El Niño (also called **El Niño Southern Oscillation** or **ENSO**). An atmospheric and oceanic phenomenon of the Pacific Ocean. Unusually warm conditions periodically appear along the coasts of Ecuador and Peru, causing climatic disturbances and unusual weather of varying severity in the southern hemisphere and over much wider areas.

Epicenter. The point on the earth's surface directly above the focus (or hypocenter) of an earthquake.

Extensional tectonics. See *plate tectonics*.

Fallout deposits (also known as **airfall** or **fall deposits**). See *airfall volcanic deposits*.

Flood basalt. Voluminous wide-spreading flows of very fluid lava. Examples occur in the Deccan region of India and Pakistan and the Karoo area of South Africa. See *basalt*.

Fluid/coolant reactions. See *hydrovolcanism*.

Focus (of an earthquake). The place within the earth at which rupture commences. Also known as the *hypocenter*.

Fractional crystallization. See *crystal fractionation*.

Fumarole. Vents from which volcanic gases are emitted at the ground surface.

Hypocenter. See *focus* (of an earthquake).

Garnet. A silicate mineral found in a variety of igneous rocks.

Geomorphology. A science concerned with the morphology of the surface of the earth and the processes that produce it.

Glowing avalanche. See *pyroclastic flow.*

Graben. A feature of a region in which the surface elevation is controlled by intersecting faults which give rise to a block-like morphology. A graben is a fault-controlled trough or valley bounded by approximately parallel block faults. Also known as a *rift valley.* In contrast, a *horst* is the raised, hilly or mountainous portion of such a region.

Holocene. The last 10,000 years of geological time. This period follows the Pleistocene; the two together constituting the Quaternary.

Horst. See *graben.*

Hydrovolcanism (also known as **hydromagmatism**). The interaction of magma and water to produce an explosive eruption. Sea, lake, ground, or glacial water may be involved, but explosive activity demands a critical ratio of water to magma. When the water/magma ratio is below 0.2, water has little influence on the eruption and is ejected as steam (so-called *phreatic* activity). As the ratio becomes critical, at around 0.35, the eruption is at its most energetic and is dominated by both hydrovolcanic and magmatic fragmentation of the melt. It is termed *phreatomagmatic* at this stage. Hydrovolcanism is analogous to fuel/coolant reactions, which are a known hazard within the chemical industry. The products of hydrovolcanism include fine-grained airfall materials and cold (or base) surge deposits. See *pyroclastic surge* and *lahar.*

Igneous rock. A rock type formed by cooling and solidification of a molten mass of magma. Plutonic rocks are formed at depth and include granite, gabbro and syenite. Volcanic rocks are formed when magma is erupted at the surface and include basalt, andesite and rhyolite.

Igneous intrusion. Igneous intrusions occur when the country rock is penetrated by a mobile body of igneous rock. See *dyke.*

Ignimbrite. The deposits generated by pumice-rich pyroclastic flows, sometimes referred to as *ash-flow tuffs.* See *pyroclastic flow.*

International Decade for Natural Disaster Reduction (IDNDR). Under a resolution of the General Assembly of the United Nations, the decade of the 1990s was designated as one that would focus global efforts to understanding natural hazards and their mitigation.

Ka. kiloyear (a thousand years).

Lahar. A word of Indonesian origin used to describe volcanic fragments that are transported by water. It encompasses all water-transported debris-flows of volcanic material regardless of grain size and water content and includes all flows regardless of whether they were formed during an eruption or later by processes of slope instability. See also *hydrovolcanism*.

Lapilli. Pyroclastic fragments with a caliber between 2 and 64 mm.

Lateral blast. See *directed blast*.

Latite. A volcanic rock or magma of intermediate composition. See *igneous rock*.

Lava. New rock, whether molten or solidified, which is emitted as a flow at the earth's surface during eruption. Lava contrasts with *magma*. This is molten rock in the earth which has not yet been erupted.

Leucite. A felsic silicate mineral typically found in undersaturated potassic magmas and lava flows.

Leucitic phonolite. A volcanic rock or magma of potassic silicic composition.

Lithic (also **lithic pyroclast**). A pyroclastic fragment of previously formed rock. Lithics may be of igneous, sedimentary, or metamorphic composition and are often pieces of lava from a vent area that have been incorporated into a pyroclastic deposit.

Mafic. See *acid lava*.

Magma. See *lava*.

Magma reservoir (also **magma chamber**). A magma-filled chamber within the earth's crust. Magma reservoirs develop as various shapes and sizes, ranging from single chambers to complexes of interconnecting sills and dykes.

Magma/water interactions. See *hydrovolcanism*.

Magnetite. A metallic mineral (iron oxide) which is widely distributed in igneous rocks. An iron ore source in some regions.

Metamorphic rock (also **metamorphosed rock**). A rock type in which the original mineralogy, texture, or composition has been altered due to the effects of recrystallization in response to pressure, temperature, or the loss or gain of chemical components.

Mindel. Under the classic subdivision of the Pleistocene, the Mindel was a major period of glacial advance at high latitudes and major climatic changes throughout the world.

Nepheline. A felsic silicate mineral found in silica undersaturated igneous rocks.

Nested caldera. See *caldera*.

Nuée ardente. See *pyroclastic flow*.

Olivine. A ferromagnesian silicate mineral which is common in rocks of a basaltic composition.

Orogeny. A tectonic process in which large areas of the earth's crust are folded, faulted, metamorphosed, and intruded. Orogeny ends with uplift and the formation of mountains. See *plate tectonics*.

Pahoehoe lava. A Hawaiian word, pahoehoe lava has a smooth crust often taking the form of hillocks and hollows. Pahoehoe lava may have areas where the crust is twisted into forms which resemble folds in heavy cloth or coiled rope. Active lava in pahoehoe flow fields is typically transported in tubes. It contrasts with *aa lava*.

Palaeosol (also **paleosol**). The soil of a former land surface, which has been subsequently buried by either geological or anthropomorphic activity.

Periglacial. In high latitude regions and in some areas of high elevation, prevailing temperatures keep the ground wholly or partially frozen for most of the year. The effects of repeated freezing and thawing and the growth of ground ice produces distinctive landforms. During the cold phases of the Quaternary many areas experienced periglacial conditions.

Phenocryst. In an igneous rock, a large crystal surrounded by a finer groundmass.

Phlogopite. A mica mineral found in volcanic rocks of a mafic composition.

Phonolite. An intermediate to acidic alkali-rich volcanic rock.

Phreatomagmatic. See *hydrovolcanism*.

Phreatoplinian. A form of hydrovolcanic activity giving rise to a high eruption column and widespread dispersal of ashes.

Pisolite. See *accretionary lapilli*.

Plate tectonics. The contemporary paradigm of the earth sciences. It is a model in which the earth's crust and uppermost mantle (i.e., the lithosphere) are divided into a number of large semi-rigid segments known as *plates*. Plates move in relation to one another and plate margins meet at convergence (subduction) zones or separate at divergence (spreading) centers. Spreading centers occur at sea (e.g., mid-Atlantic ridge), and are associated with extensional tectonics and volcanism; the latter being produced by partial melting in the upper mantle. Subduction zones are areas of active andesitic/rhyolitic volcanism. Areas of upper mantle partial melting also occur at intraplate locations (e.g., the Hawaiian Islands), associated with mantle hot spots or plumes. Although the picture is in detail very complex, basaltic volcanism is strongly associated with spreading centers and intraplate locations. More silica-rich andesitic and rhyolitic melts are associated with subduction zones (often called the *orogenic volcanic series*). Earthquakes are associated with plate margins.

Plinian eruption (including **sub-plinian**). Named in honor of Pliny the Elder who was killed in the eruption of Vesuvius in A.D. 79. The term refers to the continuous ejection of large volumes of ash and pumice lapilli and to developed eruption columns that reach to a great height. When the column collapses pyroclastic flows and hot surges are often generated. Tephra dispersal is widespread and may be global.

Porphyritic. The texture of an igneous rock containing abundant phenocrysts.

Pumice. A form of volcanic glass, usually of felsic composition so filled with void spaces (i.e., vesicles) that it is sponge-like and of low density.

Pyroclastic rock. A rock formed of fragments of volcanic rock.

Pyroclastic flow. An eruption cloud comprising hot pyroclastic fragments and gas. Driven by the energy of the eruption, fluidization of the fragments, and gravity, flows move across the ground as density currents. Many are generated by collapse of the particle-laden eruption column. Most pyroclastic flows move downslope at high velocities, often along river valleys. Alternative terms are *nuée ardente, glowing avalanche* and *ash-flows*. Pyroclastic flows are often associated with less dense, hot surges (i.e., ground and ash-cloud surges). See *pyroclastic surges*.

Pyroclastic surges. At least two sub-types are recognized:
1. Cold surges (also known as *base* and *wet surges*) are a ground-hugging blast of fragmental material traveling at hurricane velocities radially away from an explosive hydrovolcanic eruption.
2. Hot surges are associated with magmatic eruptions and denser pyroclastic flows. They move at great speed and are produced by processes that include explosive disruption of domes, gravitational collapse of domes, collapse of eruption columns and lateral blasts. See hydrovolcanism and pyroclastic flow.

Pyroxene. A ferromagnesian silicate mineral, typically associated with mafic volcanic rocks.

Resurgent caldera. See *caldera*.

Rheology. The study of the deformation (changes in shape or size) and flow (the rate of change in deformation) of materials under stress (force per unit area). It is important in understanding the physics of magma movement and lava flow.

Rhyolite. A light brown to gray compact volcanic rock, containing at least 74% silica.

Sanidine. A felsic silicate mineral associated with volcanic rocks of a potassic composition.

Scoriaceous. Having the texture of *scoria*, a congealed lava usually of basaltic composition that contains a large number of voids, or vesicles, formed by gases coming out of solution.

Sediment (also **sedimentary rock**). Materials deposited at the earth's surface by physical agents (wind, water and ice), biological agents (organisms living or dead) and chemical agents (precipitation from oceans, lakes and rivers).

Silicic. See *acid lava*.

Sill. See *dyke* and *igneous intrusion*.

Stratovolcano. See *composite volcano*.

Strombolian eruption. Activity is characterized by discrete, weak to violent explosions of basaltic or andesitic magma. Scoria, cinder cones, and lava flows are produced by this type of eruption. Less violent than plinian eruptions.

Surge. See *pyroclastic surge*.

Tectonics. The movement and deformation of the earth's crust due to folding, faulting. See *plate tectonics*.

Tephra. A collective term used for all fragmented materials, regardless of size, produced by an explosive volcanic eruption.

Tephrite. A type of volcanic rock.

Terrestrial planets. The inner or earth-like planets of the solar system: Earth; Mars; Mercury; Moon; and Venus.

Toothpaste lava. A viscous lava that appears from eruptive vents like toothpaste from a tube. It is characterized by surface grooves and drawn-out spines.

Trachybasalt. Basaltic rocks belonging to the alkali basalt-trachyte trend.

Trachyte. An alkali-rich silicic rock.

Tuff. Consolidated volcanic *tephra.*

Tuff cone. A volcano composed of indurated ash with steep slopes of 20–30°. Often associated with hydrovolcanism.

Tuff ring. A volcano with low angle outer slopes (2–10°), a wide crater, and an apron of pyroclastic debris. Often associated with hydrovolcanism.

Unconformity. A surface that separates two geological strata. It represents an interval of time in which deposition stopped, erosion removed some sediment or rock, and deposition then resumed.

Volatiles. Gaseous constituents.

Würm. Under the classic subdivision of the Pleistocene, the Würm was the last major period of glacial advance at high latitudes and major climatic changes throughout the world.